The Wa
Understanding the Water Supply
and Wastewater Industry

Leonard S. Hyman
Andrew S. Hyman
Robert C. Hyman
Edward P. Meehan
James D. Hempstead
Jose V. Kochen

Public Utilities Reports, Inc.
Vienna, Virginia

1998

First Printing, July 1998

Library of Congress Cataloging-in-Publication Data

The water business: understanding the water supply and wastewater
    industry / Leonard S. Hyman . . . [et al.].
        p.   cm.
    Includes bibliographical references and index.
    ISBN 0-910325-71-5 (pbk.)
        1. Water utilities—Management.   2. Water-supply—Management.
    3. Sewage—Purification.   4. Sewage disposal.   I. Hyman, Leonard S.
    HD4456.W38   1998
    363.6'1'068—dc21   98-33510
                                                                              CIP

Printed in the United States of America

About the Authors

Leonard S. Hyman is a senior industry advisor to Salomon Smith Barney's Global Power Group, specializing in utility and telecommunications finance and economics.

From 1978 to 1994, as head of the Utility Research Group and first vice president at Merrill Lynch, he supervised and maintained research on foreign and domestic energy and telecommunications utilities. He was also a member of privatization teams for offerings of British, Spanish, Mexican, Argentine, and Brazilian utilities.

Mr. Hyman has written and spoken on utility finance and deregulation, taken part in management seminars and briefings for electric and telecommunications companies, and presented papers at conferences on three continents. Mr. Hyman has testified before Congress and served on four advisory panels for the U.S. Congress Office of Technology Assessment, and for a study undertaken by the National Science Foundation. He was a member of a Pennsylvania state task force on electric utility efficiency, and a member of a NASA task force on fusion and other energy sources. He serves on the advisory board of the Electric Power Research Institute. In 1997, Mr. Hyman was a member of a task force advising on the reorganization of the North American Electric Reliability Council.

Author of *America's Electric Utilities: Past, Present and Future* (in its sixth edition), co-author of *The New Telecommunications Industry: Meeting the Competition* and editor of *The Privatization of Public Utilities*, all published by Public Utilities Reports, Inc., Mr. Hyman has contributed to other books and to professional journals.

Prior to joining Merrill Lynch, he was vice president and senior industry analyst with Wainwright Securities, a partner at H.C. Wainwright, and second vice president and research analyst at Chase Manhattan Bank.

For more than 10 years, Mr. Hyman was cited by *Institutional Investor* as one of the leading research analysts in his field. He is a Chartered Financial Analyst (CFA) who is listed in *Who's Who in Finance and Industry*, *Who's Who in Science and Engineering*, *Who's Who in the World*, and *Who's Who in America*. He holds a B.A. degree from New York University, where he was elected to Phi Beta Kappa, and an M.A. degree in Industrial Organization with a minor in Latin American Studies from Cornell University. He speaks Spanish and Portuguese.

Andrew S. Hyman is an associate in Coopers & Lybrand's Utilities/Energy Strategy Consulting Group in Chicago. He is involved in developing strategic uses of computer systems to collect, analyze, and disseminate energy and utilities information. Mr. Hyman holds a B.S. degree in applied physics from Tufts University. He also holds a Master of Public Policy degree from Vanderbilt University and an M.A. degree in geography from the University of Illinois at Urbana-Champaign. He contributed to *The New Telecommunications Industry: Meeting the Competition*

(1997) and *The Privatization of Public Utilities* (1995), both published by Public Utilities Reports, Inc. Mr. Hyman devoted much of his graduate study to developing ways to improve the operating efficiency of the Central Valley Project and the Inland Waterways System.

Robert C. Hyman is an economic analyst at Eastern Research Group, Inc., in Lexington, Massachusetts, where he analyzes the effects of environmental regulation on regulated industries. Mr. Hyman graduated *cum laude* from Harvard University with an A.B. degree in Earth and Planetary Sciences. Mr. Hyman was an intern at the Israel Oceanographic Institute while a student at Tel Aviv University.

Edward P. Meehan is a managing director with Legg Mason Wood Walker, Inc. He has 20 years' experience on Wall Street as a financial officer and investment banker. In his 17 years at Merrill Lynch he concentrated on raising private equity funds, on general corporate finance, and on utilities and power. From 1995 to 1998 he was a director in Smith Barney's Global Energy and Power Group.

Mr. Meehan's banking experience includes advising clients on strategic matters, raising in excess of $20 billion for corporate clients, and advising startup companies on corporate finance strategies and accessing the public capital markets. He has spoken at a variety of conferences and has published several papers on emerging utility issues. Mr. Meehan holds a B.S. in Accounting/Economics and an M.B.A. degree in International Finance from St. John's University in New York.

James D. Hempstead is a vice president in Merrill Lynch's Global Power Group. Mr. Hempstead focuses on strategic advisory and corporate finance assignments for the electric, gas distribution, gas pipeline, and water industries. His recent mergers and acquisitions experience includes advising Williams Companies in its acquisition of MAPCO Inc. Prior to joining Merrill Lynch, he worked in the Global Energy and Power Group at Smith Barney Inc. Mr. Hempstead received a B.S.B.A. from Villanova University and an M.B.A. from Fordham University.

Jose V. Kochen has played a leading role in the management and development of the water and sanitation industries of Brazil's most industrialized state, São Paulo. He is the retired chief operating officer of São Paulo's Basic Sanitation Company. Since retiring he also has served as a consultant to the Brazilian Association for Sanitary Engineering.

Mr. Kochen, a civil engineering graduate of the Mackenzie School of Engineering in São Paulo, with a graduate degree in business administration from the School of Business Administration of the Getulio Vargas Foundation, first joined the Department of Water and Sewage of São Paulo as an engineer, later moving up to supervisor of operations and maintenance. He was director of planning and then superintendent of the São Paulo Superintendency of Water and Sewage prior to joining the Basic Sanitation Company.

To our wives, children, and parents—tap water drinkers all—
who put up with us during the writing of this book.

Look at the crowds of water-gazers there.[*]

— Herman Melville

[*]Herman Melville, *Moby Dick or The Whale* (New York: Random House, 1930), p. 2.

Table of Contents

The Water Business:
Understanding the Water Supply and Wastewater Industry

List of Tables

List of Figures

Preface

Picture this scene. Three o'clock in the morning. A hot, dry summer night. A thirsty man stumbles into the kitchen. He runs the faucet a few minutes. Get cold water. He never turns on the light. Why bother? The water is always the same. Always safe. Always clear. Across town, a fireman taps a hydrant to fight a fire in an abandoned building. Water gushes out. As expected. With the pressure required to fight the fire.

Film noir with a cool jazz sound track? No, just ordinary scenes that play out across the country every day. Nobody questions the quality and reliability of the water system. Nobody thinks about it. Turn on the faucet. Water comes out. Clean water. Safe to drink, to bathe in, to wash baby's clothes. We take water for granted. We never even think about the water supply. The stuff just comes out of the faucet.

Many view their consumption of fresh water as an inalienable right. Water, they believe, should not be the property of private entities. Basically, they are correct. Water is free, at its source, at least in the United States. But most people are too lazy to carry water to their homes. They prefer that others, public and private water suppliers, bring it to them in safe form. They pay a fee for that service, the cost of collection, processing, and delivery.

Collection, treatment, delivery, and recycling of water constitutes an enormous industry, with over $50 billion of revenues in the United States alone, and possibly $300 billion worldwide. Despite the overall size of the industry, most of the thousands of community suppliers are tiny entities. Government-owned operators dominate, an unusual feature for a business in the U.S., and increasingly less common in the rest of the world. As the natural gas, electric, and telecommunications industries fall victim to competition, the water business remains the last natural monopoly in town. Perhaps rightly so. Public health and safety depend on it. You can fight only so many fires, flush out sewers or run industrial processes with bottles of spring water.

This book examines, in basic terms, how the water supply industry operates, developed, accounts for its operations, is regulated, and where it might be going. This is an introductory book. It explains the required principles of accounting, engineering, accounting, and public health. It is, however, primarily a book about water as a business (whether owned by government or by investors), not an engineering or public health text.

In order to make the sections of this book as self contained as possible, we occasionally repeat explanations, rather than force the reader to find the original explanation. Specialists might find sections of the book too elementary, and can move on to the sections that they find helpful.

This book is divided into seven sections, a bibliography, appendices, and an index.

Part One, *Water Basics*, provides a brief overview of topics covered in greater detail later in the book. Discussions of the properties of water organization of the industry, regulation and finance furnish a foundation that should help the reader understand what follows.

Part Two, *Operations*, looks at how the water and sewage industries provide their products and services, how the customers use the services, and what entities actually supply the water and sewage services.

Part Three, *Development and Structure of the Industry*, traces the history of water and sanitation services from early times, and the influence of public health and environmental issues on the development of the industry.

Part Four, *Regulation, Pricing, and Economics*, looks into how the suppliers set prices, and whether application of market principles could increase the efficiency of the water supply industry and of its customers.

Part Five, *Financial Structure*, examines accounting procedures, financial statements, how to use those arcane documents to draw conclusions, and how the companies and their owners have fared, financially speaking.

Part Six, *International Issues*, considers the difference in water supply and sanitation from region to region, and the challenges that suppliers face abroad.

Part Seven, *Conclusion*, summarizes our conclusions, and takes a look at the future of the industry.

A *Selected Bibliography* lists some easily accessible sources of information. The *Appendices* present an analysis of conservation procedures and case studies of the activities of large water suppliers. A *Subject Index* follows.

Mr. W. F. Holland of American Water Works read much of the text and provided us with many helpful suggestions. At Salomon Smith Barney, the presentations graphics crew helped us put together the many figures in the book, but we owe the most to Denise Perry, who cheerfully shepherded the manuscript, typed it, kept it in order, and put it together. At PUR, Lori Rodgers edited, checked, proofed, directed, asked questions, demanded clarification of the obscure, all with a stern affability that never failed.

We are grateful for guidance, corrections and help. We, naturally, take responsibility for all remaining errors.

Leonard S. Hyman
Andrew S. Hyman
Robert C. Hyman
Edward P. Meehan
James D. Hempstead
Jose V. Kochen

PART I
Water Basics

CHAPTER 1

Defining Water: Properties and Issues

WÁTER ... Sir Isaac Newton defines water, *when pure, to be a very fluid salt, volatile, and void of all savour or taste; and it seems to consist of small, smooth, hard, porous, spherical particles, of equal diameters, and of equal specific gravities.*[1]

Water is one of the most common and unusual substances on earth. Demand for water grows every year, but its supply is fixed. We pay over $50 billion per year, in the United States alone, for utilities to supply it and keep it clean. Providing potable (safe to drink) water is the single most effective way to improve public health in less developed countries. Some of the most productive agricultural land in the country depends on water, imported at high cost to taxpayers, from other parts of the country. We cannot live without water, but we take it for granted except during droughts.

Before diving into the topic too deeply, however, we must understand basic terminology and concepts, ranging from units of measurement to geology to economics.

MEASUREMENTS

The water industry utilizes a number of industry-specific measurements. Just understanding the language is essential to understanding the business. The fact that the United States sticks to the English system while the rest of the world has gone metric, of course, confuses matters. Furthermore, various water suppliers manage to say the same thing in different ways, which only adds to the confusion.

Volume is the space that an object occupies. A *gallon* occupies 231 cubic inches of space (a container 10 inches high, 5 ¾ inches wide, and 4 inches deep holds one gallon). The *liter* (l), the metric measure of volume, is the volume occupied by one kilogram of water, which is one cubic decimeter (a cube 10 centimeters by 10 centimeters by 10 centimeters). One gallon equals 3.79 liters. The volume of water on earth, though, is so enormous that some authors quote quantities in measures like *cubic miles* (the volume of water that fits into a cube one mile by one mile by one mile in dimension). More commonly agricultural experts talk about *acre-feet* (the quantity of water needed to cover one acre of land to a depth of one foot). An acre-foot, incidentally, equals 326,000 gallons, the amount of water than an average family of four uses in one year. *Flow* is a measure of the volume of a substance passing a point within a specified period of time, measured for instance, in gallons per second, or cubic feet per second.

Force, in physics, denotes something that changes the state of motion of a body. Force can concentrate on a single point on the surface of a solid, and move the solid body. It cannot concentrate on a single point on the surface of a fluid, because if it did, it would go right through the surface, into the fluid, and leave the body of the fluid where it was before. Therefore, the force has to exert itself over the entire surface of the fluid. *Pressure*, therefore, is force over the area pushed by the force. Where F = force, S = surface area and P = pressure, then:

$$P = \frac{F}{S}$$

The *pascal* (Pa), named after French scientist Blaise Pascal, is the standard measure of pressure. Another is the *atmosphere* (atm). Commonly, Americans speak of *pounds per square inch*, abbreviated as lb/in² or psi.

1 atm = 101,325 Pa
1 atm = 14.7 lb/in²

Water distributors must maintain enough pressure on the water to move it through water mains, to push it up the pipes of buildings, and to supply firemen with enough pressure to hose down fires.

Water *quality* has a subjective sound to it, but health authorities can measure the minerals or microorganisms that impart bad taste or carry diseases, in terms of their concentration. Consumers, for instance, may not notice the taste of a small amount of minerals in the water. A few microorganisms may not be harmful. A lot are harmful. *Concentration* is measured in grains (1/480 of an ounce) per gallon, or milligrams (mg) per liter (l), or, most familiarly, parts per million (ppm). Due to the multiplicity of measures, it is easy to become confused. The reader can translate English to metric measures through calculations, or easier yet, by using a table. Converting milligram per liter into parts per million, on the other hand, is easy. For convenience, remember that one liter of water weighs one kilogram (1,000 grams). There are one million (1,000 x 1,000) milligrams per kilogram. Therefore, a concentration of 150 mg/l equals 150 ppm. Government regulations specify the maximum safe level of concentration for each mineral and type of organism, mainly through Safe Water Drinking Act (SWDA) standards.

PROPERTIES OF WATER

Water is a peculiar substance, always in motion, used but never destroyed, found in the air, on the surface, and underground.

The ancients defined the universe in terms of four building blocks: air, earth, fire, and water. Knowledge advanced, in 1781, when British chemist Henry Cavendish showed that the combustion of hydrogen produced water. Two years later, French chemist Antoine Lavoisier, who later lost his head in the Reign of Terror, proved that water was a compound of hydrogen and oxygen. In 1804, Gay-Lussac and von Humboldt quantified the two-to-one proportion of hydrogen-to-oxygen in the water molecule, giving us the familiar chemical formula for water, H_2O.

Water has unusual properties. It exists as solid, liquid, and gas within a narrow temperature range. A large number of substances dissolve in water. Our bodies require water for the digestive processes, to transport nutrients, to build tissues, to maintain the temperature of the body, and to carry off wastes. Most people could not live more than four days without water. Plants and animals cannot survive without water. Most of the weight of living matter consists of water.

States
Water appears in three *states* or conditions: solid, liquid, and gas. Water, generally, turns into a solid, ice, at a temperature of 32°F (0°C) or lower. It is in a liquid state between 32°F and 212°F (0°C to 100°C). It boils off into a gas, water vapor, or steam, above the boiling point. Water, however, can co-exist in all three states. Water, for instance, *evaporates*, that is, turns into vapor, from the surface of water-ways, at temperatures below the boiling point. Furthermore, plants and animals *transpire*, that is emit water vapor, at temperatures below the boiling point.

Hardness, Softness, and Other Qualities
Hardness of water is not an idea cooked up by enterprising soap manufacturers and sellers of water softening devices. Hardness is a chemical concept, referring to the quantity of dissolved calcium and magnesium salts and ferrous iron in the water. Soft water, for instance, contains 0 to 60 mg per liter of hardness constituents, moderately hard water has 61 to120 mg/liter, hard water 121 to 180 mg/liter, and very hard water over 180 mg/liter.

Hard water causes problems for industrial and residential consumers. It deposits carbonate salts (scale) on the insides of pots and pans, pipes and boilers. The iron reddens water. Mineral salts hinder the work of soap, forming scum when interacting with soap. Soft water, on the other hand, does corrode metals more easily, but it is better for laundering, drinking, and swimming. (The slippery feeling when taking a shower is a sign of soft water.)

Water softeners remove offending chemicals, but water suppliers would prefer to start out with soft water, rather than having to add chemicals, or to ask customers to take their own steps to soften the water, or to give consumers an inferior product. Some entrepreneurs and water suppliers, however, want to customize water, so that consumers can optimize the hardness or softness of the water to suit their individual needs.

Water suppliers consider other measures of quality, as well. *Turbidity*, for instance, refers to the amount of stirred up sediment suspended in the water. The *acidity* of the water means just that, a measure of the acids in the water, which could corrode plumbing if they exist in too high a concentration. Acidity is measured on a pH scale (which, of course, hearkens back to all those litmus tests of high school and college chemistry days) of 0 to 14. The middle of the scale, 7, is neutral. Counts of below 7 are acidic, and 4.0 to 5.9 indicates extreme acidity by water supply standards. Iron in water causes staining. Some bacteria actually thrive on iron, and they may end up clogging the plumbing. Iron content of 0.3 ppm can cause staining. Again, what the water supplier does not remove causes inconvenience to consumers, who then take corrective measures using chemicals or devices supplied by non-utility firms.

Bottled and Tap Water

Tap water or ordinary drinking water is what comes out of the faucet, supplied by the local water utility or from a well. The water may be disinfected with chlorine and treated to remove harmful organisms and substances. The water still contains some dissolved minerals. Water sold in bottles may differ from tap water. All minerals, for instance, have been removed from *distilled water*. In contrast, *mineral water* contains minerals (which almost all water does, anyway). *Natural mineral water*, naturally, is the water that comes out of the ground, with all dissolved minerals left in it. (Carbonation may be either natural or added by the bottler.)

HYDROLOGY AND GEOLOGY

Water covers about 70% of the surface of the planet. It is probably the earth's most plentiful compound. That, of course, is fortunate, considering the impossibility of life without water. Yet, most land-locked life requires fresh water, which constitutes less than 3% of the water on the earth, and three quarters of that fresh water is frozen in glaciers, which means that we are all competing to use about 0.6% of the world's water. Roughly half of our water used is taken from underground sources and the rest from surface water, such as lakes and rivers.

The planet's water supply, incidentally, remains fixed in quantity, although demand for usable water increases as the population grows. Water supply is no different now than a century ago. Furthermore, "In 1850, the water available for each person on Earth was eight times more plentiful than it is expected to be in 2050."[2] Water suppliers have to provide cleaner water to more consumers throughout the world, without help from Mother Nature. Doing so has become an increasingly difficult challenge, thanks to new forms of pollutants, the contamination of underground aquifers, and changing meteorological patterns.

Hydrological Cycle

Water moves in an endless *hydrological cycle*. To begin somewhere, water rises as vapor from surface water (such as oceans, lakes, and rivers). Living creatures also transpire vapor into the air, adding to the supply. The water vapor rises in the air, eventually forming clouds. Rain or snow precipitates from the clouds, onto bodies of water or onto land. Precipitation hitting the ground takes one of two paths. *Runoff water*, staying on the top of the ground, runs directly into springs, rivers, and other bodies of surface water. The rest of the precipitation infiltrates the soil.

Vegetation plays a role in transpiration, runoff and capture of water. For this reason, scientists and environmentalists are concerned about the effect of destruction of large tracts of forest on water supply. (For example, clear cutting increases sedimentary runoffs, which not only reduce the land's ability to retain water but also create problems downstream.)

An *unsaturated zone* (also called *zone of aeration* or *vadose zone*) lies below the surface of the ground. Water enters spaces between soil and rock. It remains at atmospheric pressure. Plants suck up the water in this zone. Without rain, this zone soon dries out.

Water percolates farther down to the *saturated zone*, (also called *phreatic zone*) which is topped by the *water table*. In this zone, the water in the spaces between rock and soil is under pressure. Water from this zone will flow into a well, as a result of the pressure. The water table rises or falls, depending on the amount of rainfall that reaches the saturated zone. The water table, incidentally, is not always level. Los Angeles sits atop a water table. Years ago, water from the geological structure flowed like the oil wells of Texas. Unfortunately, demand has outstripped supply, pressure subsided, the water table fell, and it has never recovered. Today, Angelenos would have to install expensive pumps to bring up the water.

Water, even underground, is in motion. Underground water, too, must complete the cycle. It eventually discharges to the surface through brooks and streams, which form rivers that return the water to the sea. (See Figure 1-1.) From the surface, of course, the water evaporates, and the cycle continues. In a year, the hydrological cycle moves 100 quadrillion (100 x 10^{15}) gallons.

Aquifer

The *aquifer* is a geological formation, made up of porous or permeable material through which water can travel, which holds large quantities of water. It is, in effect, a natural, underground storage reservoir. Aquifers underlay approximately half the surface of the United States. (See Figure 1-2, which not only shows the location of aquifers but also categorizes them by the nature of the underlying formation. *Consolidated* aquifers are made up of rock, mainly limestone, basalt, or sandstone. *Unconsolidated* aquifers consist of sand and gravel. The most productive aquifers are of the latter type.)

The Ogallala Aquifer, in the middle of the country, may be the best known aquifer in the United States. About 200,000 wells suck water out of that aquifer. Despite

Figure 1-1

The Hydrological Cycle

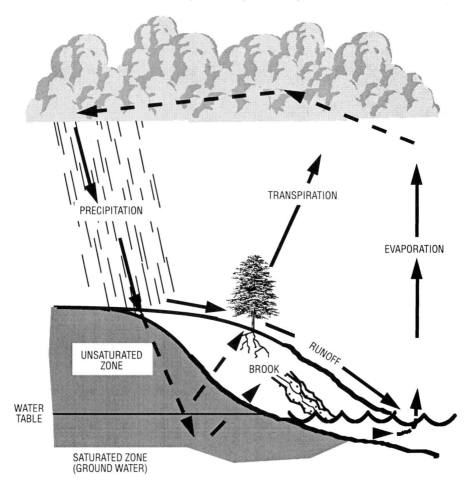

its size (156,000 square miles), all the usage is depleting the aquifer. The Ogallala accumulated its enormous supply over a half million years. In the dry region that it underlies, natural sources of recharge now equal only a fraction of the water withdrawals (see Figure 1-3).

In the *unconfined aquifer*, water filters down through the earth until it reaches an impervious layer. Then it accumulates over that layer. Unfortunately, pollution can just as easily percolate down, too. Users of water from unconfined aquifers must take care not to pollute their water source.

The *confined aquifer*, on the other hand, lies between layers of impermeable rock, which create a shield against pollution from the surface. An *artesian aquifer* is one

Figure 1-2

Aquifers in the United States

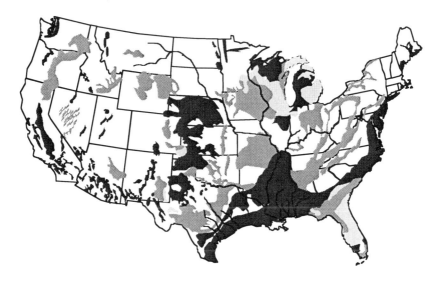

■ Unconsolidated and semiconsolidated
▦ Consolidated rock
□ Both unconsolidated and consolidated-rock

where rock layers put the water under so much pressure that it rises in wells as far as the ground surface, without pumping. The Australian Artesian Basin, one of the largest, covers 676,000 square miles.

The contamination of an aquifer by pollution is called *leaching*. Obviously, this is a scenario no government or water utility wants. Thus, they regularly test aquifers for various levels of *contaminants*. This pollution may have been introduced 50 or 100 years ago, many miles away from the aquifer. Over time, as the demands on the aquifer increase, water (and pollution) is drawn from faraway areas. This natural occurrence works in the same way as a straw draws liquid from a cup. Aquifer users can protect themselves by drilling a ring of testing wells around the aquifer. When they find a contaminant in the outlying well, they can quickly take countermeasures.

Development of land over aquifers not only prevents water from percolating into the aquifer to recharge it, but also produces pollution that could affect the quality of the aquifer as a water supply. Zoning and land use regulations, therefore, must protect a natural resource owned by nobody but used by everybody.

Figure 1-3

The Ogallala Aquifer

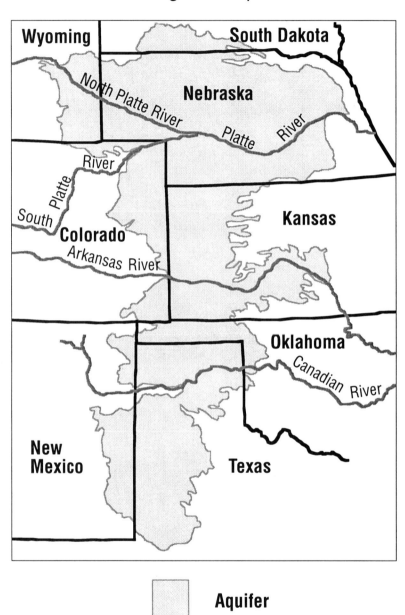

Aquifer

Watershed

In the word *watershed*, "shed" refers to the ridge or crest of a hill. The word originally signified the line on the top of a hill that divided the flow of waters into one river basin or another. (In that sense, a watershed event denotes a turning point.) Now, in the water industry, watershed is more likely to mean the drainage basin of a waterway, but usually in a local sense, not for a huge river system, such as the Mississippi. In other words, the hills, valleys, and plains whose surface runoff drains into a creek constitute the watershed for the creek (see Figure 1-4).

GATHERING AND DELIVERING WATER

Water suppliers must collect water from surface and below-ground sources, transport it, often long distances, to the population centers, and then distribute it to consumers. The system has numerous components.

Figure 1-4

Watershed

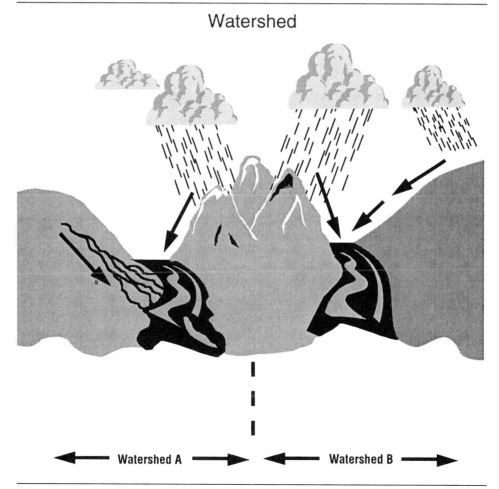

Watershed A   Watershed B

Reservoir

The *reservoir* (French word for "reserve") is a large artificial or natural lake used as a source of water by the water system. Often, the water supply entity will dam a river, causing a lake to back up behind the dam. That lake constitutes the reservoir. At the dam, the water supplier diverts some of the water into the water supply system, and allows some to continue to flow to the river below the dam. All reservoirs, though, are not designed to catch and collect water. Some serve as storage points near the consumers, in case of interruption of the flow from the distant reservoirs, some are additional storage facilities, and others serve as regulating mechanisms in a multi-reservoir system. Lake Mead, behind the Hoover Dam, is the largest reservoir in the United States, but Lake Mead does not come close to ranking in the top 20 reservoirs in the world. In fact the largest reservoir in the world, at Owens Falls in Uganda, contains six times as much water as Lake Mead.

Surface Sources

In many places, the water supplier takes water directly from a surface body of water, such as a river or a lake. The supplier, then, can dispense with the huge investment in collection and storage facilities. Chicago, as an example, takes its water from Lake Michigan.

Wells

Ground water accounts for roughly 40% of public water supply in this country. To reach that water, suppliers drill holes in the earth: wells that extend down to the underground water resource. They bring the water to the surface through the well.

A simple *dug well* suffices to reach shallow water sources. The diggers excavate a hole down to the water level, then line the wall of the hole with cement or rock. The lining extends from about a foot above ground level to at least 10 feet below ground level. The watertight lining prevents surface water or pollutants from entering the well.

Where ground water is within 25 feet of the surface and soil is not rocky, *driven wells* are common. A pipe with a cone shaped strainer at its end is driven down to the water bearing layer. If the soil is cohesive and unlikely to cave in, the well excavators may produce a *bored well*. The boring device collects soil as it digs, and it must be raised and emptied, periodically. After completing the excavation, the builder puts in a well casing and a screen at the bottom of the well where the water enters.

Many wells, however, must be *drilled*, because the ground is rocky, or the water level is far below the surface. The drill bit, at the end of a shaft, cuts away at the soil and rock, making a long hole down to the water level. The builder usually lines the hole down to the aquifer level, where a masonry device or screen allows the water to enter the well.

Modern wells usually require pumps to raise the water to surface level. (Artesian wells are an exception. The water is under enough pressure to send the water upwards, sometimes to the surface. The water in an artesian well, though, is the same as any other water.) Modern wells are a far cry from the old village well at which local citizens raised the water in oaken buckets (see Figure 1-5), but the concept is the same.

Aqueduct

The Romans built *aqueducts*, a word derived from the Latin *aqua* (water) and *ducere* (to lead). The aqueduct is a channel that conveys water, usually from a distant reservoir or other source to a populated area where the consumption takes place. Modern aqueducts are huge, closed pipes that traverse hundreds of miles, carrying the water over mountains, or in some cases, through tunnels under mountains.

Figure 1-5

Wells

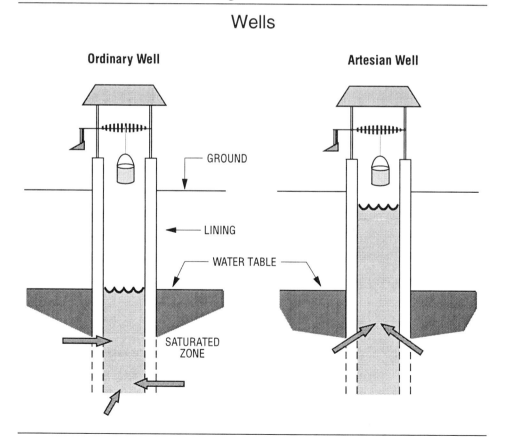

Gravity Flow and Pumping

The water supplier must find a means to make the water move from the source of supply to the place of consumption. There are two ways of dealing with the problem. If the source of water is above the place of consumption, the water supplier can build a conduit for the water that goes downhill all the way. The force of gravity causes the water to travel downhill. Modern cities and their water supplies, though, may not be conveniently located to allow gravity flow. In that case, the water supplier has to install pumps to push the water under pressure.

Desalination

Desalination is the removal of salt from water to make the water potable, using one of two basic processes. *Filtration*, passing the water through a filter, removes impurities, but it may not work well on water that has a high concentration of dissolved salts. *Distillation* means boiling the water, and collecting the vapor (which is free of the impurities), and condensing it back into pure water. Desalination is an expensive process. The water it produces has a cost several times that of ordinary tap water. Use of the process is limited to those places with insufficient supplies of fresh water.

ECONOMICS

Geology and hydrology produce the water supply. Engineers figure out how to get it to consumers. But somebody has to pay for the water, and the pricing of the product often determines whether consumers use it carefully or waste it. Having said that, and stated the case in its common form, let us take the analysis another step. In reality, the water itself costs nothing unless the government charges the utility for taking it from the environment, as is done in some countries, such as Brazil. Otherwise, consumers pay only for the collection, treatment, and transportation of the water.

Pricing, Usage, and Conservation

In most markets, price disciplines consumption. High prices encourage consumers to use a product more efficiently, or to find cheaper substitutes, for instance. Suppliers, in turn, try to provide their services more economically, in order to improve their profitability and to keep their customers by offering the product at a low price. The water industry has run differently. Many government agencies provide water at prices below true cost, which encourages wasteful usage. Some water suppliers do not meter (measure) the consumption of the customers, or charge by amount of consumption, so the users have no economic reason to consume water wisely. Water suppliers, themselves, could deliver the water with less loss along the way, but some of those suppliers operate under pricing systems set by regulators in such a way that they provide little incentive to run the company more efficiently. Undoubtedly the combination of regulated pricing plus government subsidies encourages wasteful usage and forces water suppliers to build facilities that would not be needed if users consumed water more carefully.

(Consider for instance, do you leave the water running when you brush your teeth? Do you let the gas spill over when you fill the car's tank? Do you have your outdoor barbecue grill on for hours when not cooking?)

The problems caused by this pricing regime become acute during periods of water shortage. In most commodity markets, the excess of demand over supply causes price to rise. Consumers then reduce their demand, and new suppliers enter the picture because of increased profitability at higher prices. The combination of lowered demand and new supplies eventually brings prices down. For years, water suppliers have acted as if consumers do not react to changes in the price of water, and suppliers certainly cannot bring in new supplies quickly. Thus, in times of shortages, water suppliers and governments usually resort to mandated prohibitions on certain types of usage (for example, a prohibition against washing cars or watering lawns), which clever people find ways to evade. (At the same time the California experience is instructive. The state has endured severe droughts. Consumers, apparently, stick to lower usage patterns, forced on them by the drought conservation programs, after the drought has ended. Demand rarely returns to pre-drought levels. Perhaps economists should take heed. Perhaps price helps to shape demand, but so do other factors.)

Most other public utility sectors have begun to utilize market pricing in order to induce operating efficiencies and more economic consumption of the product. Finding market-oriented solutions to problems of supply and demand could dramatically affect the efficiency of water supply and usage.

Water Rights

The eastern and western parts of the United States have developed different water use doctrines. In the East, *riparian* rights prevail. The land owner has the right to use water on his property, but does not own the water, and must submit to regulation that assures reasonable use.

In the West, the *doctrine of appropriation* prevails. California miners, in pioneer days, for instance, could take all the water they needed to work their claims. As in the case of the mining claim itself, whoever got there first got the water. This is the *prior appropriation doctrine*. Later on, Westerners developed the *beneficial use doctrine*, meaning that people who did not use their water allotment lost it.

Western water doctrine encouraged wasteful use. (One could argue that poorly priced Eastern water policies did the same, of course, but the East did not suffer from endemic shortages.) Users garnered no benefits by using water efficiently, because they could not capture for themselves the value of the water that they did not take. Policymakers have attempted to change that situation by allowing owners of water rights to sell those rights to people who need and value the water more than the owners of the rights. Thus, water rights owners gain the incentive to utilize water efficiently because they can sell the rights to the water they do not need. Purchasers of the rights, because they pay high prices for the water, have incentive to take as little water as possible. Introduction of a market for water rights could bring about a new attitude toward water use in the arid West.

Ownership

In most public utility sectors in the United States, investor-owned companies dominate the industry. In the water supply sector, though, government-owned utilities account for over 80% of the volume of the industry. Government-controlled utilities can borrow money at lower cost, thanks to tax advantages and guarantees by the parent government. Some government water projects may have emphasized social and public policy, rather than economic, objectives when formed. They may, therefore, sell water at prices that do not reflect costs, something that a private sector company cannot do. (That does not mean that privately owned utilities cannot serve public policy objectives, but rather that they have to somehow recover the costs expended, which government agencies are not obliged to do.)

CONCLUSION

Water is one of the world's most important resources. Life is unsustainable without water. Despite its seeming abundance, regions can run short of clean water. Since water supply, overall, is fixed, but demand for water is on the increase, we will have to find more efficient ways to use existing supplies. Market-based solutions may prove more effective than the old command-and-control methods of controlling demand and inducing supply.

CHAPTER 2

Water Supply and Sewage

My great wish is to abandon the system of . . . passing buckets at fires . . .[3]
— Mayor Josiah Quincy of Boston (1825)

Water supply and sewage systems are, essentially, part of the same business, which has two functions: to provide clean water for drinking and for carrying away waste, and to dispose of the waste water in a manner that neither constitutes a threat to health nor damages the environment. (Figure 2-1 shows the similarities of the two systems.)

WATER SUPPLY SYSTEM

A good water supply service provides its product continually, in accord with sanitary standards, without interruptions or shortages, at an adequate pressure, and at a price that is affordable to the community served.

Furnishing potable water involves a five-step process:

1. **Collection:** The water is collected from sources, which may be surface runoffs, rivers, lakes, reservoirs created by dams, or subterranean natural deposits.

2. **Treatment:** The water receives chemical and mechanical treatment that brings it to the standards of drinkability.

3. **Storage:** The treated water is conducted and accumulated in tanks to constitute reserve for use during peak hours of consumption, and also to guarantee supply (and maintain pressure) during emergencies.

4. **Distribution:** Large pipes bring the water to the various supply zones of the city.

5. **Supply:** Pipes transport the water from the distribution network, passing in front of houses, buildings, and industrial firms, and connecting to the water installations on private property.

Each of the stages of the process are connected by pipe systems that range from the large diameter water mains between the collection, treatment, and storage stages, through successively smaller diameters down to the pipe under the streets serving the supply function. In each of the stages, there may or may not be a

Figure 2-1

Water and Sewage

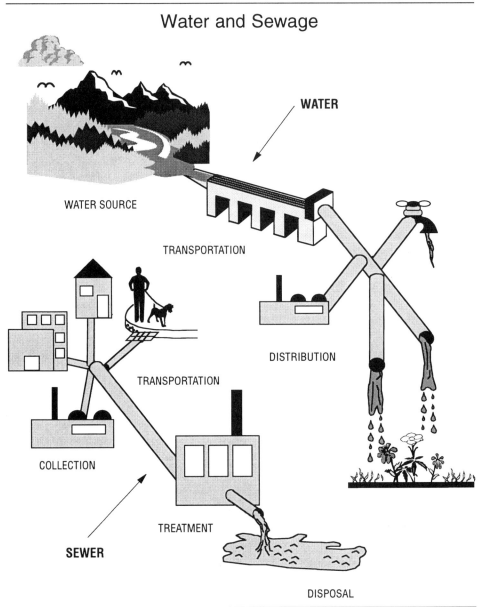

mechanical elevation of water by means of pumping stations, depending on topography.

All the activities that make the entire system function properly and provide the end product to the customer constitute the operational activity.

A good water supply service is one that guarantees the continuity of supply and the quality of the product that is supplied. Continuity of service is guaranteed by effective, corrective, and protective maintenance of all the equipment that constitutes the supply system. The physical, chemical, and bacteriological quality of the product is guaranteed by adequate control through sampling from the collection stage, and even before, through to final delivery.

SEWAGE SYSTEM

The first request of the inhabitants of a newly incorporated area is for water service. However, as the population becomes denser, sanitary problems grow, and the residents start to demand installations for the collection and removal of sewage. The existence or lack of this service directly affects public health and the environment. Lack of sewage service usually causes pollution of waterways and groundwater, as well as of the local environment as a whole, and a deterioration of the quality of life in the area. While there are a variety of types of agencies that furnish sewage services, most are municipally owned.

The sewage service function may be divided into five stages:

1. **Connections:** Pipes that connect the sanitary installations in the house, building, or factory to the collecting network of the sewer system.

2. **Sewer collecting network:** The network of pipes to which are attached the connections that carry the sewage (normally by gravity flow) to the trunk collectors which take all the flows from the drainage basin.

3. **Removal:** The assemblage of large trunk pipelines and mains that receives the flow from the trunk collectors and brings the sewage to the treatment station.

4. **Treatment station:** Facilities that treat the sewage, remove the solid waste in suspension, and bring the liquid up to standards that permit its reintroduction into the environment so that it may be reused.

5. **Final disposition:** Discharge of the liquid effluent from the treatment station, in accord with regulations that take into account the levels of treatment, at carefully determined points, so that the final elimination of impurities and inorganic materials takes place helped by natural processes, without environ-

mental damage. Solid wastes are sometimes transformed into fertilizer with restricted use.

A well-run sewage service is one that maintains its network for collection and discharge permanently free of obstructions and leakages, that treats the entire volume collected, and does so in a manner adequate to preserve the waterways water sources, and the environment as a whole.

INDUSTRY ORGANIZATION

In the United States, roughly 60,000 community water systems, of all sizes, provide water to 85% of the country's residences. Government-owned entities serve 85% of the customers of community water systems; 15% of residences have their own wells or no water. Public sewer systems collect waste from over 75% of American homes; the other 25% of homes have cesspools, septic tanks, and outhouses. Most water and sewage systems are owned by the local municipality, or constitute separate government agencies. Some, such as the Metropolitan Water District, in California, or the New York City Water and Sewer System, are enormous, multibillion-dollar organizations.

Ownership patterns vary. Most sewer systems are municipally owned and operated, even if the local water company is in private hands, but some private water companies also own sewer facilities. A large regional water agency may own the collecting reservoirs and aqueduct system, but sells the water that it collects and transports to local water distributors that may be privately or governmentally owned.

These two services, seemingly, will retain the characteristics of public utilities and natural monopolies long after the other utilities succumb to competitive influences. They might benefit from outsourcing and from regulation that creates greater incentives for efficiencies, but little of the business could be put into the competitive sector.

The functions of collection and transportation of water often require government control of land use, of extraction of water from the aquifer, and of riverways. The huge capital needs may preclude any benefits from competitive duplication of facilities. Enough different water sources may not exist in an area to allow competition, either. The water distribution system has all the characteristics of a classic public utility, too. Providing several sets of water pipes would represent a colossal waste of resources and cause disruption in the streets. In many places, the collection and long-distance transport of water is accomplished by a different entity than its local distribution, so vertical integration is not a necessity.

Many of the same comments apply to sewage collection and disposal. The city does not need competing underground lines carrying sewage from the same localities. Due to the difficulty of finding sites for the facilities, the need to safely dispose of wastes, and the fixed nature of the transport system, it is hard to envision numerous sewage treatment facilities competing with each other. Envisioning a system in which the treatment facility is owned by a firm other than the sewage collection entity is easier to do. In fact, when the need for a treatment facility arises, the sewage company could call for bids for a contract to serve it, and award the contract to the firm that agrees to provide the treatment for the lowest price. The sewage firm gets some of the benefits from competition through outsourcing.

Water and sewage supply, in many ways, is an industrial process. The private sector provides most industrial services in developed countries. The predominance of government ownership, however, may be due to several factors. For one, urban areas had to put the water and sewer infrastructure in place before development could take place, which meant that investment had to precede paying customers. Second, the water supply might be distant from the place of consumption, which necessitated heavy investment and ability to condemn property for public purposes in order to build the facilities. In the past, building the necessary facilities, under the circumstances, may have been beyond the capabilities of local private investors but the community needed the facilities nonetheless. Local interests petitioned the government to make the investment in water supply, which was recovered from subscribers in the form of a tariff for services rendered. This model for development was common, and it led many to the comfortable but false belief that water, as an essential for life, was the exclusive obligation of the government to furnish.

Faced with the tasks of rehabilitating ancient facilities and meeting more stringent water quality standards, water supply and sewage entities may have to move to new forms of ownership and operation that permit them to raise the needed funds and to operate with maximum efficiency. Changes will include sale of systems to entities more capable of operating and financing them, private/government partnerships, and outsourcing of functions to the most efficient provider of the function. Government regulations that inhibited the development of private/government partnerships are no longer in force, so the industry could modify its organization faster than in the past.

ENVIRONMENT AND HEALTH

For at least two thousand years, water suppliers have sought to prevent contamination of the water that they furnish. In the 20th century, modern water treatment methods kill off most life threatening pathogens before they can reach the consumer. But some illness-causing organisms have proved resistant to current water treatment methods, and many unhealthy substances remain in the water supply. The federal government has legislated the Safe Drinking Water Act of 1974, which sets limits on chemicals in the water supply, and the Clean Water Act of 1987, that controls pollutants in the waterways. Those laws helped to facilitate the cleanup of waterways and of water supplies, although a large proportion of our waterways are still too polluted for swimming, let alone for drinking. The laws required and will continue to require large capital and operating expenditures from those using our water resources. Clean water does not come cheap.

CONCLUSION

The water and sewer industries are vital to public health, capital intensive, unchanged in technology over many years, and possibly on the verge of new ownership and outsourcing patterns. They must confront more stringent health and environmental requirements. They must provide services to new customers. And they must rehabilitate or replace aging plant. Even without the growth evident in more dynamic industries, water and sewage firms have plenty of work ahead of them.

CHAPTER 3

Regulation, Finance, and Ownership

Every executive ... is inundated with figures ... Which ones really have something to say?[4]

— Peter Drucker

All water utilities, whether owned by governments or private investors, distribute the same product. They all need money in order to build, maintain, and operate the infrastructure required to collect, treat, and distribute the product. They have to set prices, too. (The price must not only cover the direct cost of operation but also pay for the funds raised to build the water supplier.) In doing all of this, they have to deal with outsiders, regulators, legislators, and investors.

REGULATION

Water utilities have developed into *natural monopolies*, meaning that one producer can serve customers more efficiently than can many competing producers. Imagine the inefficiencies involved if five or six water utilities each dug up streets and laid pipe that served only some customers and bypassed others. Furthermore, the water utility cannot allow third parties to use its system, a practice developing in the electric, gas, and telecommunications sectors, without knowledge and proof that the product meets the same standards and fulfills the same health regulations as the product that the utility offers. Electrons or bits are uniform. Natural gas, regardless of the supplier, is maintained at a 12,000 Btu heat rate, which insures steady oven temperature and prevents explosions. Water quality, however, varies, and the consequences of drinking substandard or contaminated water range from illness to death, sometimes on a massive scale.

When an investor-owned water utility has a monopoly, a *regulatory agency* in each state assures that the utility does not take advantage of its customers. The agencies set service standards and prices. The price (rate) is set to permit the utility to collect enough money to cover all operating expenses, including taxes, and to have enough *operating income* left to provide a fair *rate of return* on the money invested in the business. Investors supply the money used to build the plant and to buy the equipment that serves the customers (the *rate base*). The rate of return is determined from the utility's *cost of capital*. For example, suppose that a utility has invested $1,000 in facilities to serve its customers. The company borrowed $500 on which it is paying 8% interest ($40 a year). Holders of the utility's common stock furnished another $500. The regulators note that the loan costs 8%. After a lengthy hearing, the regulators decide that commons stockholders are entitled to a return of 12% on their investment ($60 a year). Thus, the cost of capital, as calculated below, is 10%, the rate of return that the utility is allowed to earn.

Type of Capital	Amount of Capital	Cost of Capital	Dollar Return		
Debt	$500 ×	8% =	$40		
Stock	500 ×	12% =	60		
Total	$1,000		$100	and:	$100/$1,000 = 10%

Regulatory agencies rarely set rates more often than annually. Certain major expenses, however, can move up or down rapidly in the course of a year. A utility might earn too little when these expenses rise, or too much when they fall. To avoid having frequent rate hearings to adjust price for these sudden shifts in expenses, most agencies allow the use of *automatic adjustment clauses*, which pass on to customers changes in certain expenses.

In most instances, state regulatory agencies do not set prices for government-owned utilities. Those firms may set their own prices, or request the local city council to set prices of service for the city-owned utility. The investors who lend money to the government-owned utility, however, may influence, or even determine, the price of service. They will lend money on certain terms that require the water utility to set prices that will produce enough revenue to meet predetermined financial standards of safety.

The standard regulatory framework is changing. Regulators are seeking new methods of regulation that will give utilities the incentive to run more efficiently. The old-style rate of return regulation may give way soon to alternatives.

RAISING MONEY

Water supply facilities are enormously expensive to build. They require large tracts of land. The construction and land acquisition process can take years, during which time the utility lays out money for the procurement of labor, materials, and property, but receives no additional revenue on the investment. Rarely do water companies set aside from the year's income enough money to pay for constructing a new filtration plant, for example. To pay for the plant, the companies often have to borrow money and to sell new shares of stock to outsiders (*external financing*).

Thus, the profits from new business that is served by the new plant have to be shared by an increased number of holders of the company's bonds and stock. If too many new securities are sold and if business does not grow as expected, the share of profits left for the holders of old securities might actually be less than before the expansion. *Dilution* takes place when so many new shares have to be sold to pay for expansion that earnings per share of stock are less than they would have been had no expansion and financing taken place. Other things being equal, an investor-owned utility is better off if it can finance as much of its expansion as possible from internal sources, especially when interest costs are high and stock prices are low.

Government-owned utilities do not sell stock. Instead, when internal funds are not sufficient to cover the cost of new plant investment, they borrow money. Usually they sell bonds. Because the bonds have been issued by a local government agency, the interest paid on those bonds is not subject to federal income taxes. Investors normally accept lower interest rates on tax-exempt bonds because they do not have to pay a portion of the interest in taxes.

RATIO ANALYSIS AND FINANCIAL STATEMENTS

The financial reports of a corporation have three key parts. The *income statement* shows revenues and expenses for the year, and the net income, which is what is left over after expenses are paid. The *balance sheet* provides a statement of assets (what is owned), money owed, and money put in by shareholders. The *statement of cash flows* tells how the company raises and disposes of cash in a particular accounting period. Government-owned utilities issue financial statements similar to those of investor-owned utilities.

The balance sheet shows the sources of all money used to build the utility since it was formed (the *capital*). A percentage of capital was borrowed and a percentage came from shareholders. The breakdown of capital between sources is the *capitalization ratio*. If a large percentage of funds came from borrowing, the company is said to be leveraged. If something goes wrong, the company will not pay dividends to the shareholders. Nor can the shareholders recover their investments until creditors (those who have lent money to the company) are repaid. Bondholders judge the quality of their securities by whether shareholders have invested a sufficient cushion of money for bondholders to fall back on if something goes wrong, and by the *pretax interest coverage ratio* ("coverage"), which measures how much income is available to pay interest charges. If $100 of income is earned and interest charges are $20, then the coverage ratio is five-to-one (5x). Financial organizations rate investment quality of bonds by letter designations. Moving from highest to lowest, designations are Aaa or AAA, Aa or AA, A, and Baa or BBB, with a plus, minus, or number added to show gradations of quality. Many investors are not allowed to own bonds rated below a Baa or BBB because they are not considered prudent investments.

Finally, to determine how profitably the firm uses stockholders' money, one must find out how much income is earned for every dollar invested, or the return on equity. If a company earns $120 for stockholders who have invested $1,000, the *return on equity* is 12%.

The government-owned utility has almost the same type of income statement, flow of funds, and balance sheet. There are three major differences, though. First, the government agency pays no income taxes. Second, the government utility will not report stockholders' equity because it has no stockholders, but it does report the contributed capital that its owner has put in, plus any earnings retained in the business. Third, the government-owned utility may show little or no net income left over after it has paid interest on outstanding debt. The bondholders of the government utility watch how many times the operating income covers the interest expense. They also watch *debt service coverage*, which looks at how many times the cash generated by operations covers the interest expenses plus payments of principal on the bonds. The rating agencies apply the same type of scale to government debt. The rating of the water utility's debt, however, may be affected by whether the local government guarantees the debt and whether the utility has paid to have its debt guaranteed by an insurance company.

CAPITAL MARKETS

Most of the money supplied to water company from outside sources is in the form of borrowings or of equity capital (money invested by stockholders who own the business). Borrowings usually come from banks, which provide *loans*, or from investors, who buy commercial paper (*short-term debt*), or in the form of bonds or debentures (*long-term debt*). In the case of long-term debt, the creditor lends money for a long period (perhaps 20 years) and receives a bond that will mature (be paid off) on a specified date. When owners of bonds need cash before the maturity date, they sell the bonds in the marketplace. Bondholders have no assurance that the market price, at any time between issuance and maturity, will equal the price paid when the bond was issued or will equal the value of the bond at *maturity (face* or *par value*). Meanwhile, the bondholder receives a fixed-interest payment (often called the *coupon*) each year. The return that the bondholder earns is called *yield*. The simplest yield is the *current yield*, the coupon as a return on the market price of the bond. If a bonds sells for $100 and has a coupon of 8% ($8), the current yield also is 8%. If the same bond with the 8% coupon ($8 in interest) sells at $80, the current yield is 10%. When the bond is selling below par, $80 in this example, the investor will not only receive $8 a year in interest, but will also receive $20 more when the bond is finally redeemed (at $100 par) at maturity. In that case, the correct yield to use is the *yield to maturity*, a calculation of return that takes into account both the current return and the increase in price as the bond approaches the maturity date. In general, yield to maturity is lower for high-rated (high-quality) bonds. That is, when risk is lower, return is lower.

Preferred and *preference stocks* also pay fixed dividends. Many preferred and preference stocks remain outstanding for the life of the corporation, i.e., they have no fixed date for repayment of investment to their owners. The shareowners must sell the shares in the market when they need to raise cash. The return is measured by the dividend yield, which is the annual dividend divided by price.

The *common stockholders* are the owners of the business. Their investment in it is called *equity*. In order of priority, the company pays interest first, then the board of directors declares preferred and preference dividends, then the board declares dividends on common stock, if anything is left. The same order applies if the company goes out of business. In liquidation, all debts are paid in full, first. Then preferred and preference shareholders get their investments back. Finally, if any funds remain, the common stockholders take what is left. When something goes wrong, common stockholders' money is used to pay the holders of bonds and preferred stock. When business is good, the common stockholders collect the profits.

If a company earns $1 million and has one million shares of common stock, it has *earnings per share* of $1. The company will keep some of the profits for the business (*retained earnings*) and pay the balance as *dividends*. The *payout ratio* is the dividend paid as a percentage of earnings. The company that pays a dividend of 60 cents per share out of $1.00 of earnings per share has a 60% payout ratio. The price of a common stock is usually valued at a *multiple* of earnings, also called the price-earnings (P/E) ratio. For instance, if the stock of a company earning $1 a share sells at $10, its P/E ratio is ten-to-one, or ten times earnings (10x). Investors often pay a higher P/E for the stocks of companies whose earnings are expected to rise rapidly. The second common measure of value is the dividend yield, the dividend return on the price of the stock. The stock selling for $10 and paying a dividend of 60 cents a share annually yields 6.0%. Shares of companies that are expected to raise their dividends rapidly often sell at lower dividend yields. A company with a high payout ratio may not be able to raise its dividend for lack of earnings from which to pay the additional dividend. As a result, shares of that company may sell at a high dividend yield. In other words, investors will pay a higher P/E ratio and settle for a lower current dividend yield if they expect substantial improvement in the future. Investors also consider the risk level of the stock and will pay a higher P/E and accept a lower dividend yield from the investment with the lower risk.

The bondholders of government-owned utilities measure their expected return in terms of *yield to maturity*, as do the bondholders of private corporations. They accept lower yields from the safer, higher-rated bonds. Usually, the bondholders of municipal utilities pay no federal income tax on the interest earned. Those bonds are called *tax-exempt* or *municipal* bonds.

Movements in interest rates affect bond and stock prices. When investors can earn a high return on money in the bank, for instance, they will not buy a stock or bond until its price has declined to a point at which the dividend yield or the yield to maturity is high enough to compete with returns offered elsewhere. On the other hand, when interest rates decline, investors bid up the prices of stocks and bonds until returns on them drop to levels that are close to prevailing interest rates. The market is a two-way street. Common stockholders can only guess at the return they will earn over time. Bondholders, on the other hand, know what return they will earn, assuming all goes well, if they hold the bond to its maturity date, at which time the issuer pays back the principal amount.

OWNERSHIP ISSUES

Investor-owned utilities raise money from expensive sources, shareholders who want profits from a rising stock price and dividends, and from creditors who demand the highest possible interest rates. Those utilities also pay federal, state, and local taxes. Government-owned utilities raise money by selling tax-exempt bonds that usually pay lower interest rates than corporate bonds. They do not pay federal, state, and local taxes, either. Thus, the government-owned utility has a seeming cost advantage over the investor-owned utility. Some of that cost advantage, though, is illusory. First, the market for the securities of the government agencies of any state is limited. To the extent that the water agency raises money from investors, that action may depress the demand for the securities of other agencies, which might then have to pay higher interest costs in order to snare investors. If that happens, part of what the customer gains in lower water bills might be offset by higher taxes required to pay extra interest of other government agencies. In the same sense, the local, state, and federal taxes not paid by the utility have to be made up by extra taxes paid by everyone else, including the customers of the water utility. There is no such thing as a free lunch.

Yet, some water projects are too big or too long-term for private investors, especially investors who have to work under the profit-limiting rules of public utility regulation. Ventures that involved public financing combined with private management know-how have been rare, until recently, thanks to unfavorable tax rulings. Now, it looks as if privately owned companies will be able to offer services to government-owned utilities in a manner that could erode the barriers between government- and privately owned water utilities.

CONCLUSION

Whether investor or government-owned, water utilities utilize the same financial concepts and face the same financial challenges. Government-owned utilities may avoid some of the hurdles erected by state regulators, and they may have access to less costly capital than their private brethren, but those privileges may be offset in other ways. The development of public-private partnerships that meld the advantages of government financing and private operating management may provide a solution to many of the financial challenges that the industry faces.

CHAPTER 4

Summary

Not only is water in short supply, but there are no substitutes for it.[5]

— Jose Kochen

The supply of water is "affected with a public interest,"[6] to use the words of Lord Chief Justice Hale, more so than the services of most public utilities. To collect the water, the suppliers tap a vast watershed, much of which they do not own, or an underground source, which nobody owns but anyone can use or abuse. They need cooperation of others or coercion of others by the state in order to maintain a safe water supply. Any slip-up in treatment of water leads to illness or epidemics. Failure to provide a sufficient water supply hampers economic development. Inadequate sewage disposal not only degrades the environment but also affects the safety of the water supply.

Building and maintaining water and sewer systems requires a long-term view and large sums of money. When the price of water does not reflect its true cost, consumption rises, which not only involves waste of a precious natural resource but also waste of the financial resources required to meet uneconomic demands for more water. Often, one region of the country attempts to maintain its low-priced water supply at the expense of other regions. That sort of water policy not only encourages waste but transfers income as well.

Water suppliers often emphasize the public service nature of their task, implying that provision of water is too sacred a task to be sullied by considerations of economics or profit. That attitude confuses ownership with regulation, a confusion most common in less-developed countries. Perhaps, in an era of limited government resources, we will apply economic tools to the water business, and, in the process, economize on the use of another limited resource.

NOTES

1. Samuel Johnson, LL.D., *A Dictionary of the English Language* (New York: Barnes & Noble, 1994), p. 813.

2. U. S. Filter, *1997 Annual Report*, p. 5.

3. Nelson Manfred Blake, *Water for the Cities: A History of the Urban Water Supply Problem in the United States* (Syracuse: Syracuse University Press, 1956), p. 173.

4. Peter Drucker, *Managing for Results* (New York: Harper & Row, 1964), p. 25.

5. Jose Kochen, "Privatization of Water Supply and Sewage," in Leonard S. Hyman, ed., *The Privatization of Public Utilities* (Vienna, Virginia: Public Utilities Reports, 1995), p. 87.

6. Cited by Chief Justice Waite in *Munn v. Illinois,* 94 US 113 (1877).

PART II
Operations

CHAPTER 5

Introduction to Water Operations

When the well's dry, we know the worth of water.[1]

— Benjamin Franklin

Water supply and sewage are peculiar services: big businesses, each with more than 121,000 employees and revenues of over $26 billion per year. Yet the public pays little attention to either except in time of drought or when sewage escapes just when everyone wants to go to the beach.

Oddly enough, these two industries handle only a small percentage of water used in society. Direct human consumption accounts for about one-sixth of water withdrawals. Power plants take four times as much water as do people. Power plant operators, at least, return the water clean, to the environment, although at a higher temperature. Farmers, however, take three times as much water for irrigation purposes as do people for domestic consumption. Much of the irrigation water evaporates, and part of the rest returns to the waterways in polluted form. In some regions, urban and agricultural interests battle each other in order to obtain water supply.

Both industries play a vital role in maintaining public health and environmental cleanliness. They treat water to make it safe for drinking, and treat sewage before returning it to the environment. Untreated sewage affects the safety of water supply, as well. The two services are linked.

Government-owned utilities dominate both industries, an oddity in America's private sector economy. Most of the suppliers, moreover, are small and entirely local in service and ownership, also oddities in modern America.

Those firms will have to deal with increasingly complex environmental demands, as well as greater reluctance on the part of governments to spend money. Will they have the resources to do so? Is the extreme fragmentation and parochiality a consequence of municipal ownership or of the peculiarities of the economics of the industry? All other utilities have moved in the direction of regional or national scope.

Operating a water and sewer utility is simpler, technologically, than the operation of other utilities. But government regulation of the industry, while not centered on profitability, is more pervasive and prescriptive due to public health considerations. People don't pay much for water compared to the bills for other utility or health services, but a poor quality product has expensive consequences.

CHAPTER 6

The Public Water Supply System

A great fire ... proved to the Tarrytowners the necessity of a municipal water supply. The fire gutted 19 buildings ... and one of the reasons for the widespread destruction was the lack of an effective water supply and distribution system.[2]

— Jeff Canning and Wally Buxton

The public or community water supply system performs many functions: it develops and maintains the source of water supply, stores the water for use, transports the water to a treatment plant, treats the water to improve its quality, moves the water from the treatment facility to intermediate points closer to the customers, and then distributes the water to the individual customers. The local water system need not own and operate all the parts of the system, but some entity must provide each of the functions, and the various participants in the process must coordinate their activities. Smaller water systems can telescope the process into fewer functions because of the proximity of the water supply to the wells. In 1996, the public water supply systems, with 122,000 employees, collected over $26 billion for their services. (In comparison, the electric utility industry had revenues of over $200 billion, and an employee count of over 500,000.)

WATER SUPPLY

As a first step, the water authorities must locate the water designated to supply the system. They can choose *surface* or *groundwater* or both (unless they choose to desalinate sea water). Both, of course, depend on the amount of rainfall, how much of it runs off into lakes and rivers, how much infiltrates the soil to become groundwater, and how much evaporates.

Water suppliers take groundwater from natural springs or draw it from wells that tap underground water resources, where water exists in spaces between sand and gravel, and in cracks and pores of rocks. (Aquifers, those underground storage areas, in other words, are not large, underground swimming pools.) Their intake or recharge areas (where water enters the underground resource) may be located far from where the water is withdrawn. Thus, even distant rainfall, land development or disposal of wastes could affect the viability of a particular source of groundwater. (Land development, such as extensive parking lots, prevents water from percolating down into the aquifer. The water is more likely to run off into storm sewers. Improper waste disposal might lead to leaching of poisons into the underground water supply.) Roughly half the population obtains its water supply from groundwater sources, including those people who take water from their own wells. If withdrawal of groundwater exceeds the natural recharge rate, the groundwater level falls. Users of groundwater are, to some extent, at the mercy of other users of groundwater, unless restrictions are placed on everyone's usage. One user that takes too much out of an aquifer reduces the supply for everyone else. Too much withdrawal from the aquifer lowers the water level, which forces those using the aquifer to drill deeper, more expensive wells.

Large urban water suppliers rely more on surface water sources, namely rivers and lakes. Where the water supply is steady, the system may have a simple intake that removes water out of the lake or river. In some cases, the water system will build diversion dams to assure adequate flow to the intake all year round. In the case of water from large lakes, the water supplier might place the intake far out and deep in the lake, and connect it to shore by pipeline. Doing so will assure better quality water (farther from pollution sources) and mitigate difficulties caused by freezing. Surface water, too, suffers from the problem that the action of neighbors affects the quality or quantity of supply. Someone who dumps pollutants into a river upstream of the water intake affects the quality of the water taken in, and raises the cost of purification to the water user. For that matter, a water supplier that takes too much out of the water source may affect the value of the body for recreational use, diminish its environmental qualities, or reduce the ability of others to take water out of the same source. (As an example, New York City proposed to take fresh water out of the Hudson River. An upstate water supplier that used the Hudson as a source claimed that by removing the fresh water from the river, New York City would make Hudson River water saltier farther north, thereby affecting the quality of water that the upstate supplier took in. The Hudson, after all, is a tidal estuary.)

Water suppliers can develop two other sources of supply. They can de-salt sea water (desalination), an expensive, energy-intensive process used mainly in arid lands like Arabia, or they can use *brown water,* which is the purified water that is an end product of the sewage clean-up process. While brown water may be potable, it is more likely to be used for irrigation in areas with scarce water resources, such as Israel. In addition, water consumers can develop a third source: *grey water,* waste water from bathtubs and washing machines. Grey water, however, does contain impurities beyond soap, and has limited uses.

STORAGE NEAR THE SOURCE

Suppliers that rely on surface water face a reliability problem. The amount available depends on patterns of precipitation. Supply is unsteady, varying by season, and patterns of demand for water may not coincide with patterns of supply. Furthermore, droughts may reduce supplies for years at a time. Cities need reliable supplies at all times. The water supplier cannot control rainfall, but can store enough water to provide reliable supplies, even during periods of low water flow or drought. The reservoir stores water. The water system builds a dam on a river or stream. Water flowing in the waterway backs up behind the dam, forming an artificial lake that fills the valley behind the dam. A large water supplier will build reservoirs in several different watersheds as an insurance measure against poor water conditions in any one watershed. The water supplier must prevent pollution on the streams entering the reservoir, and forestall activities that will pollute the surface runoff that goes into the reservoir.

Some reservoirs serve multiple purposes: public water supply, irrigation, flood control, navigation, and hydroelectric generation. In such cases, the water company cannot depend on the reservoir as a supply of water unless water supply is the primary purpose and other uses are secondary. Reservoirs of the large Eastern urban areas are almost exclusively dedicated to water supply. The vast Southern and Western federal water projects, however, favor multi-purpose usage.

At the reservoir, sunlight and air help to clean the water. Sediments sink to the bottom, too. That reduces the *turbidity* (lack of transparency) of the water. From the reservoir, the water moves through screens that remove fish, wood, and other nonmicroscopic objects. Screening is the first and simplest part of the treatment process.

TRANSPORTATION TO THE TREATMENT PLANT

The system has to transport the water from place of storage, often a distant reservoir, to the place of treatment, generally by means of a long pipeline called an aqueduct. (If place of treatment is at or near the reservoir, then the aqueduct system's main job is to move the water from that point to the city.) The water in the aqueduct may flow downhill, thanks to gravity. Otherwise, pumping moves the water to the required destination. In the New York City system, whose water supplies are located in the mountains and hills upstate, most water flows by gravity. In contrast, Los Angeles, which takes water from distant sources, has to pump the water over mountain ranges.

Open canals that carry water must follow the *hydraulic grade line*, that is they must go downhill, continuously, to permit the water to flow in the right direction. To keep the grade, they may have to wind through the landscape, avoiding hills, or go through tunnels that cut through the hill at the right grade. Pipelines, operated under pressure, follow the ground, because the pump or other source of pressure can push the water uphill, if necessary.

Material selected for use in aqueducts has to prevent seepage, withstand pressure, endure for a long period of time, and not poison the water. Water tunnels, going through the right type of rock, may be unlined. Otherwise, aqueduct builders use cement, steel, and cast iron, with the metals often covered by corrosion-resistant materials. Plastic has been introduced for small diameter lines.

TREATMENT

The water treatment facility should remove impurities and kill harmful organisms. Treatment should take out organic compounds, remove substances that produce color, taste, and odor, and chemicals that cause hardness, or other untoward effects. Iron, for instance, stains laundry. Sulfate is a laxative. Chloride adds unpleasant taste. Pesticides may cause cancer.

The treatment process (see Figure 6-1), in simplest terms, consists of five stages:

1. **Chemical**—Chlorine kills living matter. Alum (aluminum potassium sulfate) traps pollutants in clumps. Lime helps the process. Powdered carbon traps more chemicals. Ammonia removes odors and bad taste.

2. **Flash mixer**—Mixing makes the water interact with the chemicals.

3. **Slow mixer**—Slow mixing in the flocculator helps the alum and lime to form glops of chemicals known as flocculant or "floc."

4. **Settler**—Floc settles out and is removed from the water.

5. **Filter**—Water moves slowly through a bed of coal, gravel, and sand. Chlorine, added a second time, prevents a buildup of bacteria in the pipes.

In reality, of course, the treatment process is more complex. For instance, one could argue that sedimentation is a pretreatment process. *Sedimentation,* the settling to the bottom by particles in a liquid, occurs as a natural process in reservoirs or any place where water stands still or flows slowly. The silt and other fine materials

Figure 6-1

Water Treatment

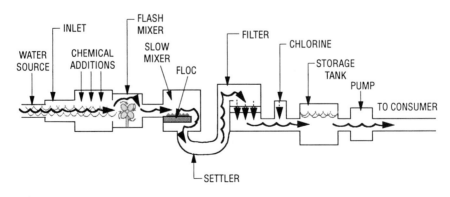

settle to the bottom. Treatment plants have settling tanks in which the water may remain for hours or days. The water might flow horizontally, and solids would sink to the bottom of the tank. Or the water could flow upwards, and the solid particles will sink to the bottom.

Coagulation (curdling of substances in a fluid into a gelatinous mass) removes fine particles and *colloidal matter* (large organic molecules that will not diffuse through animal and vegetable membranes) by causing them to combine into a wooly looking, gooey precipitate called flocculate. Some water, with the right combination of chemical and organic content, coagulates naturally, when mixed. Usually, though, the treatment process adds a chemical, such as an aluminum salt, which forms an insoluble hydroxyl (chemical containing the OH radical) flocculant. The bacteria, colloids, and fine particles in the water get stuck on the surface of the gooey floc, which is then removed.

Filtration, the process of passing liquid through a substance to remove particles within the liquid, cleans out suspended solids and organisms in the water. The slow sand filter is like a giant sandbox, with a layer of sand about two to four feet deep on top, a bed of gravel underneath, and drain pipes below the gravel. Water passes slowly through the sand and then through the gravel to the pipes below. The system does not work well with turbid water, and requires a large land area and labor force. Rapid sand filters operate at more than 25 times the volume of a slow sand filter of the same size. The top bed (about two feet deep) consists of sand or crushed anthracite coal above the gravel that tops the drains. The water flows faster, and the system has a washing mechanism to keep it clean.

Disinfection, the process of destroying disease-causing organisms, can be accomplished in many ways. Boiling the water may be the simplest and surest method. Applying chlorine gas or a chlorine compound to the water may be the most common means of disinfection in the United States. Unfortunately, chlorination produces a bad taste in some water, and it leaves a residue of harmful chemicals. Application of ozone (popular in Europe) and of ultraviolet light kill living organisms, too, without the side effects of chlorination.

Granulated activated carbon, finely powdered, can be placed on the top of filters. The powder reduces tastes and odors, and helps to filter out harmful chemicals, including carcinogenic (cancer causing) substances, many of which are formed as a result of chlorination.

Many facilities have to *soften* water, which means removing the calcium and magnesium salts that give hard water the qualities that makes it hard to wash with, cause scum, and form scales in boilers. Municipal authorities generally act when the hardness components reach 150 ppm. They may treat the water with lime (calcium oxide or CaO) or soda ash (sodium carbonate or Na_2CO_3), which causes the offending hardeners to precipitate as part of new chemical compounds.

As an alternative, the water supplier passes the water through a porous cation exchange (possibly made from a sand called zeolite) that substitutes the sodium ions in the exchange for the calcium and magnesium in the water. Some water, for industrial uses, requires a more thorough process.

Aeration exposes water to the air, which requires the pumping of air through the water, or the pumping of water through air. Aeration adds oxygen to water and removes gases that impart tastes to the water.

That completes the treatment process, which has removed particles, filtered out bacteria, eliminated odor and taste, and killed pathogenic organisms. In some cases, the water supplier adds chemicals to soften the water, as well. Water treatment, then, removes unsafe substances and also makes the water more palatable.

TRANSPORTING TO INTERMEDIATE POINTS

Water must move from the treatment facility to a central distribution facility or directly to the pipes that lead to the customers' homes. In a large system, the company will pump the water from the treatment facility to an intermediate storage facility, such as a large, elevated water tank or a distribution reservoir. The water supplier will locate those facilities throughout the area served, in order to protect supplies in case of emergencies. The system may move water to and from particular facilities in order to assure adequate supply and pressure to all customers. Proper layout of intermediate facilities will reduce the supplier's pumping load, which, in turn, will bring down the supplier's large bill for electricity.

DISTRIBUTION TO CUSTOMERS

The distribution system must supply clean water to customers throughout the system at adequate pressure under almost all circumstances. Water supply must not decline to a dribble due to fire fighting emergencies, demand on hot days, or broken pipes somewhere.

Water systems normally operate at pressures of between 30 to 100 pounds per square inch (psi). Pressure prevents inward leakage into pipes, which would allow pollutants to taint the treated water. Pressure raises water supply in the pipe above ground level. Forty to 50 psi will push the water to the fourth floor. Firefighters without pumping engines need 75 psi. At the same time, too much pressure causes the system to lose too much water and adds to equipment maintenance and operating costs.

In the New York City system:

> Water pressure is regulated within a range of 35 to 60 pounds per square inch ('psi') at street level. Generally, 40 psi is sufficient to supply water to the top

of a five or six-story building. About 95% of the total consumption is normally delivered by gravity. It is necessary to pump only the remaining 5% to areas of higher elevation to keep the pressure within this desired range.[3]

Gravity is a powerful force. So is atmospheric pressure. It is no accident that water tanks are elevated in water towers. (See Figure 6-2.)

Figure 6-2

Water Pressure

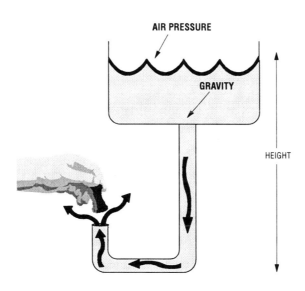

Where:

P = pressure

H = height of liquid

D = density of the liquid

G = acceleration of gravity,

then:

P = HDG

meaning that "the pressure at the bottom of the vessel depends on the height of the liquid above it, the density of the liquid, and the value of g at that place."[4] Water

41

supply from elevated reservoirs coming down the mountains creates pressure in the same way.

Finally, at the end of the pipe, where the system connects to the customer's plumbing, there may or may not be a meter that keeps count of how much water the customer uses. Customers without meters pay a flat rate, that is, the same price per billing period, no matter how much water they take. The price might be based on a formula that takes into account the size of the building and number of water-using fixtures.

Simple System

Small towns do not require the elaborate facilities found in major cities. The town probably takes its water from a nearby well. It pumps the water to ground level, runs it through a desander and chlorinator, pumps it up to a water tower, which serves as a storage and pressure-equalizing reservoir, and then the water flows through the distribution system to the consumers. (See Figure 6-3.)

Major City System

Denver provides an example of a complex city water system. The city is located in an arid region. Nearby groundwater and local surface water are inadequate in quantity. The problem, simply, is that Denver is located on the eastern slope of the Rocky Mountains. More rain falls on the western slope, but that water

Figure 6-3

Simple Water System

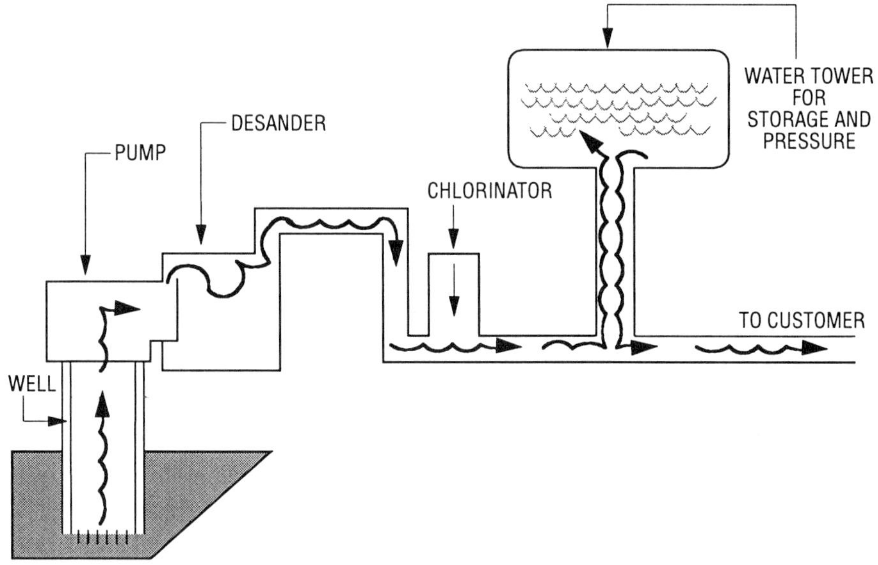

WATER TOWER
FOR
STORAGE AND
PRESSURE

DESANDER

PUMP

CHLORINATOR

TO CUSTOMER

WELL

flows westward, away from Denver. Denver's water system engineers decided to bring water from the western slope across the Continental Divide to the eastern slope. They completed the first project in 1936. On the western slope, the city collected water, built reservoirs to store excess flow, and sent the water, by gravity flow, through canals and tunnels, across the Continental Divide, to the eastern slope. There, the water flows to storage reservoirs and to treatment plants. Then pumping stations send the water through the distribution system. (See Figure 6-4.) Today, private industry participates. For example, Vidler Water, an investor-owned entity, owns one of the two transcontinental-divide tunnels that move the water east.

Suburban Regional System

New Jersey-American Water Company needed an additional water supply for 55 communities in southwestern New Jersey. Groundwater supply was inadequate, so the company, in conjunction with the state and other municipal water systems in the area, decided to use Delaware River water. This plan became the "Tri-County" project. Planning for the Tri-County project began in 1986, the company broke ground in 1993, and the project began operations in 1996.

The water intake is located on the Delaware River. The company's allocation is 40 million gallons per day (mgd), compared to the 2,000 mgd that passes the site during a period of drought. The water flows by gravity through two 54-inch-diameter pipes a distance of one-third of a mile, to a pumping station. From there, electric pumps send the water another two miles, through a 54-inch-diameter pipe, to the treatment plant.

The treatment plant began operations with a capacity of 30 mgd, but it was designed for expansion to 100 mgd. Treatment begins with ozone not chlorine. A new method of chemical coagulation removes solid matter. Activated carbon granules remove the remaining particles, organic matter, and taste. Chlorine is the final disinfectant.

Another pumping station sends the water through a pipeline system whose transmission mains (large pipes) vary in diameter from 24 to 54 inches. The pipelines carry the water to the communities served by New Jersey-American and other municipal systems. The company will mix water from the Tri-County project with water from other sources, all of which must meet the standards set by New Jersey-American.

COSTS

The cost of providing water varies, depending on whether the system has a distant supply, whether it has to pump the water (and thereby pay big electric bills), how much treatment the water requires, and the complexity and difficulty of maintaining the system in the big city. The cost of water, including return on

Figure 6-4

Denver Water System

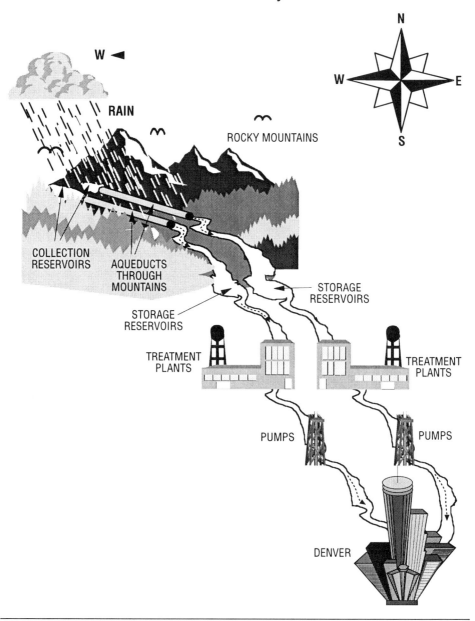

investment, could range from 0.1 cent to 0.4 cents per gallon, which works out to an annual bill of perhaps $300 to $500 for the average water user. The water supplier, however, might have invested $1,500 per customer in water supply plant in order to provide that water. Of that investment, perhaps $1,000 went into distribution facilities, $150 into water treatment, and $350 for supply.

Providing water requires large amounts of investment relative to revenue collected. The ratio is roughly $4 to $5 of investment to $1 of revenue, compared to a $3 to $1 ratio in the electric utility business. The water utilities have to build plant to meet demand at peak periods, which may be twice average daily demand. Customers want the water when they want it, not when it is most convenient for the water utility. Water suppliers build reservoirs and other storage facilities for average conditions. But the biggest investment is elsewhere, and:

> transmission and treatment facilities, as well as major feeder mains, pumping stations, and local storage facilities, are designed to meet maximum-hour demand, or maximum-day demand plus fire protection flow requirements, whichever is greatest.[5]

Operating and maintenance expenses consume roughly half the revenue of the investor-owned water utility. Another 15% goes to paying taxes, 10% to cover wear and tear of plant and equipment (depreciation), and the balance pays creditors (interest expense) and owners (profit). Government-owned water utilities would show a different breakdown, because they do not pay taxes. Their ratios might look more like this: 65% operating and maintenance expenses, 15% for depreciation, and 20% for interest payments and profit.

Table 6-1 provides a breakdown of revenue for four large investor-owned water utilities in four regions of the country, based on 1995 data. Table 6-2 presents operating statistics for the four regional groups. Note how much of a gap exists between average production and the production capacity that the company has in place. The water utility has to build its plant large enough to handle demand at peak periods. (One cannot expect the fire department to put off its demand to another hour.) In a sense, the water utility has to support almost twice as much plant as it needs on an average day. To add to the expense, the utility loses almost 20% of the water produced before it reaches the customer. Furthermore, it has to invest $1,500 to $2,500 per average customer and support that investment (whose depreciation and return is at least $120 to $200 per year) whether the customer takes one gallon or the expected 400 gallons a day. Interestingly, it is possible that the variable costs involved in producing the incremental gallon sold equal only 20% of the price of that gallon. This is, clearly, a business with high fixed costs.

CONCLUSION

The public water supply system collects, purifies, and reliably delivers water at a reasonable price to roughly three-quarters of the population, mainly in urban areas. And it does so at a price so low that many people just about disregard the

Table 6-1

Revenue and Expenses Breakdown[1],[2]
Regional Water Utilities[3]
1995 (% of Revenue)

	Four Eastern Water Utilities	Four Midwestern Water Utilities	Four Southern Water Utilities	Four Western Water Utilities
Revenues[4]	100.0	100.0	100.0	100.0
Operating and maintenance (O&M) expenses[5]				
Production	14.5	10.0	12.0	39.5
Purification	2.0	8.5	8.5	1.5
Transmission and distribution	7.5	9.5	7.0	6.5
Customer Service	5.0	6.5	5.5	5.0
Administrative and general	15.0	16.0	18.0	12.5
Total O&M Expenses	44.0	50.5	51.0	65.0
Depreciation	9.5	10.0	9.0	7.0
Taxes and misc.	21.0	14.5	15.5	10.5
Total Expenses	74.5	75.0	75.5	82.5
Revenue available for owners of capital (interest paid plus profit)	25.5	25.0	24.5	17.5

Notes:
[1]Expense breakdown may vary due to classification by company and by whether company undertakes activity on its own or purchases services or water from others.
[2]Data from National Association of Water Companies.
[3]Four largest water utilities in region, after removing companies in same state.
[4]Gross plant in service as a multiple of revenue was $4.5\times$ (Eastern), $4.3\times$ (Midwestern), $4.5\times$ (Southern), and $3.5\times$ (Western).
[5]Payroll expenses included in O&M as a % of revenue are 18.0% (Eastern), 24.0% (Midwestern), 17.5% (Southern), and 14.5% (Western).

water bill. Price of service, however, could go up, unless either the water suppliers or the water users make a significant breakthrough in developing new supply and consumption technologies. In may ways, this appears to be a 19th-century industry heading into the 21st century.

Table 6-2

Operating Statistics for Four Water Utilities
In Each Region
1995

	Eastern (Total)	Midwestern (Total)	Southern (Total)	Western (Total)
Productive Capacity (mgd)	586	850	214	1,696
Maximum daily rate (mgd)	533	660	193E	1,016
Peak hourly rate (mgd)	696	869	210E	1,119E
Average daily production (mgd)	358	384	138	586
Annual water delivered (mg)	131,634	140,017	50,321	213,835
Water sold (mg)	105,888	119,965	43,020	179,244
Customers (1,000s)	734	749	292	866
Estimated population served (1,000s)	2,344	2,586	891	3,461
Employees	1,534	1,468	722	1,465
Revenues ($ millions)	390	252	143	411
Gross plant in service ($ millions)	1,742	1,071	639	1,445
Net plant in service ($ millions)	1,404	828	516	1,058
Miles of main	10,915	9,945	4,085	10,203
Water sold as % of water delivered	80.4	85.7	85.5	83.8
Maximum daily rate as % of average daily production	148.8	171.9	171.5	173.4
Water sold/customer (annual)	144,261	160,167	147,329	206,979
Revenue/customer (annual)	$531	$336	$490	$475
Revenue/gallon sold (annual)	$0.0037	$0.0021	$0.0033	$0.0023
Customers/employees	479	510	404	591
Customers/mile of main	67.2	75.3	71.5	84.9
Gross plant in service/customers	$2,377	$1,430	$2,188	$1,669
Gross plant in service/productive capacity	$2.97	$1.26	$2.99	$0.85

Note:
mgd—million gallons per day
 mg—million gallons
 gd—gallons per day
  E—estimated

CHAPTER 7

The Collection and Treatment of Sewage

Small boys still paddle up and down the stream on rafts and angle for catfish;
raw sewage . . . has driven off . . . other species . . . —but sewage doesn't show
much . . . and catfish thrive on it and boys survive anyway.[6]

— R.E. Banta

Suppliers first clean the water for public use. Then the sewage systems collect
and clean the wastewater before returning it to the environment. And the cycle
continues. Environmentalists decry the loss of organic matter, which could be
converted to fertilizer, that the sewage systems dump into the water. Neighbors
complain about odors from treatment plants. Municipal governments resist expensive improvements to their systems. Taxpayers vote down capital expenditures
destined to repair and upgrade facilities. Sewage however, is more than an environmental issue or a budget annoyance. It is a big, growing business, with 121,000
employees and over $28 billion revenue per year.

COLLECTION

The sewage system collects, carries, and treats wastewater, and then disposes of the
treated effluent (outflow). The system collects human, household, and industrial
wastes and some systems still collect rainwater and surface runoff, as well,
although mixing the waste and run-off operations causes major pollution
problems.

In simple terms, the sewage system collects wastewater from residences and
businesses through pipes that connect the customers' premises to a network of
sewer pipe under the streets. Toilet, bathtub, and garbage disposal units all empty
into the sewer system. (So does the runoff of rains from driveways and streets.
A modern, well-designed sewer system, however, separates the storm from the
sanitary sewers, and surface runoff goes into its own sewer system.) Sewage
contains harmful substances, so the pipes are made of corrosion-resistant materials. They vary in size, from eight inches to eight feet in diameter, depending on
their placement in the system and the volume that they are expected to carry. In
order to avoid the need for pumping, engineers try to lay out the collection
network on a downgrade, so that the wastewater flows by gravity. Obviously,
though, they will install pumps where needed, in order to keep the flow moving.
The system must not only pump the sewage in the right direction in places where
gravity flow will not carry the sewage to the proper destination, but it must also
maintain a velocity of flow that removes solids left in the pipes during periods

of low flow. Bacterial activity in material left in the pipes could produce explosive or poisonous gases.

The system's treatment facilities may not have the capability to handle some industrial wastes. Industrial customers, therefore, may have to pre-treat the materials that they release into the sewer system. The average user of the system should not have to pay the costs required if the system's plant had to be modified to deal with unusual purification problems. Unfortunately, due to the open nature of the sewer system, malefactors can dump damaging or illegal substances into the sewer system to the detriment of all other users.

Where the collection pipes meet, manholes permit entry into the system for purposes of cleaning or maintenance. (Manhole covers, incidentally, are round so that they cannot fall into the manholes.)

Surface runoff from rains presents another problem. The word "sewage" (also sewerage) derives from the Old Norman French word *seuwiere*, which was the channel that carried off the overflow water from a fishpond. Perhaps the connection between sewage and runoff is older than that between sewage and sanitary wastes. Surface runoff from streets drains into storm sewers, whose openings (collecting points, in reality) are those holes, covered by grates, on the sides of streets and roads. In old-style sewer systems, the storm sewers connected to the main sewer system. The storm water, mingled with the waste water, flowed to the discharge point, and then into the nearby river or lake. The sewer system discharged all its contents, no matter what, untreated. So mingling the two streams of waste did not make any difference. Eventually, however, the systems began to treat the wastewater before returning it to the environment. A rush of runoff after a heavy rain could overwhelm the capacity of the treatment plant, causing the discharge of untreated sewage into the environment. In order to avoid this problem, authorities today rarely build combination sewer systems that handle both surface runoff and wastewater.

To sum up, the collection network of the sewer system begins with small pipes that collect wastewater from customers. Those pipes join to larger pipes that meet at large junction chambers. From those chambers, an even larger pipe conveys the wastewater to a treatment facility. The system is designed to flow downhill, as much as possible, to utilize the force of gravity, but wherever necessary, powerful pumps push the wastewater to its destination, the treatment plant. (See Figure 7-1.)

TREATMENT

Wastewater contains solids, usually categorized as colloidal matter, floating matter, matter in solution, and matter in suspension. The wastewater has other physical characteristics that make it offensive or dangerous: acidity, alkalinity, tempera-

Figure 7-1

Sanitary Sewer System

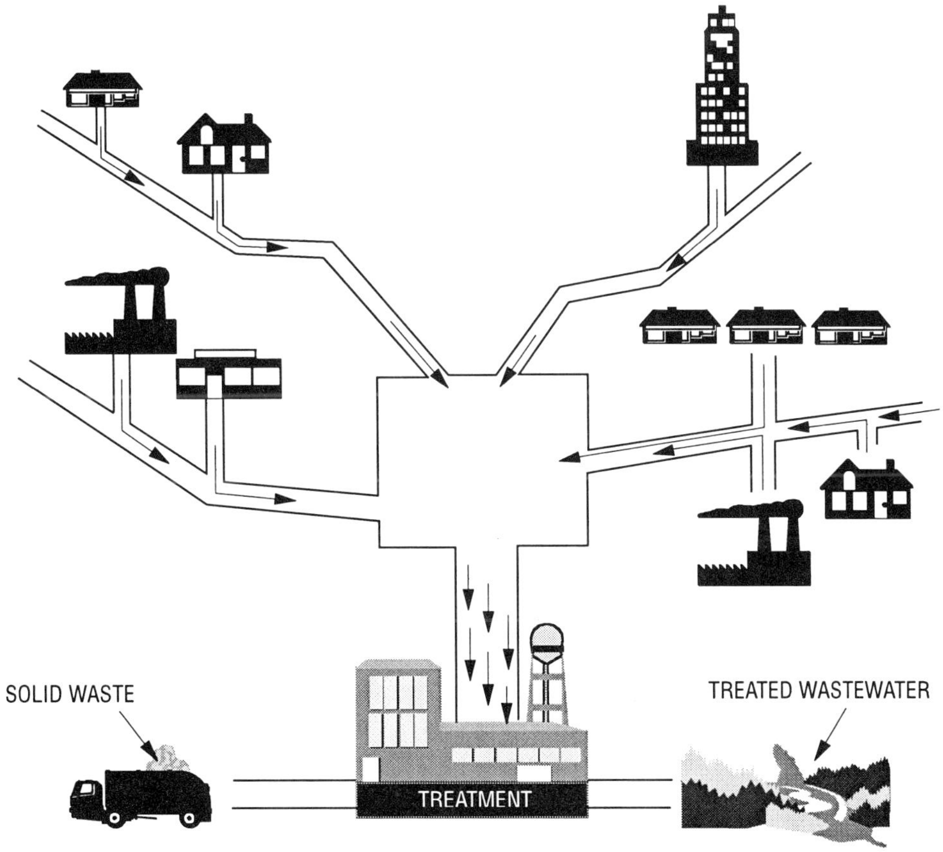

SOLID WASTE

TREATED WASTEWATER

TREATMENT

ture, color, odor. And, of course, the wastewater contains pathogenic (disease causing) organisms. How the wastewater is treated is determined by its contents and by the regulatory requirements that apply so that it may be returned to the environment in a safe form.

Originally, in the good old days, nobody treated sewage. The stuff was dumped in the nearest body of water. After all, people believed that water had a naturally cleansing effect that would take care of the problem. As a precautionary matter, one did not put their water supply intake downriver close to the sewage discharge outlet. Of course, another water supplier might have its intake downstream of the discharge point, but, presumably, the cleansing power of water did its magic before the pollution reached the unfortunates downstream.

Eventually, public health authorities insisted on the treatment of raw sewage, to remove matter dangerous to health before its discharge into the environment. The treatment process developed through three stages (Figure 7-2).

First, sewage authorities utilized what later was called *primary treatment*. The sewage treatment plant screened out coarse solids, and removed others by a process of sedimentation (letting them settle to the bottom of the tank). It removed floating oil and grease. It compensated for excessive acidity or alkalinity. It added in a mixture of microorganisms that broke down organic materials.

Then, in order to clean the sewage even more, treatment plants moved to *secondary treatment*, adding more biological processes to break down organic substances, and more chemical processes to remove solids. Primary and secondary treatments together remove about 90% of suspended solids, half of nitrogen, and one-third of phosphorous in the sewage.

In some places, not even secondary treatment is sufficient. *Tertiary treatment* adds more advanced procedures to the process. Carbon *adsorption* (gathering dissolved substances onto a surface) removes traces of organic materials. Chemical precipitation or ion exchange techniques concentrate and remove toxic metals. (They introduce a chemical into the sewage that combines with the metal to form a compound that falls to the bottom of the tank.) Filters remove any solids still suspended in the wastewater. Only a small percentage of sewage systems employ tertiary treatment.

Figure 7-2

Primary-Secondary-Tertiary Sewage Treatment

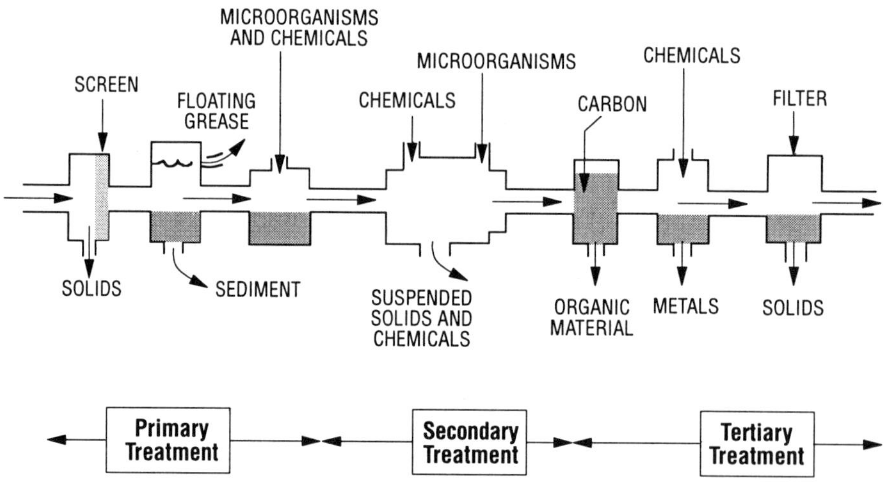

Figure 7-3

Sewage Treatment Process

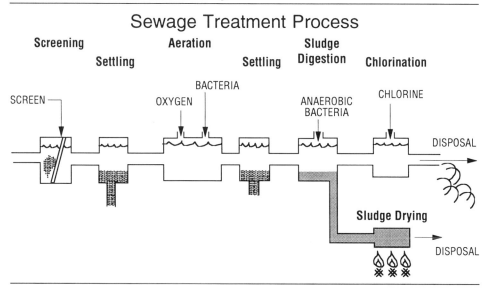

Generally, the sewage treatment process has seven parts (see Figure 7-3).

1. **Screening**—Remove large items from the wastewater.

2. **Settling**—Take out grit (sandy particles). Move wastewater to a tank. Let particles settle out and fall to the bottom for removal.

3. **Aeration**—Add bacteria to the sewage (sludge). Add oxygen to stimulate the activity of these oxygen-using (aerobic) bacteria. The mixture of sewage and bacteria is called activated sludge. The bacteria eat the harmful organic material. The end products of this process are carbon monoxide, water, and secondary sludge.

4. **Settling**—In the second settling tank, even more sediment settles out of the wastewater.

5. **Sludge digestion**—Secondary sludge goes into a digestor. Add non-oxygen-using (anaerobic) bacteria. They break down the sludge over a 15-day period, turning it into a soil-like substance.

6. **Sludge drying**—Dry out the wet sludge, making it easier to dispose of.

7. **Chlorination**—Add chlorine to remaining waste water. That kills the bacteria in the water (many of which were added during the treatment process). Other

disinfecting processes may substitute for chlorination, incidentally. Wastewater, now cleaned and disinfected, can return to the environment.

DISPOSAL

Treatment of sewage produces two products: water and a solid. The water that emerges from the treatment plant varies in quality, depending on the degree of treatment. People could drink water that received tertiary treatment, although the chances are that only sewage engineers would do so voluntarily, at the present time. Water shortages and the cost of bringing in fresh water, however, might change attitudes. In water-short regions the treated water is used for irrigation purposes. (Israelis irrigate with sewage water, as do many American golf courses.) Otherwise, the treatment plant will discharge the treated water into rivers and streams.

The solid byproduct, the sludge, presents another problem. It contains enough organic matter to qualify as a fertilizer, but it may also contain concentrations of toxic chemicals that would poison crops or the people who eat them. The sewage authorities cannot dump the sludge into the ocean or into the nearest waterway, as before. Neither fertilizing the water nor poisoning it is socially acceptable (or legal) anymore. Disposal, then, depends on the contents of the sludge. Cities have fertilized nearby farms, helped to reclaim strip-mined areas, produced compost for sale, or buried sludge in landfills.

COSTS

Roughly speaking, the treatment and disposal of wastewater costs about the same as the treatment and delivery of clean water, or about $130 per person served in the United States. Of that amount, perhaps 70% goes to paying operating expenses, including labor, and 30% to meet fixed costs, including return on invested capital. Wastewater collection and treatment may be even more capital intensive than water supply. Those estimates, however, assume that cities and towns properly allocate their sewer costs, revenue, and whatever taxes replace revenues, which may qualify as heroic assumptions. Furthermore, the costs of sewage treatment could rise significantly. Not only does existing infrastructure need major rehabilitation but the elimination of combined sewers would add to sewage costs in the older cities of the Northeast and Midwest.

CONCLUSION

Disposing of wastewater (sewage) is a big business, possibly bigger than furnishing clean water. Because of the public health and environmental aspects of sewage, government takes an even greater role than in the water industry. Conceivably, sewage providers have made even less use of economic signals than water suppliers, which may indicate the possibility of a less-than-efficient sewer system, but that is another matter. Sewer operations and water supply, though, have similar networks, similar treatment of product, the systems often are parallel to each other, and they have the same customers. In the United States, municipal govern-ments often provide both water and wastewater services, and they reap the benefits of whatever operating economies derive from providing the two services to the same customers. Private water companies, however, are less likely to provide wastewater services as well. Separating the two functions in the same location for the same customers might reduce the potential operating efficiencies for both services, to the detriment of the consumer.

CHAPTER 8

Supply, Demand, and Suppliers

. . . Kublai Khan . . . boasted that his magicians had the power of controlling bad weather, and obliging it to retire to any quarter of the heavens. Marco Polo . . . neglected to verify this claim.[7]

— Lewis Mumford

The earth's total inventory of fresh water remains unchanged. It is the same as it was 100 years ago and it will be the same 100 years from now. In some regions, the usable supply is unreliable or inadequate for the size of the population settled there, and for the demands they place on the water supplies. In other regions, water supply exceeds any possible human use for it. Thanks to periodic droughts or unusual rainfall of Biblical proportions, regions of plentiful water swing to scarcity, and vice versa. By and large, though, water supply exceeds need, but uneven distribution of water resources, pollution of existing supplies and growing demand create serious problems in many parts of the world. The United States is not an exception.

INVENTORY

The human population requires fresh water, but 97.6% of the world's water is salty, 1.8% is locked away in glaciers, and only 0.6% is liquid and fresh. Mother Nature did not put the fresh water on a platter for the taking, either. Over 97% of all fresh water is underground. (See Tables 8-1 and 8-2). People, in essence, have to mine for water in the same way that they mine for gold.

Table 8-1

World Water Inventory (%)

	Total	Fresh	Unfrozen Fresh
Oceans	97.6%	—	—
Ice	1.8	73.9%	—
Groundwater	0.6	25.7	98.4%
Lakes, streams and atmosphere	0.0	0.4	1.6
	100.0%	100.0%	100.0%

Source:
Carla W. Montgomery, *Environmental Geology* (Dubuque, IA: Wm. C. Brown Publishers, 1992), p. 214.

Table 8-2

World Fresh Water Inventory
(Excluding Ice)

	Cubic Miles	Millions of Acre Feet	Quadrillions of Gallons	%
Groundwater	2,000,000	6,760,000	2,202.7	97.74
Lake water	30,000	101,500	33.1	1.47
Surface soil water	16,000	54,000	17.6	0.78
River and stream water	300	1,000	0.3	0.01
Total	2,046,300	6,916,500	2,253.7	100.00

Source:
Encyclopedia Brittanica

The hydrological cycle that maintains and recirculates the water inventory is a closed one. As Figure 8-1 shows, more water evaporates from the ocean than precipitates into it, but runoff from the land makes up the deficit. More water precipitates on land then evaporates from land or transpires from living organisms on land. That difference flows into the sea. So far, we have developed no economically feasible, large-scale mechanisms to make more rain over land or to stop the water from running into the ocean.

In the United States, rainfall averages about 4,200 billion gallons per day. Evaporation and transpiration subtract about 2,800 billion gallons per day from the potential supply, leaving around 1,400 billion gallons per day to recharge ground water storage or to flow into surface waterways. Americans then withdraw over 400 billion gallons per day from the remaining supply for various uses. Of that amount, after use, about three-quarters discharges back into the waterways or into the ground, and the rest evaporates. The problem, then, is not a countrywide lack of water, but rather a combination of lack of abundant water supplies in the fast-growing West, falling ground water levels in agricultural regions, pollution of aquifers and of surface water sources, and periodic droughts. Lake Superior will not run dry. Not many people, though, live near Lake Superior. They prefer, instead to live in the Arizona and California deserts, while maintaining a Lake Superior lifestyle. A vast part of the United States receives little rain and many people live there. (Figure 8-2.) And a lot more people are moving there.

USAGE IN THE UNITED STATES

The average American uses about 123 gallons per day at home, one-third of that amount outdoors, to water lawns, clean cars, fill pools, and grow tomatoes. The bathroom accounts for most indoor water use, for toilets, baths, and showers. (See Table 8-3.)

Figure 8-1

World Hydrological Cycle Quantified
(Billions of Cubic Meters/Year)

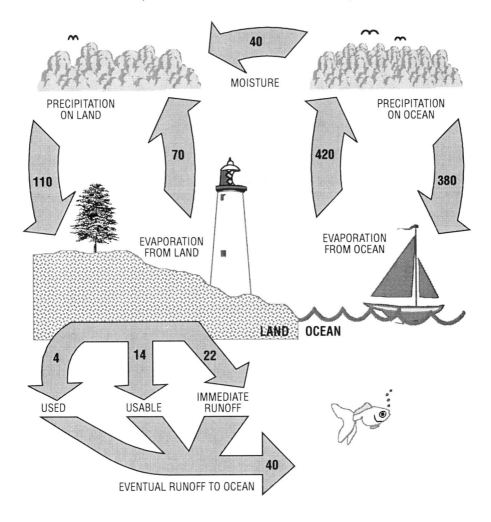

Note:
One cubic meter equals 2.8 gallons. All data rounded.

Source:
Geoffrey Lean and Don Hinrichsen, *WWF Atlas of the Environment* (Santa Barbara, CA: 1994), p. 60.

Figure 8-2

Rainfall Patterns in the Continental United States

☐ Under 50 cm (127.0 in)
☐ 50-75 cm (127.0-190.5 in)
▨ Over 75 cm (190.5 in)

Despite all the fuss about low-flush toilets, efficient showerheads, and leaky faucets, America's households account for less than 15% of water usage and consumption. (See Tables 8-4 and 8-5.) Electric utilities, for steam generation, withdraw more water than any other sector, but they return almost all of it to the same stream in clean form, so they put little strain on the system. Irrigation, the sector with the second largest withdrawal, is by far the biggest consumer of water. More than half of irrigation water evaporates rather than flows back into neighboring streams. Furthermore, agricultural chemicals and pesticides pollute much of the irrigation water that returns to waterways, making it unusable to others.

Since 1900, groundwater has furnished about one-fourth of the water used in the country. Groundwater, however, accounted for only one-tenth of irrigation needs in 1900, and two-fifths in the 1980s and 1990s. (See Table 8-6). Agricultural interests, in essence, have been mining the groundwater.

Table 8-3

Water Use per Day for Residential User
(Gallons per Capita)

	Gallons	%
Outdoor	45	36
Indoor		
Toilets	27	22
Laundry	17	14
Shower and baths	22	18
Other	12	10
Total indoor	78	64
Total	123	100

Source:
Dr. Janice A. Beecher, "PUC 2000: The Water Utility Industry," *Water*, Vol. 36, No. 2, Summer 1995, p. 37.

Table 8-4

Average Daily Water Use in the United States
(Billions of Gallons per Day)

	Total	Irrigation	Public Utilities	Rural Domestic	Industrial and Misc.	Steam Electric
1900	40	20	3	2	10	5
1910	66	39	5	2	14	7
1920	92	56	6	2	18	9
1930	111	60	8	3	21	18
1940	136	71	10	3	29	23
1950	184	89	14	4	37	40
1960	273	110	21	4	38	100
1970	379	130	27	5	47	170
1980	445	150	38	6	45	210
1990	408	137	34	8	30	195

Source:
For 1900–1930, George Thomas Kurian, *Datapedia of the United States 1790–2000* (Lanham, MD: Bernan Press, 1994), p. 170.
For 1940–1990, U.S. Department of Commerce, *Statistical Abstract of the United States* (Washington, D.C.: U.S. Government Printing Office).

Note:
Data rounded and adjusted.

Table 8-5

Average Daily Consumptive Use in the United States
1960–1990
(Billions of Gallons)

	Total	Irrigation	Public Utility	Rural	Industrial and Misc.	Steam Electric
1960	61	52	4	3	3	0
1965	77	66	5	3	3	0
1970	87	73	6	3	4	1
1975	96	80	7	3	4	2
1980	100	83	7	4	5	3
1985	92	74	8 E	4 E	3 E	3 E
1990	94	76	8 E	4 E	3 E	3 E

Source:
Statistical Abstract

Note:
Estimates in 1985, 1990 required due to reallocation of data between consumer categories, eliminating Public Utility category. Data have been rounded and totals may not add.

Table 8-6

Average Daily Groundwater Use in the United States
(Billions of Gallons)

	Total	Irrigation	Public Utilities	Rural Domestic	Industrial and Misc.	Steam Electric
1900	7	2	1	2	2	0
1910	12	5	1	2	3	0
1920	16	8	2	2	4	0
1930	18	9	2	2	4	0
1940	23	11	3	3	6	0
1950	35	20	4	4	7	0
1960	57	35	6	4	12	0
1970	68	40	7	5	16	0
1980	90	62	7	6	15	0
1990	81	55	8	8	10	0

Source:
Statistical Abstract and *Datapedia*

Note:
Partially estimated 1950–1990. Data have been rounded and totals may not add.

The huge increase in water destined for irrigation, largely in the arid west (see Table 8-7), has had two impacts on public supply. First, it has limited the amount of water available to urban water consumers, forcing them to seek more distant and expensive resources. Second, it has lowered aquifer water levels by withdrawing more water than the sparse local rainfall can recharge, thereby limiting the water available for future urban development, and increasing the cost of accessing that water.

On a per-capita basis (see Table 8-8) water use doubled between 1900 and 1940, but four-fifths of the increase came about from increased demand for irrigation and for steam generation of electricity. From 1940 to 1990, water usage per capita rose 60%, with three-fifths of the increase attributable to irrigation and electric generation. Individuals did use more water, as they installed indoor toilets, bathtubs, and washing machines, and as they moved from apartments and houses on tiny lots to suburban homes with big lawns, but they did not drive the increase in total usage. (From 1940 to 1990, the percentage of dwelling units with indoor plumbing rose from 52% to 99%. That fact, alone, could have explained a significant part of the increase in usage per residential consumer, but only a small fraction of the increase in overall water usage in the country.)

Demand for water has grown with the economy and with population. (See Table 8-9.) Obviously, more people need more water, and as they move to larger homes, and add on plumbing and appliances, they take more water per dwelling unit.

Table 8-7

Irrigated Farm Acreage
(1,000s)

	Total	17 Western States	31 Eastern States
1900	7,789	7,543	246
1910	11,667	11,259	408
1920	14,482	13,883	599
1930	14,689	14,086	603
1940	17,983	17,243	740
1950	25,787	24,271	1,516
1960	33,700 E	31,200 E	2,500 E
1970	39,500 E	35,000 E	4,500 E
1980	49,700 E	42,200 E	7,500 E
1990	48,200 E	38,100 E	10,100 E

Sources:
U.S. Department of Commerce, *Historical Statistics of the United States, Colonial Times to 1957* (Washington, D.C: Bureau of the Census, 1960), p. 240, and *Statistical Abstract*.

Notes:
1960–1990 estimated from bracketing years, by extrapolation.
E—estimate

Table 8-8

Per Capita Water Use in the United States, 1900–1990
(Gallons per Day)

	Total	Public Utility	Groundwater	Population (Millions)		
				Total	Served by Public Utilities	% Served by Public Utility
1900	528	—	92	76.1	—	—
1910	719	—	131	92.4	—	—
1920	859	—	149	106.5	—	—
1930	898	—	146	123.1	—	—
1940	1,027	133 E	174	136.3	E	55.0
1950	1,185	145	225	151.9	96.6	63.6
1960	1,500	151	313	180.0	139.1	77.3
1970	1,815	166	326	203.9	162.6	79.7
1980	1,953	183	395	225.3	185.8	82.5
1990	1,620	195	319	251.9	210.3	83.5

Sources:
Based on series in *Statistical Abstract* and *Datapedia*. 1940 data, as issued, appears wrong and has been adjusted by authors.

Notes:
Per capita use by those on public utility water system.
E—estimate

Industry, however, has grown far faster than its consumption of water. The same applies to steam electricity generation. On the other hand, farm output has increased at half the rate of growth of water applied for irrigation purposes. For the first half of the century, water use and economic activity moved together. With the subsequent slowdown in expansion of western water projects, the rise of environmentalism, and the move toward a service economy, the connection between water usage and economic activity has weakened. In individual years, water consumption may depend more on weather conditions than economic indicators.

PUBLIC WATER SUPPLIERS

Water service is the most local of all public utilities. Everyone needs the product. Public health requires a clean and safe supply. The product is heavy, expensive to transport, and sells at a low price per unit. Water utilities move water for long distances only if they have no choice, that is, there is no local water source. As a result, individual water suppliers size their operations to local or regional needs. Most operate at the size that other utility sectors would consider far below that necessary to reach optimal levels of efficiency. The majority of the suppliers, in fact, are so limited in scope that they do not even qualify as community water

Table 8-9

Water Use and Economic Indicators, 1900–1990
(1900 = 100)

	Total Water Usage	Gross National Product	Industrial and Misc. Water Usage	Industrial Production Index	Gross Farm Product	Irrigation Water Usage	kWh Generated	Water Use Electric Generation
1900	100	100	100	100	100	100	100 E	100
1910	165	156	140	170	109	195	400 E	140
1920	230	182	180	246	117	280	1,020	180
1930	278	239	210	310	120	300	2,065	360
1940	340	295	290	425	131	355	3,232	460
1950	460	462	370	748	145	445	7,007	800
1960	683	634	380	1,100	164	550	15,036	2,000
1970	948	940	470	1,773	178	650	29,705	3,400
1980	1,113	1,244	450	2,430	188	750	44,455	4,200
1990	1,020	1,617	300	3,063	264	685	56,013	3,900

Sources:
1. U.S. Department of Commerce, *Long Term Economic Growth 1860-1970* (Washington, DC: Bureau of Economic Analysis, 1973), pp. 184-185.
2. U.S. Department of Commerce Bureau of the Census, *Historical Statistics of the United State 1789-1945* (Washington DC: Bureau of the Census, 1949), p. 158.
3. *Statistical Abstract.*

---

systems. Of the 58,000 community systems, only a small percentage even fall under public utility regulation. (See Table 8-10.)

A sample of the water industry in 1994 (Table 8-11) shows the vast number of tiny water systems in the country, both publicly and privately owned. At the same time, a mere one-half of one percent of the companies served 44% of the population. Government-owned companies predominate, serving four-fifths of the population. Furthermore, all the giant water systems, including the Los Angeles Department of Water and Power, the Chicago Water Department and the Dallas City Waterworks and Sewer System, are government-owned.

Wastewater is just as local and monopolistic a service as water supply. Water utilities may collect supply at a distance, and then bring it to consumers. Wastewater utilities collect the supply from consumers, and then dispose of it at a distance. Wastewater volume tends to correlate with public water supply volume, for the obvious reason that the water taken from the supplier has to go somewhere after it is used. In much of the country, the same entity provides water and wastewater services, so generalizations made about the size, ownership, and number of water utilities apply to the wastewater industry, as well.

Table 8-10

Water and Wastewater Systems in the United States
1994

	Number of Systems	%
Total Water		
Non-community systems	142,000	71
Community systems	58,000	29
	200,000	100
Regulated Water Systems		
Investor-owned	6,650	59
Municipal	1,680	15
Water districts	1,270	11
Other	1,620	15
	11,220	100
Regulated Wastewater Systems		
Investor-owned	2,450	74
Municipal	630	19
Water districts	190	6
Other	30	1
	3,300	100

Source:
Dr. Janice A. Beecher, "PUC 2000: The Water Industry," *Water*, Vol. 36
No. 2, Summer 1995, pp. 35–36.

Even the large, investor-owned utilities (Table 8-12) are small by utility standards. Two holding companies, American Water Works and United Water Resources, own almost half of the large companies in the business. The holding companies have aggregated some of their properties for administrative convenience, but retain a bewilderingly large number of affiliates spread among many states.

In the aggregate, water and wastewater industry revenues have risen steadily, at a pace that probably reflects price increases to cover additional costs as well as wider coverage of the population. Employment in the industries has grown rapidly, as well. (See Table 8-13.)

BOTTLED WATER

In the 1960s and 1970s, drinking bottled water in the United States seemed an affectation limited to those who frequented continental restaurants, yuppies, those who did not want to order an alcoholic beverage but did not want to order a soft drink either, and, of course, office workers gathered around the water cooler. Sales took off after the introduction of small bottles on store shelves in 1984, and

Table 8-11

Public Water Supply Systems in the United States
1994

	Total	Population Served by System			
		Up to 3,300	3,301– 10,000	10,001– 100,000	Over 100,000
Number of Systems and Ownership					
Public	22,609	16,605	3,265	2,491	248
Private	29,691	28,644	586	406	55
Unreported	4,303	4,002	193	102	6
Total	56,603	49,251	4,044	2,999	309
Population Served (Millions)					
Public	188.2	15.3	19.3	69.5	84.1
Private	43.5	8.5	3.4	12.0	19.6
Unreported	6.1	1.5	1.1	2.4	1.1
Total	237.8	25.3	23.8	83.9	104.8
Population Served (%)					
Public	79.1	6.4	8.1	29.2	35.4
Private	18.3	3.6	1.4	5.1	8.2
Unreported	2.6	0.7	0.5	1.0	0.4
Total	100.0	10.7	10.0	35.3	44.0
Average Population Served per System (Thousands)					
Public	8,324	921	5,911	27,900	339,113
Private	1,465	297	5,802	29,557	356,364
Unreported	1,418	375	5,699	23,529	183,333
Average	4,201	514	5,885	27,976	339,159

Source:
American Water Works Association Water Industry Data Base, Compiled from U.S. Environmental Protection Agency Federal Reporting Data System (FRDS), 1994, Tables 1-3.

Note:
Public: Government-owned
Private: Investor-owned, cooperatives, mixed ownership.
Unreported: Ownership not reported

then showed renewed growth after the introduction of half-liter bottles that fit into vending machines. From 1984 through 1997, sales in small bottles rose from 4.4 million gallons to 750 million gallons. The total bottled water market, in the same time period, rose from 843 million gallons to 2,950 million gallons. Revenue of bottlers reached about $2.7 billion in 1997. Contrast those numbers with those of the public water supply industry in 1997. It produced 14 trillion gallons, but collected only $26 billion for its product.

Table 8-12

Size of Investor-Owned Water Utilities
1995

	Number	Affiliate of Holding Company[a]	Affiliate of American or United[b]
Revenues over $1 million	87	72	36
Revenues over $100 million	7	5	3
Revenues over $50 to $100 million	8	7	5
Revenues over $25 to $50 million	13	12	4
Revenues over $5 to $25 million	33	29	13
Revenues $5 million or less	26	19	11

Source:
1995 Financial & Operating Data for Investor-Owned Water Utilities (Washington, DC: National Association of Water Companies, 1996).

Note:
[a]Affiliate of one of 18 holding companies, some of which have only one principal subsidiary.
[b]Affiliate of American Water Works or United Water Resources, the two largest holding companies.

Table 8-13

Revenue and Employment
1980–1996

	1980	1990	1995	1996	% Change 1980–1996
Water treatment revenue ($ billions)	$ 9.2	$19.8	$27.3	$28.6	+211%
Water utility revenue ($ billions)	11.9	19.8	25.3	26.3	+121
Water treatment employees (thousands)	53.9	95.0	118.2	120.9	+124
Water utility employees (thousands)	76.9	104.7	120.5	122.2	+59
Estimated population served by public suppliers (millions)	186	210	235 E	242 E	+30
Consumer Price Index (1982–1984 = 100)	82.4	130.7	152.4	156.9	+90

Source:
U.S. Department of Commerce, *Statistical Abstract of the United States* (Washington, D.C.: U.S. Government Printing Office, various years).
E—estimate

To do some simple arithmetic, bottlers charged about 91 cents per gallon, wholesale. Consumers pay 30 cents to $1.00 per half-liter bottle, which equals a price range of $2.27 to $7.58 per gallon, for "just water ... and no guarantee that it's greatly different than what comes out of your tap,"[8] which, of course, costs consumers one one-thousandth the price of the bottle product.

Clearly, the water bottlers have learned how to segment the market. They have proved that consumers will pay for what seems a better product, and charge a price that no regulator or public water supplier would dare to even think about. In the meantime, water treatment firms sell their products to others who do not trust the product that comes out of the tap. Perhaps those developments indicate that the public water suppliers will, in the future, provide the bulk of the water, while others will furnish the high-margin specialties. As the public suppliers struggle with new health requirements, though, the question arises whether or not more reasonably priced specialty products (such as bottled water or home water treatment equipment) might not be economical alternatives to full-scale upgrading of the public water supply system.

CONCLUSION

Public water supply and sewage is a mature business. Demand, at best, grows with the economy. Year-to-year changes may depend more on the weather than business conditions. A plethora of water and sewage suppliers serve the public. Even where they have a common water supply, the small water suppliers run separate companies, or better yet, separate water departments. Water is a parochial, multibillion-dollar cottage industry in many ways. Even if the geographic distance between facilities reduced the potential operating economies derived from mergers, water suppliers could still benefit from joint development of water resources, economies of scale in purchasing, billing and administration, and from the lower interest costs available to larger borrowers. Furthermore, water suppliers have given little heed to the business possibilities inherent in having millions of satisfied customers that might buy other utility or home services from the water company. Nor have they considered sufficiently the operating and administrative savings that could come from working together with other local utilities. Tiny water suppliers could cooperate in order to benefit both shareholders and customers, although consolidation might produce greater efficiencies.

CHAPTER 9

Summary

Of all our natural resources water has become the most precious ... In an age when man has forgotten his origins and is blind even to his most essential needs for survival, water ... has become the victim of his indifference.[9]

— Rachel Carson

In an era of commercialization, privatization, and deregulation, the water and wastewater supply industry remains a monopoly, tightly regulated on health issues, owned largely by government, and economically regulated when privately owned. Those characteristics differentiate the industry not only from other public utilities, but also from almost all other major businesses in the nation.

This is a capital-intensive business, requiring over $4 of investment in plant to bring in $1 of revenue. Roughly two-thirds of that plant is in distribution assets. Thus, this is a pipes business, in terms of investment, but the public and the health authorities probably pay more attention to treatment that prevents disease-causing organisms from entering the water supply or discharged sewage from despoiling the environment, than they do to the collection and distribution infrastructure, much of which is both aged and decrepit. Water and sewage treatment have remained low-tech processes, little changed over many years.

Public ownership predominates among suppliers, reflecting decisions made over a century ago. Many tiny organizations serve customers, probably because small municipalities have had little incentive, in the past, to work together. After all, water and sewer services account for only a small portion of the family budget, so there has been little public outcry for more economical operations. (That situation may change as water suppliers raise prices in order to comply with environmental requirements.) Even given the localized nature of the water and wastewater business, larger organizations should be able to find ways to accomplish some tasks more efficiently than existing, tiny entities.

Demand for water has risen as the economy and population has grown. But with more emphasis on curtailing waste, less expansive federal irrigation budgets, more metering of water consumption, and the virtual end of growth in the generation of electricity from conventional steam turbines, the growth in demand for water could slow down, too. Public water suppliers, though will have enough work ahead of them, dealing with new environmental regulations, replacing aged infrastructure, and, possibly, meeting requests from specialty markets for ultra-pure water. To date, though, those companies have done little to explore business opportunities other than furnishing the standard product through the pipe. In contrast, unregulated water supply and treatment companies have moved aggressively to exploit opportunities in associated lines of business.

Despite the maturity of the market, the glacial rate of change in industry structure in the recent past, minimal technological innovation, public indifference, and the monopolistic nature of the service that has seemingly rendered the water and sewage industry impervious to calls for competition and deregulation, water suppliers cannot rest on their laurels. Aggressive entrepreneurs have muscled their way into many seemingly unexciting businesses, looking for better ways to make money off the customer base. All those millions of water customers, buying nothing but tap water from the water company, may represent a temptation to outsiders. And to some extent, the activities in the water field by NIPSCO, an Indiana gas and electric utility that purchased a large water utility, and United Utilities, a British electric utility that purchased a nearby water utility, provide tangible evidence that the temptation exists.

NOTES

1. Benjamin Franklin, *Poor Richard's Almanac*, as quoted in *Ben Franklin's Wit and Wisdom* (White Plains, NY: Peter Pauper Press, no date), p. 46. Of course, Thomas Fuller (1608–1661) said it first, in *Gnomologia*, number 5451: "We never know the worth of water till the well is dry."

2. Jeff Canning and Wally Buxton, *History of the Tarrytowns* (Harrison, NY: Harbor Hill Books, 1988), p.92.

3. New York City Municipal Water Finance Authority, *Prospectus*, August 7, 1997, p. 49.

4. Henry Semat, *Fundamentals of Physics* (New York: Rinehart & Co., 1957), p. 169.

5. Dr. Janice A. Beecher, "PUC 2000: The Water Industry," *Water*, Vol. 36 No. 2, Summer 1995, p. 37.

6. R.E. Banta, *The Ohio* (New York: Rinehart & Co., 1940), p. 124

7. Lewis Mumford, *The Myth of the Machine: The Pentagon of Power* (New York: Harcourt, Brace Jovanovich, 1970), p. 176.

8. Constance L. Hays, "Now, Liquid Gold Comes in Bottles," *The New York Times*, 20 January 1998, p. D1.

9. Rachel Carson, *Silent Spring* (Boston: Houghton Mifflin, 1962) p. 39.

PART III

Development and Structure of the Industry

CHAPTER 10

Introduction

Decaniis, Oriás, que a esperança
Têm de sua salvação nas ressonantes
Águas do Gange . . .[1]

— Luis de Camões

Water supply started out as a great business opportunity for American private enterprise and ended up, largely, as a business of government. Sewage, in most places, started and ended as a government service. What caused these industries to move in the opposite direction from almost all other public service industries in this country?

Public health and safety issues dominated many decisions. So did questions of regional development. Those matters still influence decisions. Is the private sector incapable of running profitable businesses that also serve public policy? If so, why is this the case for water and sewer, and not for other public utilities?

For that matter, have the public agencies necessarily kept in the forefront of health issues, or have they bogged down in complacency, worried about budgets and taxes in the same way that a private company worries about budgets and profits? Have the great federal water projects, once pioneering development agencies, turned into nothing more than means of transferring cash from taxpayers to special interests? Are public health measures aimed at remediation of the public water supply the most cost-effective means of achieving their goals? Would a market-based water industry, with proper regulation, produce at least the same public welfare achievements in a more economical manner than the present system?

Most people in this country have access to clean water, and most of the urban population has access to sewage systems. In the sense that most people take the services, and population growth is slow, these industries are mature. But they still face environmental and budgetary challenges of enormous magnitude.

CHAPTER 11

The Old World

. . . I caused a canal to be dug to the meadows of Ninevah. Over deep-cut ravines I spanned a bridge of white stone blocks. Those waters I caused to pass over upon it.[2]

— Sennacherib, King of Assyria

Western civilization began in the arid Middle East, in Mesopotamia, sandwiched between the Tigris and Euphrates Rivers, and in the Nile Valley. The ancients had to transport water long distances. They irrigated fields. They channeled raging rivers. They built water and sewage systems for their cities. King Hezekiah, in whose reign an angel struck down the 185,000 invading Assyrian soldiers of Sennacherib, "made the pool and the conduit and brought water into the city" of Jerusalem.[3]

MESOPOTAMIA AND EGYPT

In the Indus River Valley, now in Pakistan, the ruins of Mohenjo-daro and Harappa, possibly dating to 2500 B.C., show evidence of sanitary sewers, wells, bathrooms, cesspools, and lavatories in larger houses. Babylonian texts of the same period refer to canals and reservoirs. The Code of Hammurabi (c. 1800 B.C.) provides instructions on the proper care of irrigation ditches. A clay tablet dating around 1200 B.C. describes a water-raising wheel. Horizontal tunnels, called *qanats*, driven into hillsides, carried water to the fields of Persia before 500 B.C.

Mesopotamians built low dams, levees along the Euphrates, spillways to carry excess river water into basins, and reservoirs. Dams that stored water made irrigation possible in Yemen from about 1000 B.C. to 600 B.C. Sennacherib, King of Assyria and self-proclaimed ruler of the world, in the seventh century B.C. erected an aqueduct about 34 miles long to carry water to Ninevah. At about the same time, Sennacherib's enemy, Hezekiah, ordered the construction of a 1,750-foot-long tunnel to carry water from the spring of Gihon to the pool of Siloam, in Jerusalem. Laborers, cutting solid rock, worked from both ends and, after a few misses, met. In the sixth century B.C., Cyrus the Great may have dammed the main channel of the Tigris and diverted water into 30 canals.

The Egyptians, living in a narrow valley that could not support the population without irrigation, built dams and canals in order to water the desert. The first recorded dam, probably put up around 4000 B.C., diverted the Nile in order to clear a site for Memphis. Around 2000 B.C., the Theban (Eleventh) Dynasty

dammed ravines to impound water used to irrigate a basin in the Faiyûm Desert
west of the Lower Nile. Another project, the Canal of Joseph, carried Nile flood
water into an artificial lake.

In the water-scarce Middle East, the early civilizations could not simply live
next to water supplies. They had to manage, divert, and transport the water.
Civilizations in arid regions today continue to do the same, with remarkably
similar techniques.

GREECE AND ROME

The Minoan civilization of Crete (around 2100 B.C.) may have had better sanitary
facilities than anything that followed in the next 3,900 years. The palace of Knossos
had bathrooms, tubs, and flush toilets. Gutters carried rain water. Settling basins
caught sediment. Sunlight cleansed the water as it ran to storage cisterns or to
washing rooms.

The Greeks had simple public water supply systems. Ditches conveyed spring
water to reservoirs. Clay pipes then carried the water to public fountains and
basins, from which people took the water they needed. Herodotus, however,
described an unusual project on the island of Samos, one of

> the greatest building and engineering feats of the Greek world ... a tunnel
> nearly a mile long, eight feet wide and eight feet high, driven clean through
> the base of a hill nine hundred feet in height. The whole length of it carries a
> second cutting thirty feet deep and three broad, along which water from an
> abundant sources is led through pipes into the town. This is the work of
> ... Eupalinus.[4]

That system dates to the sixth century B.C. As in the case of Hezekiah's tunnel,
work crews began at each end and met in the middle.

By the Hellenistic period, the Greeks had developed a more sophisticated knowledge of water engineering. Around 200 B.C., they built the water system of
Pergamon, in Asia Minor. An aqueduct 35 miles in length, containing three seven-
inch tile pipes, carried the water to a reservoir on a hill located about two miles
away from and about 200 feet above the level of the city. The water then ran
down through a 10-inch pipe, probably of wood, up and down several valleys
and ridges, at a high pressure, until it reached the city's fountains. The Greeks
had learned the principle of the inverted siphon. They could make water run
uphill under pressure.

The Romans, masters of massive engineering projects, developed their aqueduct
and water system over a 500-year period. The sources of water were in the
mountains, about 1,000 feet above sea level. From dammed streams, through
feeder canals and settling basins, the water moved downward through underground aqueducts that followed the contours of the hills, except where the Romans

had to tunnel through hilltops to keep the downward slope, or had to build bridges to carry the aqueducts over valleys. Near the Eternal City, the Romans erected the bridgelike, arched, high structures that everyone thinks of as aqueducts. (The word "aqueduct," incidentally, is derived from the Latin words *aqua*, water, and *ducere*, to lead.) The aqueducts delivered the water to water castles that contained reservoirs, located about 200 feet above sea level. The water then descended through pipes to the public and private fountains, in which it continuously flowed. (The pipes, often, were of lead. The word "plumbing" is derived from *plumbum*, the Latin word for lead.)

The first Roman aqueduct, Aqua Appia, was an underground conduit, built around 312 B.C. during the administration of Appius Claudius Caecus. The last, and eleventh, was constructed in 226 A.D. Sextus Julius Frontinus, water commissioner, in his treatise *De aquis urbis Romae (Concerning the waters of the city of Rome)*, asked, "Will anybody compare the . . . Pyramids, or . . . other useless though renowned works of the Greeks with these aqueducts . . .?"[5]

At the time of Frontinus, in 97 A.D., Rome had eight aqueducts, with a total length of 260 miles. They carried water from several sources. Spring waters flowed into the public fountains. Turbid stream water flowed to public baths and laundries. The Cloaca Maxima, or Great Sewer, which drained the Roman forum, remains in service today. Overflows from the aqueducts flushed streets and sewers. Some wealthy people tapped into the public system in order to bring water to their homes. Water was free. The system may have transported 84 million gallons per day, but possibly only 38 million gallons reached the population, thanks to leakages, theft, and other diversions, which occasionally brought the system to a standstill. Rome's population at the time was about one million.

The great Roman engineers could make unbreakable concrete, but they built most of their aqueducts of stone, probably because of the difficulty of erecting the forms needed to cast the concrete. As for the conduits themselves, the Romans may have realized that the concrete would burst under high water pressure. They knew about inverted siphons, and used them in places, but not extensively, because they could not build pipes that would contain the water pressure. They could make lead pipes, but Vitruvius, in *De architectura (On architecture)* warned about lead poisoning and recommended clay instead. The Romans, in addition, did not use force pumps to raise water. Vitruvius, however, described those pumps, probably invented by Ctesibius (300-230 B.C.). Their remains have been found in Roman ruins, so the Romans did know the technology. They preferred the simpler gravity flow method of moving the water.

Vitruvius had a checklist for choosing a good source of water: healthy people lived near the source, the water sprinkled in a vase left no spot, when boiled the water precipitated no sand or mud, and the water was clear. The Romans did not treat the water in any way to purify it, but they designated only the cleanest water sources for drinking. Pliny, the Roman writer, however, noted that boiled water was a healthier drink. Nero, incidentally, did boil the water that he drank.

To the east, engineers of the Byzantine Empire copied Roman techniques. According to the historian Procopius, the emperor Justinian built enormous underground cisterns in Constantinople, one of which had a capacity of nine million gallons. Byzantine engineers—best remembered for the great church of Santa Sophia—built aqueducts and two crescent-shaped dams with flood gates.

The Roman and Byzantine engineers built water supply and sanitary facilities that set the standards that Western cities did not reach again for a thousand years.

FROM THE FALL OF ROME TO THE INDUSTRIAL REVOLUTION

Medieval towns often used the durable Roman aqueducts. Some of the towns' water supply systems had reservoirs, water pumps, and other water-raising devices connected to water wheels and long water pipes. More commonly, though, townspeople would draw their water supply from a stream or well, and haul it home in buckets.

Monasteries built elaborate water supply systems, often with extensive aqueducts. Many of the monasteries extended their systems to the neighboring towns. The dissolution of the monasteries of England, in the 16th century, led to transfer of facilities to ownership by the town.

Some cities instituted water supply systems even earlier. Dublin set up its operation in the 13th century. Bruges, by the 14th century, had an underground delivery system. Water from a reservoir flowed to a *water huis*, was raised by buckets on a chain to a storage area, and then distributed by gravity flow.

Human excrement and other garbage thrown into the streets, rivers, or wells fouled the water supplies. Outdoor privies leaked into nearby wells. Eventually, city residents installed privy vaults and cesspools, whose contents they periodically cleaned out, and then either spread on nearby fields as fertilizer or dumped into conveniently located rivers. Both Pliny the Elder and Vitruvius, in Roman times, thought that drinking impure water might lead to disease. In 1310, Jean Pitard, surgeon to Louis IX, dug a deep well at his Paris home that provided clean water for a period of 300 years, but his achievement may have been an exception.

By the Renaissance, European cities had begun to introduce the antecedents of the modern municipal water system. In the reign of the King Francis I of France (1515–1547), the engineer Le Roy designed and installed a water system for the planned community of Le Havre. It conveyed water by gravity flow, three miles from the spring, in clay pipes, to fountains within the city. The locals then had to carry the water home. Augsburg, in Germany, though, set the new standard.

Its waterworks had no need for long, expensive aqueducts to carry water from distant source by means of a gravity flow. The city, instead, raised the water 130 feet above its source, a local stream, into water towers, from whence it flowed to public fountains and to individual homes. Undershot water wheels, operating on the same stream, may have powered Archimedean screw pumps or force pumps to lift the water. About the same time, an Italian clock maker, Giovanni Turriano, concocted a marvelous system of waterwheels and scoops to carry water uphill from the Tagus River to the Alczár of Toledo, but the system did not work for long. Gloucester, England, in 1542, utilized a windmill to pump water into a raised reservoir that supplied the town.

Peter Morice, in 1582, built Elizabethan London's first municipal water works. He placed undershot wheels under the arches of London Bridge. The tidal flows generated over 100 horsepower, powering piston pumps that raised the water taken in to a reservoir tower 128 feet above river level. Gravity then took the water down through lead pipes for distribution. The water works could pump four million gallons per day. Morice and heirs had the right to use five arches of the bridge as a location for pumps for a period of 500 years. (Parliament abrogated the grant in 1822.) The water supply, however, was insufficient to extinguish the London fire of 1666.

Meanwhile, the idea of using water for sanitation (other than for cleaning streets) made little progress. People continued to employ chamber pots and privies. The rich preferred to live right next to a waterway, with their garderobe (privy) extending out over the water, thereby eliminating disposal problems. In 1596, Sir John Harrington did install a sophisticated flush toilet for Queen Elizabeth. Harrington devised the "privy in perfection" in order to get back in the good graces of the Queen, who had banished him from court for passing around racy literature. Unfortunately, after installing the privy, Harrington's literary instinct got the better of him again. He wrote a book about his invention, entitled *The Metamorphosis of Ajax.* ("Jake" was slang for chamber pot.) Elizabeth again banished Harrington from court. The flush toilet fell out of favor for another two hundred years.

London needed cleaner water. Merchant Hugh Myddelton, with the financial backing of King James I, built an aqueduct in 1608–1613. It brought 13 million gallons per day to the city, from springs 21 miles north, by means of a canal 16 feet wide and five feet deep. The canal, though, was 40 miles long, wending its way at an average drop of 3 inches per mile. It crossed valleys in lead-lined wooden troughs. The aqueduct reached Islington, where a pump of some sort, initially sail-powered, then horse-powered, raised the water into a reservoir. From there, it flowed by gravity into London. Fifty-eight pipes, some of elm and some of lead, brought the water into the city, to houses or to common pumps. At the time of the Industrial Revolution, the water company installed steam engines in order to increase water pressure. The New River Company was a financial success, staying in business until the Metropolitan Water Board took it over in 1902.

Paris had relied on aqueducts for some of its supply. Henry IV decided, in 1608, to utilize the Seine, despite the quality of its water. Flemish engineer Jean Lintlaer installed water wheels under the Pont Neuf. Those powered the Samaritaine pumps that fed the water to the Louvre and Tuileries palaces. They operated until 1813. In 1624, Marie de' Medici, widow of Henry IV, built an aqueduct to supply safer water to her palace, to the Luxembourg Gardens, and to 14 public fountains. France's greatest achievement, however, was the water works of Marly, built in 1682 by Flemish engineer Rennequin Sualem, to supply water to the fountains and gardens of Versailles, at enormous expense. Fourteen undershot water wheels powered 250 pumps, connected to the wheels by means of rods and chains, that raised water to a reservoir 533 feet above the level of the Seine. The system may have operated at 5% efficiency. Most of the power went into moving the rods and chains, not the water. Sualem, for the first time, used cast iron for pipes, as opposed to its normal use for cannons. The system operated until 1804. Needless to say, the water was for show. Versailles, which housed 1,000 aristocrats and 4,000 attendants, had no indoor plumbing for bathing or sanitary purposes.

THE INDUSTRIAL REVOLUTION AND BEYOND

The increasingly urban populations of the newly industrialized world needed water and sanitation services. Fortunately, the advancing technology of the day enabled the water suppliers to expand their operations.

First came the cast iron pump. Then, in the early 1700s, the water companies replaced horse-powered pumps with the steam-powered pumps developed for mining. In 1787, the venerable York Building Waterworks of London installed a Boulton and Watt steam engine. Other London waterworks followed the example. In 1800, Benjamin Latrobe installed a steam pump in Philadelphia.

Pipes had to withstand the pressure of the pumped water. By the middle of the 18th century, several water systems had installed cast iron pipes, which, however, presented problems due to defective joints. In 1785, Thomas Simpson of London's Chelsea Water Company, devised ball and spigot and lead joints. In 1810, James Watt, working for the Glasgow Water Company, invented the ball-and-socket flexible joint. Cast iron became the material of choice in the 1820s. Jonathan Bell of Saratoga, New York, in 1845, developed a coating to prevent corrosion, and Dr. Robert Angus of England came up with a corrosion-preventing coating in 1848 that is still used. California mining operations began to use wrought iron piping in 1856. By 1890, steel came into use, especially for aqueducts. Steel pipes are larger, lighter, and lack joints.

Despite this progress, citizens did not have a dependable water supply as we know it. For instance in London, in the mid-1800s, houses had cisterns that the water company filled only at stated times. Only in 1873 did London institute around-the-clock water supply.

The first flush toilet, patented by British mathematician Alexander Cummings in 1775, began the trend toward public sewer systems to convey wastes. By the mid-1800s, public health authorities understood that a connection between foul water and disease did exist, but it was not until the end of the 19th century that they began to treat sewage rather than dumping it raw into waterways that also provided drinking water.

CONCLUSION

One thousand years after the fall of Rome, the public water and sewage systems were inferior to those of the Eternal City in the days of the empire. In the early 19th century, water suppliers applied industrial technologies to expand their output, and late in the century they took advantage of new scientific discoveries to make the water supply safer. Developments in the United States, though, tended to lag those of Europe.

CHAPTER 12

The Eastern Half of the U.S.

. . . the water of wells must gradually grow worse, and in time be unfit for use . . .[6]

— Benjamin Franklin

The eastern half of the United States has abundant rainfall. Its major cities are located on bodies of water. Many still do not meter a large part of their customer base. Farmland requires little irrigation. Water policy has centered on these issues:

- Clean water to improve public health.

- Water for fire protection.

- Sewage disposal that does not affect quality of drinking water.

- Government versus private ownership of water distribution systems.

- Water conservation programs where needed to combat drought-induced shortages.

The Eastern and Midwestern cities, by and large, worked their way through the same sets of problems. They tended to act only after fires, water shortages, or epidemics. They delayed action because of unwillingness to raise taxes and because they underestimated the water needs of the population.

EARLY DAYS

Perhaps the Massachusetts Water Works Company, set up in 1652, qualifies as America's first water utility. It carried water from its source to a 12-foot-square reservoir, kept filled for fire prevention and use by neighboring families. By 1658, New Amsterdam, under the Dutch, had a public well in front of the old fort. The English, when they arrived, dug six more wells. Town dwellers favored cool, clean spring water over well water, which was often polluted by leakage from nearby privies, but the springs were inconveniently located out of town. To serve their inhabitants, towns dug wells and erected public pumps. The Moravian settlers of Bethlehem, Pennsylvania, in 1754, built a water works that pumped water from a stream through log pipes to a reservoir 400 feet away, from which it flowed to every house in town. When the Moravians moved to Salem, North Carolina, they did the same. In 1774, Christopher Colles sold New York's Common

Council on a plan to construct a water works. By April 1776, the project was operating, pumping well water to an elevated pond, using a Newcomen steam engine. Wooden pipes from the reservoir then carried the water into town. The American Revolution halted the project.

In the early days of the Republic, a few private water companies served the populated areas, but most cities thought of water systems in terms of number of public wells. Fire brigades passed the buckets or employed hand pump engines. Doctors pleaded for water to clean the streets. Meanwhile, back in London, the Chelsea Water Company (founded in 1721), the Lambeth Water Works (1783), and five more companies organized between 1805 and 1822, provided London with 28 million gallons per day, 13 million through the New River Canal and 15 million pumped from the Thames.

PHILADELPHIA

In the mid-1700s, Philadelphia's well water was famous for its quality. By the 1790s, Philadelphia water had lost its reputation. In 1792, the Commonwealth of Pennsylvania chartered the Delaware and Schuylkill Canal Company to build a canal and "to supply the city of Philadelphia . . . with water . . . Provided . . . the said company shall not be entitled to . . . the annual profit of ten per centum on the capital it expended for that particular purpose . . ."[7] Unfortunately, the company ran into financial difficulties. An attempted government bailout in 1795 failed to raise sufficient funds for the company to continue building its project. After the yellow fever epidemic of 1797, Benjamin Rush, a leading physician (famed for Rush's pills, which cleansed the system, and an advisor to Thomas Jefferson), said that yellow fever came from "putrid exhalations from the gutters,"[8] which meant that the city needed a water supply to wash the streets. The city and the canal company came to terms, but the state killed the deal. Another yellow fever epidemic struck in 1798.

Benjamin Henry Latrobe, considered America's first professional architect, proposed a novel solution to Philadelphia's water shortage: use steam engines to pump water from the clean Schuylkill River, then send the water to the center of town where a second set of steam engines would pump the water up into two elevated wooden tanks. From the tanks, the water would flow by gravity to wooden mains for distribution to consumers. The canal company objected to the competition but the city raised money through sale of bonds anyway. Then the project ran out of money, another yellow fever epidemic took its toll, and the project finally opened January 1801, 21 months after the start of construction and 18 months after the proposed completion date. Latrobe designed a magnificent system, conceptually and architecturally, but the steam engines kept failing, the system did not function during the fire of September 1804, and customers took more water than expected. From March 1799 to September 1815, the city spent $657,398.81 on its water system and received only $105,351.18 in revenues. By

1811, the Watering Committee had asked Frederick Graff and John Davis to come up with a better plan. They proposed a new system, which involved raising Schuykill water by pump at Fairmont to reservoirs at the top of the hill, from whence it would flow into the water mains. They installed the new system in 1815, put in iron mains to replace the log pipes on major streets, but had poor luck with the steam engines, which blew up in 1818 and 1821.

In 1822, Philadelphia built a dam on the river, and began to rely on water power for pumping. Philadelphia soon became the model for public water supply.

By 1850, water supplies were inadequate. Then began a long period of temporizing. In 1858, an engineer's report urged the city to find new sources beyond the no-longer-clean Schuylkill River. The city, instead, enlarged the intake from the Schuylkill. In 1886, after a new report, the city took no action. Finally, in 1940, Philadelphia conceded the need to overhaul the system, but the war intervened. In 1945–1946, Philadelphia decided to turn to the Delaware River for its supply.

NEW YORK

New York endured more difficulties than Philadelphia, thanks to the activities of some of the colorful political scoundrels that livened up the city. Manhattan Island depended on notoriously bad well water. In 1786, the Common Council decided that water supply was the responsibility of the municipality, but the city fathers could not decide on what to do, because they did not want to raise taxes to pay for a better water supply. The yellow fever epidemic of 1798 moved the city to action. One newspaper article on water ended with the couplet:

> For plague will make a yearly slaughter
> until you furnish better water.[9]

Table 12-1

Water Supply of Philadelphia in 1823 and 1837

	1823	January 1837
Power supply	3 wheels and pumps	6 wheels and pumps
Iron pipes	6½ miles	98 ¾ miles
Tenants supplied	4,844	19,678
Deliveries per day	1,616,160 gallons	3,122,164 gallons
Annual revenue	$26,101.05	$106,432.37
Reservoirs	2 with 7 million gallons storage	4 with 22 million gallons storage
Bathrooms with running water	(Not available)	1,492

Source:
Nelson Manfred Blake, *Water for the Cities: A History of the Urban Water Supply Problem in the United States* (Syracuse: Syracuse Univ. Press, 1956), p. 80.

The Common Council again decided that private parties should not profit from water supply. The councilmen had been advised that Manhattan wells were contaminated. An engineer estimated that the city needed three million gallons per day. The city petitioned the state for powers to set up a water system. Then came the surprise.

Aaron Burr, Democratic-Republican politician, and later U.S. vice president, secretly rewrote the city's request, turning it into the charter for a private water company. Federalist politicians, supposedly Burr's opponents, approved the idea on the grounds that it would be too difficult for the municipality to raise funds. A number of them became shareholders in the new company. Burr, in 1799, pushed for quick approval, in Albany, of the astounding charter of "The President and Directors of the Manhattan Company." That body could use any land it needed, dam or divert any streams, dig up streets to lay pipes with no obligation to put the street back in order, had no obligation to provide free water for fire fighting, and had the right to fix its own water rates. The company, however, within 10 years, had to "furnish and continue a supply of pure . . . water"[10] to all who agreed to the company's terms, or it could be dissolved. That was the only limitation on the company. The charter, though, had another amazing aspect, for a time when the state legislature had to charter individual corporations. The Manhattan Company could use its surplus capital for any other purpose, and those activities would have an unlimited life. That clause, alone, constituted a colossal giveaway. In those days, the state legislature had to approve the chartering of a bank. It usually set a limited life for the institution. Aaron Burr had wanted a Democratic-Republican affiliated bank (the other two in the city had Federalist leanings), but prominent Federalists quickly came on board the Manhattan Company as shareholders. The city government began to worry that the company had no real intention of supplying water. On September 1, 1799, the Manhattan Company opened its banking office. The directors, too, decided not to pursue a water source on the Bronx River, north of Manhattan, because that project would require too much capital that they could better utilize in the bank. (The bank, incidentally, is still in business, none other than The Chase Manhattan Bank.)

The Manhattan Company decided to stick with local Manhattan well water, despite the fact that the local well water constituted the problem in the first place. In 1800, the company completed a 132,600-gallon reservoir, filled with water pumped from wells. It distributed water through wooden pipes. (Iron was too expensive.) Not surprisingly, New Yorkers chose to take less from it than the company expected. Well water was well water and existing free well water cost less. Carters continued to bring spring water into the city, providing competition to the Manhattan Company, and many takers gave away the unmetered Manhattan Company water to neighbors or to their business customers. By 1801, the Common Council was complaining about what the company was doing to the streets, and about the expense of buying water to clean streets. (The company did allow free water to fire companies, which drilled directly into the wooden pipes for their supplies, and then, to close it, inserted a plug into the hole, from whence comes the term "fire plug." In 1807, the company installed wooden fire hydrants, but supply was never adequate.) In 1804, the Common Council began further investigation of water supply. The Manhattan Company, at that point, would have gladly given its water supply franchise to the city, if it could have figured out how to do so without losing its valuable perpetual charter.

Aaron Burr lost control of the Manhattan Company in 1801, when the Jeffersonians took over the party. De Witt Clinton, in 1803, was both mayor of New York and director of the Manhattan Company. He tried to change the charter to give the company the power to sell its water rights to the city, but failed in the effort. In 1808, the Manhattan Company, puffing itself for possible sale to the city, claimed 2,316 customers and net income of $10,061 or a 6 ¾% return on water investment. The Federalists said the profit was overstated: it did not take into account depreciation or allowances for repair. In that year, the legislature did approve sale of water assets, with terms that extended the charter 30 years beyond the date of sale. The Manhattan Company then saw no pressing need to sell out. In 1809, 1811, and 1812, Manhattanites went without water for extended periods of time, thanks to the incompetence or lack of interest of the Manhattan Company.

By 1821, in the administration of Stephen Allen, the city began to look northward, again, for water. But despite a yellow fever epidemic in 1822, the city took no action. Meanwhile, two new private groups muddied the waters. The New York and Sharon Canal Company, in 1823, acquired the right to bring Westchester County water to New York City, but could not raise capital. Then, in 1825, the New York Water Works Company received a charter, promised iron pipes, good citizenship in street repairs, and it easily raised capital. Unfortunately, the Canal Company already had rights to Westchester water, and the Manhattan Company had rights to Manhattan water, so the new company had no sources of supply. Then the report to the council came in: take water from the Bronx River, bring it 13¼ miles by closed canal or tunnel to a reservoir north of the Harlem River (in the Bronx), transport it over a bridge into Manhattan, and then south down Third Avenue, for a cost of $1.325 million. The Canal Company did not have the money, and had the nerve to request banking privileges to raise money to pay for a water supply operation. The New York Water Works had money but no water rights. The city did nothing. The Manhattan Company began an improvement program, substituting iron for wooden pipes, and it launched a well drilling program that added little to supply. In 1829, the Fire Department committee of the Common Council complained that the Manhattan Company laid pipes only where doing so would be profitable, which meant that firefighters had to rely on inadequate water supplies from cisterns elsewhere. The city, in fact, had to build its own reservoir and lay pipes with hydrants down Broadway and the Bowery for fire protection. An 1830 report by the Common Council claimed that the Manhattan Company served only one-third of the built-up parts of the city, the wells did not provide wholesome water, the company took out fire hydrants where it replaced the wooden with iron pipes, and the company had not fulfilled its charter obligations. A local scientific society said that one could not find a wholesome water supply on Manhattan Island. An 1831 report to the Common Council denounced the Manhattan Company:

> ... incorporated for the purpose of supplying the city ... with pure and wholesome water ... more intent on making money by ... banking operations ... Manhattan Water ... is unfit for the use of men ....[11]

An 1832 report to the Council showed the pathetic nature of the Manhattan Company's water business. The company collected $10,000 per year in water revenues. Carters, who brought in spring water, collected $273,750 per year. Suppliers of water to ships in the port had sales of $50,000 per year. Furthermore, an adequate water supply would save New Yorkers $250,000 a year in losses from fires.

After failing to dislodge the Manhattan Company from its position through a court case, the state set up a board of five water commissioners to figure out what to do. Their report recommended the Croton River (in Westchester County) as a source, with water flowing to the city without use of any machinery. A new board drew up more detailed plans. New Yorkers considered the experience of London (where eight companies created eight monopolies, rates were unregulated, water supply was uncertain, and sewers discharged into the river used for water supply). Taking into account their own problems with a private developer, they came out in favor of a municipally owned water system: "Water is ... as necessary to existence as light and air, and its supply ought never be made a subject of trade or speculation."[12]

The Croton Aqueduct would cost $4.2 million, plus another $1.3 million for distribution pipes. In contrast, the 1834 fire probably cost the city's citizens $1.3 to $1.8 million, said the Fire Committee. The Common Council passed the law. Voters then ratified it in April 1835. In December of that year, a catastrophic fire bankrupted all the city's insurance companies. New York needed the water.

Under the direction of chief engineer John B. Jervis, the project moved ahead, although slowed down by the financial panic of 1837 and the Common Council's nasty habit of dipping into the bond funds to pay current expenses in order to avoid a tax hike. In 1838, the estimated cost rose to $8.5 million. In the summer of 1842, the project opened for operations. A massive dam created a reservoir on the Croton River. An aqueduct with a uniform grade carried water to New York City. The total cost of water improvements reached $13 million. The city celebrated with fireworks, cannons roaring, a five-mile-long parade, and water gushing from fountains.

The Croton Aqueduct, in 1845, had a capacity of 90 million gallons per day, but the pipes at High Bridge (across the Harlem River) could handle only 42 million gallons per day. Three years later, higher elevation sections of the city suffered from undependable supplies. In 1862, the city added pipes to correct the bottleneck at High Bridge, and put new reservoirs into service. By the 1880s, pressure in the summer was insufficient to bring water above the first floor in tenements. In 1885, the city added two new sources to the system, but the expanding population of the Bronx needed that water. The city completed the second Croton Aqueduct in 1893: a 31-mile tunnel, with capacity of 300 million gallons per day. Total water supply rose to 425 million gallons per day, although consumption reached only 183 million gallons per day. In 1906, the New Croton Dam created a larger reservoir.

The city, however, continued to grow. In 1898, the formation of Greater New York added the boroughs of Brooklyn and Queens, which depended on wells and streams, to the city. The new consumption level touched 372 million gallons per day. Furthermore, a wave of immigration was swelling the city's population. The city still needed another source of water. What about the Catskill Mountains? At this point, the city headed into another bizarre encounter with a shady, privately owned, politically connected entity, the Ramapo Water Company. Organized in 1887, that company benefited from a special legislature act in 1895 that gave it the power to supply water to any municipality or person, to condemn property, and to choose its own routes for transport of water. Then, in 1896 and 1897, the legislature passed laws that prevented New York City from developing any new source of water. The Ramapo Water Company held water rights in the Catskills, the ability to get the water to the customer, and it had arranged to circumscribe New York City's ability to act independently. In 1899, the city's commissioner of water supply arranged a lucrative 40-year contract through which Ramapo would deliver to the city line 200 million gallons per day from the Catskills. The Tammany Hall majority in the city's legislature tried to rush the agreement's signing. Fortunately, the city comptroller, Bird S. Coler, stopped the contract, going to court to prevent its signing. Observers saw the deal as a sleazy arrangement between Tammany's Boss Croker and the upstate Republican machine leader, Boss Platt. Governor Theodore Roosevelt denounced the deal as criminal. An investigation showed that Ramapo's price was twice the city's water costs. The city would lose money on the contract. In 1901, the legislature repealed the restrictive 1895 law. It set up a new Board of Water Supply in 1905. The city moved ahead on its own. From 1907 to 1917, it built the Ashokan Reservoir, and the Catskill Aqueduct, a closed tunnel that burrowed under rivers, with a length of 120 miles from its northern end to southern terminus on Staten Island. In 1927, New York added the Schoharie Reservoir to the system. The Catskill Aqueduct then delivered 535 million gallons per day.

By 1921, though, New York had its eye on an additional water source: the upper reaches of the Delaware River. New Jersey and Pennsylvania objected, but the U. S. Supreme Court ruled in 1931 that New York City could take 440 million gallons per day from the Delaware watershed. The Interstate Commission on the Delaware Basin, set up in 1936, then surveyed the water needs of the area. In

1937, construction of the Delaware Aqueduct began, resumed after a hiatus for World War II, and the first water delivery took place in 1951. The city had bored an 85-mile aqueduct through solid rock to connect the new sources to the city system. Between 1953 and 1964, New York added three more reservoirs to the Delaware system. The modified Delaware compact allowed the city to withdraw 800 million gallons per day.

New York has not added new sources of supply since 1964, despite periodic shortages. It is constructing a third water tunnel from the Hillview Reservoir in Yonkers to increase delivery, though. At the same time, half the water mains in the New York City system are made of unlined cast iron, and were installed before 1930. They break and leak. An effort to meter more of the consumption may have dampened the level of demand for water, but demand still is greater than what is considered a safe level of supply. The water system faces other problems. Economic growth in the watershed increases the risk of pollution in the reservoirs. The federal government may demand the installation of filtration system that could cost up to $4.5 billion. An area development and environmental protection pact signed in 1997 by city and upstate governments might control pollution for sometime, thereby deferring the need for filtration on those systems. At the same time, city officials have to find a site for a $500 million to $900 million filtration facility for the downstate Croton Reservoir system, and "it is not difficult to foresee that opposition to the plant could be intense."[13] Have the elected officials, as they have done in so many cities, put off corrective measures until those measures are either extraordinarily expensive or almost impossible to implement?

BOSTON

In June 1794, the Aqueduct Corporation petitioned to bring fresh water from Jamaica Pond to Boston by pipe. The legislators approved the petition in 1795, with the provisos that the company would put the streets back in good repair, provide free water for fire protection, and would let the General Court regulate prices. Service began in 1798. The aqueduct carried water from Jamaica Pond to the Fort Hill Reservoir, and then to customers through wooden log pipes. The company was a resounding failure, financially speaking. Original shareholders paid $300 per share. Shareholders subsequently paid additional assessments to bring the cost to $1,000 per share. They received no dividends for the first 12 years, and those dividends averaged $51.76 per share in the next 20 years.

After the 1825 fire, Mayor Josiah Quincy decided to get Boston beyond the system of passing buckets. The water system was inadequate. That year, the Common Council reported that the city needed 1,600,000 gallons per day (100 gallons per day per family). Boston asked the Philadelphia water supply people for advice. The Philadelphians said that 150 gallons per day was a more realistic number, that the Bostonians had chosen too small a pond for supply, and they warned the Bostonians against "... the fatal error of suffering interested individuals to have supply of an article of the most indispensable nature ..."[14]

Mayor Quincy opposed the idea of a private water company but the city could not afford to act on its own. Joseph S. Lewis of Philadelphia, in 1833, wrote to Boston's new mayor, advising against the formation of any "... company whose interest would be to furnish the smallest quality of water at the highest possible price, while it would be the interest of the city to get the greatest supply at the smallest cost."[15]

In that same year, the Aqueduct Company supplied only 1,000 families. The rest used wells. An 1834 survey showed that Boston had 2,767 wells, of which seven furnished water soft enough for washing clothes, and 682 produced water too poor to drink. Eight years of dispute followed. The city tried to decide on a water source, insisted on municipal operation, failed to get legislative approval, several private companies fought for the franchise, and voters kept approving municipal ownership, to no avail.

A newly elected Common Council, in 1844, opted for municipal ownership, choosing Long Pond, 18 miles away, as the source. The city would soon need 7,125,000 gallon per day. Long Pond had the required supply. The plan, however, had to leap additional hurdles. In order to move the process, pro-water enthusiasts set up Ward Water Unions, grassroots efforts that demanded that politicians standing for election pledge to support the Long Pond project. In 1846, the Water Act passed the legislature, created three Water Commissioners, granted the city the right to water from Long Pond and other sources within four miles of Long Pond, and enabled the city to buy out the Aqueduct Company.

At a party held to celebrate the beginning of construction, in August 1846, Mayor Quincy announced a discovery. Long Pond, he said, was originally called "Cochituate" by the Indians, and that word, by coincidence, translated into English as "an ample supply of pure and soft water, of sufficient elevation to carry into the City of Boston, at a moderate expense."[16]

The 14-mile aqueduct carried water from newly renamed Cochituate to a reservoir at Brookline (capacity 100,000,000 gallons), then by iron mains to two distributing reservoirs, Telegraph Hill (7,500,000 gallons capacity) and Beacon Hill (2,600,000 gallons capacity), and then through 60 miles of iron pipe to customers. The project cost $4.0 million.

In October 1848, Cochituate water reached Boston. By August 1849, the city had 10,851 private takers of water and 750 fire hydrants in place. In February 1855, the system had 17,999 takers, 1,210 fire hydrants, and 110 miles of pipe. In January 1851, the city bought the Aqueduct Company.

Growth, of course, continued. In 1860, the city investigated the high water usage at hotels, which had installed showers, apparently an unexpected development. The city installed meters in order to collect payment for the extra usage. The hotels protested. In 1895, Boston and neighboring municipalities created a Metropolitan Water District. However, the next big water source, the Quabbin Reservoir, did not come into service until 1931.

BALTIMORE

Baltimore had a happier experience with private enterprise. The city council and the local insurance industry worried about fire and disease, but an attempt to build a water system in 1799 failed due to a dispute over water rights. The state would not give the municipality the right to expropriate property until the yellow fever epidemic of 1800 made it clear that something had to be done. After that, though, the city's finances were too shaky to allow it to raise capital. In 1804, the Baltimore Water Company took on the task of building the new system, backed by a big investment from the insurance companies.

John Davis, superintendent of the Philadelphia Water Works, drew up the plan: water from Jones Falls transported one-quarter mile by mill race, to a reservoir on a hill, and then down through bored logs to the homes of customers.

Over a 24-year period, the water company's annual dividend return averaged 3% of investment. The city continued to buy up springs within the city to supply water to the public, but the privies and the population encroached on the springs. By 1825, the water company still served only 1,640 families. Profit was not high enough to induce investment for expansion. The company put in pipe only where it saw the possibility of connecting to paying customers. By 1827, the mayor complained about the scarcity of water. The water company launched an expansion and modernization program that brought length of pipe up to 13¾ miles (of which about six miles were of iron). By 1830, the city's springs were contaminated and half the population went without a public water supply. The water company said that it could expand, but would be willing to sell out to the city. Nothing happened.

The company, in 1835, again offered to sell. The Water Committee of the city government wrote another report denouncing private ownership: "it could not be expected that a private corporation would consult the public good when the benefit of the community could only be served by the sacrifice of corporate interests . . ."[17]

Furthermore, the company would not extend water pipes to those neighborhoods of the city that "offered no hopes for remuneration . . ."[18] And, just to make its point abundantly clear to those who had not followed the thread of argument, "the important trust of supplying our . . . population with water ought never to have been committed to a private corporation."[19] Having thunderingly denounced private enterprise, the city figured that it could buy out the water company without cash, by paying with municipal bonds. It hired an engineer who proposed that the city build a dam at Great Gunpowder Falls, 10 miles to the north, and transport the water by aqueduct to a reservoir from which it would be distributed.

Then came the panic of 1837, which dissolved the city's righteous indignation over the evils of private water supply. The city fathers rescinded the ordinance that had called for the survey that had led to the recommendation.

The Baltimore Water Company kept plugging away:

	1835	1852
Miles of pipe	15	47
Annual revenues	$27,000	$80,000

Of course, there were no fire hydrants in parts of the city, and the company made no bones about the reason why: "The Water Company could not be expected to extend the pipes without some prospect of remuneration."[20] In 1849, the year of another cholera scare, the company served between one-quarter and one-half the populated parts of the city. In 1851, another study said that water from Jones Falls, the company's source, was impure in summer and autumn. Great Gunpowder water was purer. So, in 1852, the city appointed still another group, a board of water commissioners, to find another source and to buy out the water company. In 1853, voters supported the decision. In 1854, the city bought the Baltimore Water Company at its asking price.

Then the problems began. According to the engineers, the water company's assets could supply 2,500,000 gallons per day. The city needed 13,000,000 gallons per day and would require 41,000,000 gallons per day in 1880. The engineers selected Great Gunpowder as the best source. They also provided a construction cost estimate that the mayor refused to accept. He would not sign on. Shortly afterwards, the Know Nothing Party candidate won the mayoralty, and demonstrated the validity of his party's name by selecting Jones Falls as source of new supply. Meanwhile, the water distribution system kept growing:

	1854	1860
Miles of pipe	50	127
Annual revenues	$8,750	$16,300

In 1874, the water works ran dry. As predicted, the Jones Fall supply was inadequate in quantity, the water unclean, and the money spent on Jones Falls wasted. In 1881, Baltimore belatedly began to take water from Great Gunpowder Falls which required a new dam, a seven-mile tunnel, and two new district reservoirs.

In 1910, Baltimore added a new dam to the system, still another in 1933, and more afterwards.

CHICAGO

The Chicago Hydraulic Company, chartered in 1836, started to serve customers in 1840. It pumped water from Lake Michigan, using steam engines. The company had a short life. The city bought the franchise in 1852.

The city had plenty of problems, due to flat, non-porous terrain, barely above the level of the lake. When it rained, Chicago became a swamp. Sewage drained into Lake Michigan, the source of the water supply. In the 1850s, cholera and dysentery plagued the citizens. In 1855, the Chicago Board of Sewage Commissioners appointed Ellis Sylvester Chesbrough, who had executed the plans for Boston's Cochituate Aqueduct, as its chief engineer. Chesbrough told the city to get rid of its system of privies and drainage sluices. He envisioned what may have been the "first comprehensive sewerage system undertaken by any major city in the United States."[21]

Chesbrough offered the Board four choices for disposal of sewage:

1. Drain the sewage into the Chicago River, which would carry it to Lake Michigan.

2. Drain it directly into Lake Michigan.

3. Drain it into reservoirs and then use it as fertilizer.

4. Drain it into the Chicago River, then pump it into a steamboat canal that would take the sewage to the Des Plaines River and then westward.

He dismissed the fourth solution as "too remote,"[22] that is, too expensive at that time for a system the size of Chicago's. He did not like the third solution, because he was uncertain about demand for fertilizer. The second solution entailed having longer sewer lines, greater cost, risk to water supply intake, and problems with the sewer outlet in times of severe weather. Chesbrough picked the first solution, even though the water intake was near the sewer outlet, and the drainage into the river could create obstacles to navigation.

Now Chesbrough had to build the system. Drainage was the first problem. The banks of the Chicago River stood only a few feet above water level. Chesbrough would have to elevate the sewers in order to get them to drain into the river, but street level was too low to allow drainage from below surface sewers. Chesbrough proceeded to lay the three-foot to six-foot-in-diameter brick sewers on top of the streets, and then raise the level of the street to cover the sewer. Since Chesbrough had to dredge and widen the river anyway, he used the dredgings to create a higher street level. Raising the street level created a new problem: the buildings along the streets were now too low. George Pullman, who had not yet developed his railroad car, devised a means of raising brick buildings to the new street level, and enjoyed a thriving business in Chicago.

The city then sent Chesbrough to Europe to investigate the techniques used there. He made two prescient observations. For a starter, he noted, from the experience of an English seaside town, that, "discharge of filth into the sea gives no security against its being cast back in a more offensive state . . ."[23] Could that apply to stormy Lake Michigan? Then, after considering work planned for London, he commented:

> The thorough cut for a steamboat canal, to the Illinois River, . . . if ever constructed, would give as perfect relief to Chicago as is proposed for London by the latest intercepting scheme.[24]

Chesbrough's sewer system polluted the Chicago River. The pumps of the Illinois and Michigan Canal did dilute pollution. By 1858, people realized that they could send sewage to the canal. A deeper canal would carry more sewage. Aside from that, though, Chicagoans complained about the water supply, whose intake went a few hundred feet into Lake Michigan, a half-mile north of the mouth of the Chicago River.

In 1859, the water commissioners proposed a new intake, a wrought iron pipe extending a mile into the lake. Chesbrough countered by proposing a tunnel. Two years later, the Board of Water decided to investigate filtration as a means of purifying the water supply. As an alternative, Chesbrough proposed a five-foot-diameter tunnel that extended two miles into the lake, after dismissing other choices as unsafe or too expensive. Chesbrough's tunnel constituted an impressive engineering project, and ameliorated the problem for a while, but it also put off a real solution.

In 1889, the Sanitary District of Chicago was established to do what Chesbrough seemed to have thought was the best but most expensive scheme. By 1910, Chicago opened the Drainage Canal. It reversed the flow of the Chicago River, from eastward to westward, and sent Chicago's wastes down the Des Plaines and Illinois Rivers to the Mississippi. Typhoid cases fell, as Chicago, Hog Butcher to the World, solved its sewage problem by sending the stuff down state.

WASHINGTON, D.C.

The government took care of its own, installing Washington's first bathtubs in the White House and the Capitol Buildings in the 1840s. In 1850, Congress told the U. S. Army Corps of Engineers to build a water supply system, using the Potomac River as its source. Subsequently, the government installed sewers that mixed street runoff and domestic waste and discharged them both into nearby streams.

In the early 1900s, the government built a new system that sent domestic waste to the Potomac south of the city, and took storm drain water to the Anacostia River. The Potomac, incidentally, was viewed as a perfect dumping ground because of the flushing action of the tides. By the 1920s, people had begun to worry whether the Potomac could absorb the increased sewage load. The Public Health Service, in 1932, said that the river would not handle the pollution during periods of low water flow.

The federal government awarded funds to build a treatment facility, Blue Plains, that would remove 90% of organic matter from the sewage. District of Columbia authorities, however, decided to modify the Blue Plains plans. The Blue Plains facility, built in 1934–1938, removed only 36% of organic matter, and that percentage fell as population increased. In 1950, the government started a program to increase the plant's capacity. It introduced the activated sludge process, developed in Britain 40 years before, to remove 70% of organic matter. The plant's capacity rose from 130 million gallons per day in the 1930s to 290 mgd after the postwar expansion.

Since the District shares use of the rivers and drainage areas with the surrounding counties in Maryland and Virginia, the D. C. sewer system interconnected with surrounding systems in 1959. Payments from outlying areas help to support the District's water pollution control facilities. Working together, presumably, pays off.

CONCLUSION

In the 19th century, many private companies constructed the original water works, but fell victim to municipalization, often because they could not afford to provide public services, such as extension of pipes into poor areas for fire protection and sanitary purposes, and still offer water to paying takers at reasonable prices, and earn sufficient profit to satisfy investors.

The cities, though, vacillated in their resolve to anticipate demand and extend service because they did not want to stretch their finances or raise taxes to pay for expansion. Those policies often cost more, in the long run. City governments did not want to charge water users enough to finance the water system. By not charging enough, they encouraged uneconomic demand and needless expansion. In recent years, cities strapped for cash have not rehabilitated old systems.

Private ownership failed to meet the needs of the public during a period of rapid expansion. Public ownership may fail the test when the problem is not growth but the need for the most effective economic stewardship of resources.

Chapter 13

Western Water Resources

"A Westerner's priorities are, in order 1) water, 2) gold, 3) women; you may tamper with the other two, but not the first."[25]

— Barry Goldwater

In the frontier days of the American West, they used to say, "Whiskey is for drinking and water is for fighting over." That statement stills sums up the passion associated with water issues in the region, for in no other part of the nation has water played such an important role in shaping patterns of settlement and economic success. The high cost of obtaining water has kept most of the American West barren, and, with the exception of portions of California and Texas, relatively unpopulated. Scarcity of water has constantly threatened the viability of western agriculture and hampered the economic development of the western states, which account for over 60% of the land area of the continental United States but less than 40% of the population. (Omitting Texas and California, the western states contain only about 20% of the nation's population in over 45% of the nation's area.) For purposes of water resource discussion, the 17 states with territory west of the 100th meridian (see Figure 13-1) constitute the "West." Although there are moist pockets, most of this land is extremely arid or desert, an environment hostile to unirrigated agriculture. Proceeding westward from the Atlantic Ocean, the 100th meridian marks the start of the American desert. At that point rainfall drops below the 20 inches per year needed for non-irrigated agriculture.

The scarcity of water in the West, its highly uneven distribution, and a regional culture that is pro-economic expansion, make water resources a key political issue. It is an issue with national consequences because the federal government has stepped in to provide water supply, a function handled elsewhere by the private sector or by local governments. Although both the East and the West have similar concerns about water quality, finding water in the East is usually not difficult, and despite periodic shortages and drought emergencies, lack of water is rarely an ongoing concern. In the West, however, water is scarce. It may have to flow great distances through pipeline and canal systems before reaching its destination. The growing population and vested agricultural interests attempt to share that scarce resource. Public water supply issues are inextricably tied to agricultural and environmental issues.

Figure 13-1

The Hundredth Meridian
100° W

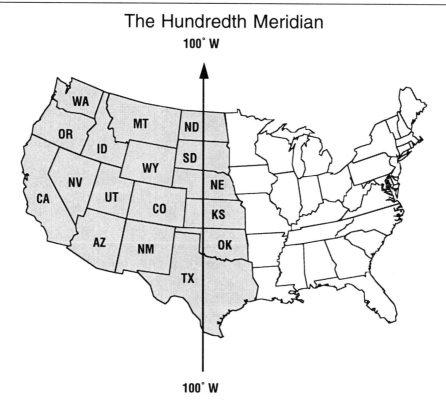

100° W

Shaded areas = The West, for purposes of water resource discussions

ENVIRONMENT

Climate is the key to Western water policy. The West is dry. Much of it is desert. Over half of the area of the western states receives less than 20 inches of rainfall per annum, the minimum rainfall required by agricultural crops without artificial irrigation. Some areas receive less than 10 inches of rain per year.

Seasonality compounds the problem caused by low rainfall. In the East, precipitation may peak in the summer, but it is still well distributed over the year. In parts of the West, the bulk of the precipitation may fall in the winter, with almost no rain for months during the rest of the year. As a result, the water suppliers have to store water for irrigation use during the dry season and for urban uses, such as filling swimming pools, and watering lawns and golf courses during the same time of year. (In the humid East, on the other hand, agricultural irrigation is usually unnecessary, because rainfall is less seasonal, and often, as in the case of Illinois, the rainiest season coincides with most of the growing season. Less seasonality also means that water suppliers require less water storage.) The highly seasonal nature of western precipitation means that western rivers have highly seasonal variations in water flows. In fact, many streams marked on maps would not exist at all during dry summer months, if water suppliers had not erected dams to store water in lakes and even out the water flows during the year. Those dams and lakes provide the West with irrigation water. They store the melting snowpack as usable water, rather than letting it go to "waste" by running to the ocean. Those same dams also serve to control floods during periods of peak flow.

Locational issues add to western water problems. Some of the fast-growing urban centers are located in arid regions, so suppliers must bring the water great distances. In addition, most of the major agricultural projects are located on the flatlands, while most of the water lies in snowpack in the mountains. Consequently, the water must be transported to the crops.

Aside from rivers, the aquifers—underground water reserves trapped in rock formations—are the other major source of water in the West. The Ogallala Aquifer, under the High Plains region of South Dakota, Nebraska, Colorado, Kansas, Oklahoma, Texas, and New Mexico, is one of the largest in the world. It contains water accumulated from glacial sources over half a million years. In recent years, the low rate of precipitation on the land overlying the aquifer and the high rate of withdrawal since World War II have caused a considerable drop in the water level of the aquifer. Therefore, the Ogallala, the main source of water on the High Plains, represents a stock of water, rather than a regularly renewed flow. Many commentators have described the methods of extracting Ogallala water as "mining," because withdrawal rates far exceed replenishment. They consider the Ogallala as a finite resource, comparable to an oil field. And, as is the case with the contents of the oil field, the lower the water level drops as a result of exploitation, the harder and the more expensive is its extraction.

Geographic and climatological factors create the uneven water distribution in the American West. (See Table 13-1 and Figure 13-2.) To begin, remember that prevailing winds in the continental United States blow from west to east, while the major mountain ranges run north to south.

The climate of the Summer-Dry region that stretches along the Pacific Coast reflects the pattern of winds and storms that carry moisture-laden winds to the Cascade and Sierra Nevada mountain ranges that parallel the coast. The winds cool off as they rise over the mountains, and deposit the moisture in the form of precipitation on the western slopes of these mountains. (Little moisture is left for rainfall to the east of the mountains.) The Pacific storms that bring the moisture to the region move onto the coast during the cooler months, thereby creating the wet season. The summer remains dry, hence the name for the region. Even the well-known "wet" city of Seattle receives little rainfall in the summer. The winter

Table 13-1

Climates of the Continental United States

Climatic Region	Characteristics
Summer-Dry Climate	Due to the Pacific Ocean weather patterns, this area receives very little rainfall in the summer months. Most precipitation falls in the form of snow on the western slopes of the Cascade and Sierra Ranges. The eastern side of the mountains is very dry.
Arid Region	Little precipitation. In the south, where the prevailing winds come from Mexico, summer is the wet season, while in the north, influenced by the same weather system as the summer-dry climate, winter is the wet season. Most precipitation falls in mountainous areas, and runs into rivers, where it is tapped for use.
Great Plains	Region of highly variable rainfall. Climate ranges from humid to arid, but overall the area is relatively dry. Most rainfall occurs in summer months when moist warm air from the Gulf of Mexico collides with cooler polar air, producing a large amount of precipitation in a short time.
Subhumid Lands	Transition area between the arid areas of the west and the humid areas of the east. Arid in the western sections, humid in the eastern sections. Precipitation is concentrated in the warm season, when moist warm tropical air masses come off the Gulf of Mexico.
Humid East	Most humid area of the continental United States. Almost all rainfall comes from interaction of polar continental air masses from Canada and warmer maritime air from the Gulf of Mexico or Atlantic Ocean. Precipitation is more evenly spread throughout the year than in the west.

months account for a disproportionate amount of the year's precipitation, much of it snowfall in the Cascades and Sierras.

The winds descending the eastern slopes of the Cascades and Sierras warm as they drop. They are dry, having deposited their moisture on the west side of the mountains. The Arid Zone, to the east of the mountains, is about 600 miles wide, and stretches to the Great Plains on the east. In the southern part of the region, below the Arizona-Utah line, prevailing winds come from Mexico and the summer is the rainy season. Pacific winds that cross the Cascades and Sierras influence the northern region, in which the winter is the rainy season. However, in both areas, rainfall is scarce. In the lowland areas, precipitation is minimal. Most precipitation falls in the higher elevations where the mountain ranges cause air currents to rise and cool, depositing their moisture at the higher altitudes. Water collected there in snowfall feeds the river systems, which in turn are tapped for water. Most major settlements in the Arid Region are situated near mountain-fed waterways.

Figure 13-2

Weather Regions in the United States

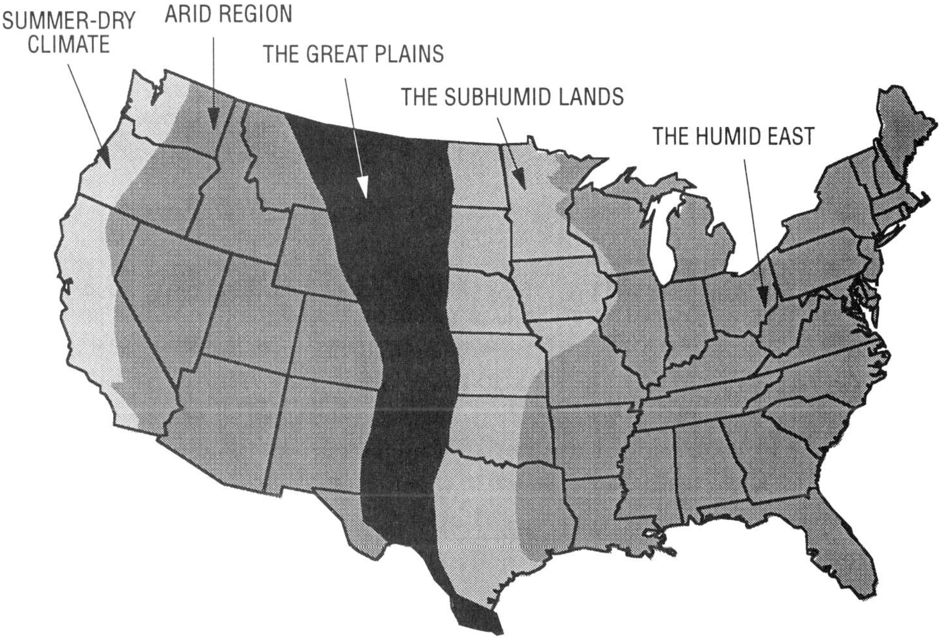

SUMMER-DRY   ARID REGION
  CLIMATE
           THE GREAT PLAINS
              THE SUBHUMID LANDS
                  THE HUMID EAST

The Great Plains lie to the east of the Arid Region, extending almost to the 100th meridian. This region has highly variable rainfall as it has variable climatic influences. Areas within the Great Plains range between arid and humid in character. On the Great Plains, most warm air comes from Mexico and is quite dry. Thus, when it meets cooler polar air there is not much precipitation when the warm air cools. Periodically, however, moist warm air comes from the Gulf of Mexico, collides with the cool air, and produces a great amount of precipitation in a short period of time. A significant proportion of annual precipitation in this region may come from only a few storms. Most precipitation in this area falls during the summer months, creating a better match between agricultural needs and water supply than in the Summer-Dry climate. Despite its variability, the Great Plains area tends to be relatively dry, compared to the East, and drought is often a major concern.

East of the Great Plains lie the Subhumid Lands, the prairie zone that marks the transition between the dry West and the humid East. The boundaries of the Sub-humid Lands are marked by the probability of the occurrence of a dry year, with their demarcation stemming more from precipitation than from physical features.

> . . .the subhumid prairie lands are fairly well bounded on the west by the line between 10 and more than 10 dry or semiarid years in 20, and on the east by the line between 0 and 1 dry year in 20. In other words, in the subhumid lands

from 1 to 10 years out of 20 are likely to be so deficient in rainfall as to be designated dry or semiarid.[26]

This region has some of the finest soils for agriculture in the world, and they are quick to produce, which has made this area highly favorable for farming. The main threat to agriculture is drought, because, "the climate of the subhumid lands errs on the side of having too little precipitation and too many droughts rather than too much rainfall."[27] Fortunately, most of the rainfall falls in the warm season, especially early summer, when grain needs moisture the most. Trewartha describes the precipitation and its causes in the Subhumid Lands:

> The concentration of the year's rainfall in the summer season is associated with the prevalence over the region of warm tropical air masses in summer, in contrast to cold polar air masses in winter. The former not only have a higher capacity for moisture because of their higher temperatures, but they have their origin over the Gulf of Mexico. To be sure, a considerable part of the moisture is precipitated before the Gulf air reaches the prairies, which accounts for their being less humid than regions farther east.[28]

The eastern United States is the most humid area of the nation. Its climate is influenced by its proximity to the Gulf of Mexico and the Atlantic Ocean. Thornthwaite describes the formation of precipitation in the East:

> In the eastern part of North America nearly all rainfall is caused by the interaction of great masses of air originating over the vast arctic tundra of northern Canada and over the Gulf of Mexico and the Atlantic between Bermuda and the Bahamas. In the northern region the air becomes cold, dry, and heavy and is called polar continental; in the southern, it becomes warm, very moist, and light and is called tropical maritime. At irregular intervals the polar continental air masses advance southward and eastward, spreading across the area east of the Rockies, where they generally encounter along their route maritime air advancing northward from the Gulf or the Atlantic. Being lighter and more moist, the maritime air is forced to ascend, is cooled, and yields a portion of its water vapor as precipitation.
>
> The path followed by the tropical maritime air characteristically curves across the Gulf, up the Mississippi Valley, and thence eastward to the Atlantic, thus tending to avoid the Great Plains altogether.[29]

In reflecting on western water policy it is essential to remember that the west is dry, and there is little man can do about it. Water can be transported to various locations, but in the near future, there does not seem any way to increase the total volume of water available without a major climate change.

HISTORY

Little or no rain during the Western growing season makes irrigation imperative, especially in California, the nation's leading agricultural state. California and the West drew prospective farmers and settlers as a result of promotion by the railroads, which received land grants from the U.S. government in compensation for building railroads across the West. The various railroad companies enticed settlers to California in the 1890s, and then transported the agricultural production of those settlers. Extreme weather and drought conditions in the late 19th century, however, hampered agricultural development. Nevertheless, the pioneers simply saw nature as an obstacle to overcome in the name of Manifest Destiny, the 19th century political doctrine that held that the United States was destined to expand westward to the Pacific. The government encouraged western settlement, and nature was but an inconvenience.

The goal of conquering the desert was unquestioned by those planning the future of the American West. However, the effort was poorly thought out and planned. For example, the General Land Office decided that 160 acres was the appropriate size of land parcels to be distributed to settlers in the West. However, the office did not consider whether that was a sufficient amount of land for a successful farm in a dry region. John Wesley Powell, the geologist and explorer who had surveyed the West for the U.S. Geological Survey and led the first party to completely navigate the Colorado River, felt that settlement was proceeding haphazardly and would not succeed without scientific knowledge and planning. He pointed out that the water resources of the West were sufficient only to reclaim a fraction of the available land, and that promoting the opening of the West as the solution to all the nation's population pressures would not succeed because of the region's modest precipitation and hostile environment. Powell believed that a slow, orderly, federal plan to develop the West was more likely to succeed than one based on the less-than-honest promotions of railroads that had land to sell to farmers along their rail lines.

Amid the stirrings of Manifest Destiny, the United States began to receive many immigrants who settled primarily in the cities of the East and Midwest. Lawmakers worried that crowding people in urban areas would lead to social instability and foster revolutionary attitudes among the working poor. Perhaps if the cities were less densely populated, and people were out earning their living on farms, lawmakers reasoned, that would lessen social unrest building in the cities and diminish the appeal of radical forces. On September 14, 1901, the day Theodore Roosevelt succeeded the assassinated William McKinley, the country gained a president concerned with what he perceived as an underpopulated western flank of the United States, one that was vulnerable to attack by Japan. Roosevelt felt that settlement of western lands would strengthen the United States against an attack from the so-called "Yellow Peril of the Orient."[30]

There were many attempts to conquer the desert through private irrigation and small-scale local/state projects, but none were large enough to succeed. Small companies had attempted to set up programs in some of the driest parts of the West and failed. The state of California tried to stimulate irrigation by passing the Wright Act, which allowed farmers to organize into groups called irrigation districts for the purpose of combining resources to build irrigation works. These districts, unfortunately, had trouble selling bonds, lacked technical expertise, and did not distribute water evenly, which created unrest among members of the districts. (Colorado tried a similar approach, but the five reservoirs built under the program were so poorly planned that they never stored water for delivery.) Ultimately, California's agricultural population growth slowed, and growth actually ceased in 1895.

Theodore Roosevelt was a conservationist in the sense that he disliked waste of natural resources. Waters flowing to the sea not fully utilized was one such example of waste. The states and private investors had failed to make the West habitable and Roosevelt believed that the federal government could do a better job. Some historians, in fact, hold the view that small western farmers and the urban poor exhibited little support for reclamation projects. The major supporters of such initiatives were the interests that stood to benefit most from federal intervention: large corporate farmers and the railroads.

The push for a federal reclamation program was spearheaded by Senator Francis Newlands, who had failed at developing his own private reclamation project. Not surprisingly, the motives of the major backers were revealed in implementing the National Reclamation Act of 1902. This act:

> . . .authorized the Federal Government to undertake surveys, to design and construct irrigation projects financed from the Reclamation Fund (set up to operate as a revolving fund), and to contract with water users for repayment, without interest, on the capital investment. The act provided also for the installation of power plants to assist in construction or to pump water.[31]

The funds for the Reclamation Fund came from the federal government's sale of land held in the public domain. The Reclamation Act originally limited irrigation with federal water to 160 acres (or 320 acres for a married farmer). These limits were designed to encourage small farmers. However, the Bureau of Reclamation ignored these regulations from the start, which eventually led to a group of large, entrenched, landowners feeding at the public trough. In addition to the Bureau's failure to enforce acreage limitations, the program failed financially. Reclamation projects did not come close to recovering the majority of their costs. Congress kept bailing out the system for farmers by increasing the subsidy. The original act specified a 10-year repayment period for the water "loans."[32] In 1914, Congress increased the repayment period to 20 years. In 1922, the service had recovered only 10% of the capital costs of the projects it had built, and farmers were still failing to reclaim the West.

Alarmed, Congress chose to fix the problem by allowing the Bureau to price water based on a farmer's ability to pay and by using hydroelectric power revenues generated by Bureau dams to subsidize the water projects. However, with the election of Franklin Delano Roosevelt as President, the Bureau took on a new role: job creation. Entering the presidency with a mandate for change, and facing a 25% unemployment rate, Roosevelt believed that the best way to preserve the social order was to create jobs for people. The Bureau of Reclamation provided opportunity of employment through huge dam construction projects.

These projects, and the water they provided, had special impact on California. In the 1930s, as the Southwest became the Dust Bowl, large numbers of destitute farmers abandoned worthless farms and headed for California, seeking prosperity and farming opportunities. Unfortunately, California, the nation's leading agricultural state, had great difficulty absorbing these immigrants. Concurrently, the federal government took over the Central Valley Project, a California state water project which suffered serious financial problems. The Central Valley Project was a system of canals and dams designed to bring water from the San Joaquin and Sacramento Rivers to the Central Valley to irrigate agricultural holdings. The Bureau of Reclamation's objective was to not only create jobs through the construction projects, but also to open up new land for farming. In the end, however, most of the area made available went not to small farmers but to large land companies, with holdings far exceeding 320 acres. Those Dust Bowl refugees who came to California seeking prosperity became migratory laborers, not new farmers.

Notwithstanding the blatant violations of acreage limits, the Bureau of Reclamation proceeded onward, its dams producing the electric power during the Second World War that powered the West Coast military industrial effort. However, near that war's end, Roosevelt again worried about social stability. Despite a booming war economy, President Roosevelt feared another depression would arise with the war's close. He envisioned troops returning home unable to find work in a nation gripped in economic malaise. President Roosevelt reasoned that the best way to forestall trouble was to establish a job-creating mechanism at the Bureau of Reclamation. The Bureau grew and prospered. In the 1950s, water projects became the grease that lubricated congressional wheels. The Bureau's work began to diminish in the 1960s, as a result of opposition from the environmental movement. Its projects were slowed in the 1970s by President Jimmy Carter's objections based on environmental and economic considerations, and ground to a complete halt in the 1980s, as President Ronald Reagan sought to reduce government spending.

WATER LAW

In the United States, two doctrines of law govern water distribution: the *riparian* system and the *doctrine of prior appropriations*. Riparian doctrine grants equal water use rights to all property owners abutting a stream bank or lake. Riparian doctrine, borrowed from English common law, governs the Eastern United States, the wetter part of the nation. A riparian user is allowed to withdraw water in "reasonable" amounts that do not impair the withdrawals of those other landholders, with "reasonable" use often determined by courts of law when disputes arise.[33] In the West, doctrine of prior appropriations dominates. Prior appropriation grants the water to the first person who can find a use for it. That doctrine originated in the frontier West, when water for mining or farming often had to be transported far from its source. The prior appropriations system arose, in a sense, because of a lack of water. In the East, mines could be located near a water source and farms received sufficient rainfall for growing crops. Out West, however, mines did not necessarily abut waterways to permit exercise of riparian rights, and farms were not always adjacent to a river. Under the prior appropriations doctrine a user receives the right to divert the flow of a certain volume of water, provided he can put it to use (the doctrine of beneficial use). While diverters have rights to water flows, not all rights are equal. Water rights have different levels of priority, depending on when they were established. The flows of the senior (earlier in time) diverter must be met before those of the junior (later in time) diverter. The doctrine of prior appropriations permits the trading of water rights as a commodity. In the 19th century, water was traded according to four basic principles:[34]

1. Seniority of water rights was time based.

2. Diversion was allowed for use on non-riparian lands.

3. Appropriators forfeited rights to unused water.

4. Transfer and exchange of rights between individuals was permitted.

Here is how the system worked. The first user of the water had priority over other potential users. It did not matter which party might put the water to better use. The user could divert the water away from land next to the body of water, to somewhere else. If the appropriator of the water could not use it, he lost all right to the unused water. However, he might be able to sell his right to use the water to someone else. For example, suppose the owner of a mine needs water to wash the ore. The nearest water is located in a stream a mile away. Nobody currently is taking water from the stream. The mine owner builds a pipe from the stream to his mine. Because he got to the water first, and uses it, nobody can object, and he pays nothing for the water. Ten years later, two new businesses come to town, a farming company that wants to grow high-value specialty vegetables, and an electronics firm. They both need lots of water. Meanwhile, the miner is digging lower and lower quality ore, and wasting much of the water he consumes. The townspeople, the farming company, and the electronics manufacturer ask the miner to let them have some of the water. They explain that he can use less water if he puts in some modern equipment. The miner, if rational, will turn them down. If he uses less water, he loses the right to that water, and he has the right to the water because he got there first. He has no economic incentive to spend the money on new equipment. He does not care that townspeople will lose out on new jobs, or that the water, in other hands, would produce more for the economy. But, he may sell the rights to that water (gained by getting there first) to other users, such as the farming company or the electronics manufacturer, that can put the water to a more valuable use. That is the only way, under the prior appropriation doctrine, to dislodge the holder of the original rights, no matter how wasteful or ridiculous his use of the water may be by present day standards.

The trading system for water rights waned early in years of the 20ᵗʰ century, as government centralization of water development increased. Recent laws, such as the 1992 Omnibus Water Bill, relaxed controls on trading. But there is no state that relies purely on either water rights doctrine. Most use a combination of both doctrines. In addition, government agencies often can allocate water based on the principle of highest beneficial use, which in time of drought prioritizes water for municipal water supplies in order to meet basic human needs.

PROBLEMS WITH WATER PROJECTS

Large water projects and subsidized irrigation damage the environment in one of two ways:[35]

1. Construction of large irrigation projects alters the natural environment, in a manner that is difficult to reverse.

2. Overapplication of water adversely affects the land.

Large water projects transform their environments by flooding previously dry areas, and changing the flow patterns of rivers. Large dams on rivers that flow into the ocean interfere with the migratory habits of many fish species. Often large reservoirs will flood wetlands, destroying wildfowl habitats, altering flyways for migratory birds.

Applying too much water to the land creates economic and environmental damage. The economic damage is felt by taxpayers who subsidize water projects that could be smaller in scale if the users of cheap water did not waste so much of it. Urban dwellers feel the impact because they have to pay more for the water that they need. They compete for the water with agricultural interests that apply more water than is necessary to the land. The environmental damage comes about because overwatering increases the salinity of the soil and raises the water table.

Irrigation water can cause salinity when it is applied to the land:

> Irrigation water normally contains some salts. When irrigation water is evaporated from the land surface, or is transpired by plants, the salts are left behind. If provision is not made for removing the salts, they will accumulate until the land becomes useless for farming. If drainage is satisfactory and flow is sufficient to leach out and carry away the salts accumulated from irrigation in one field, the degraded water moves down in the aquifers or surface streams to the farm of another irrigator. As the water moves from the upper to the lower end of an irrigated valley or river basin, it may have become so highly mineralized as to be no longer useful when it reaches the lower end.[36]

Bower and Fireman elaborate further on the relation between irrigation and salinity problems:

> Saline and alkali soils are soils that have been harmed by soluble salts, consisting mainly of sodium, calcium, magnesium, chloride, and sulfate and secondarily of potassium, bicarbonate, carbonate, nitrate, and boron.
>
> Salt-affected soils are problem soils that require special remedial measure and management practices. . . .
>
> Salt-affected soils occur mainly in regions of an arid or a semiarid climate. . . .
>
> Saline soils usually occur in places that receive salts from other locations; water is the main carrier. . . .
>
> Irrigated lands are often located in valleys near streams; because they can be irrigated easily, the lower and more level soils usually are selected for cultivation. Such soils may be adequately drained and nonsaline under natural conditions, but the drainage facilities may not be adequate under irrigation. . . . Considerable quantities of soluble salts thus may be added to irrigated soils in a short time.[37]

In addition to problems with salinity, "Overirrigation increases the amount of water that the drainage system must convey; if the capacity of the system is exceeded, the water table will rise to an unsafe level."[38]

In California's Central Valley, the soil is naturally salty, so the excess water becomes salty, and stays on top of the underlying clay. Unfortunately, California irrigation processes encourage this overwatering. Even when there is proper drainage, the problem remains of what to do with that highly saline water, which is not hospitable to animal or plant life. Often irrigation water contains toxic elements picked up from the soils, which are also harmful to animal life. Thus it is important to consider where the irrigation water goes after it is used on the fields. During the 1980s, the Bureau of Reclamation directed drainage water from California's Central Valley into the Kesterson Wildlife Refuge. Unfortunately, the water contained high levels of selenium, an element common in the arid west. While not considered harmful to plant growth, selenium is dangerous to animal life, a fact that has been known since the 1930s. The selenium, predictably, caused deformation and death among the waterfowl in the refuge.

Subsidizing the price of water encourages overwatering, because the water is so cheap. That overwatering damages the environment. In addition, subsidized water engenders economic inefficiency. Before examining those inefficiency issues (or, why water is inefficiently allocated at great cost to the taxpayer) let us first examine the four subsidy mechanisms that create those inefficiencies:

- Farmers do not have to repay back interest on the cost of the project. The federal government loses money, because it could have earned interest on the loans.

The value of this lost interest is especially significant over the 40-year period that many reclamation water contracts last.

- Hydropower revenues from Bureau of Reclamation dams subsidize the price of Bureau water. The taxpayer pays to build a dam, which further subsidizes water users.

- When property receives irrigated water, it increases in value compared to its unirrigated state. If the landowner decides to sell his property, he has received a windfall profit as a result of improvements paid for by the federal government. However, the federal government receives no benefits from the increased value of property, outside of capital gains taxes upon sale of the property.

- The government charges water users based upon what the Bureau believes is their "ability to pay," with the difference coming from government funds.

We can now examine the three categories of inefficiencies that these water subsidies create:

1. **Subsidies distort the natural functionings of the market.** The current system of water development engenders inefficiencies in the market because farmers do not pay a price for water that represents the true value of the water to society. Thus the resource will not be used efficiently according to classical market theory, creating a loss to society. Subsidies distort markets, and underpricing water encourages waste, leading to shortages of the resource. In addition, subsidies lead to the growth of crops that have less value than the water's unsubsidized cost. In other words, the cost of the water applied to grow the crop exceeds the value of the crop itself. Many areas in the West would not be tilled without subsidized water. This hurts farmers elsewhere who grow crops without water subsidies and have to compete with subsidized crops.

2. **Benefits of projects do not exceed cost.** Many projects do not pass a cost-benefit test. These projects are not economically viable due to the low price the Bureau charges for water.

3. **Subsidized water expands production of federally price-supported crops.** This is a process known as double dipping: using federally subsidized water to grow federally subsidized (price-supported) crops. Essentially, federally subsidized water is used to increase production of crops covered by federal price supports. The government is bound to buy the crops at a minimum price, exacerbating federal agricultural expenditures. By subsidizing water, thus increasing crop surpluses, the government spend more than if the crops were not grown.

Some observers also have questioned the equity of current federal programs for water distribution. For example, in California, 85% of subsidized water goes to farmers, although the urban areas are willing to pay more for the water. The 1902 Reclamation Act originally intended for water to flow to small farmers (160- to 320-acre farms). In fact, however, it is not primarily small farmers who benefit from the Act. In 1981, eight landowners, with combined holdings of at least 227,545 acres, held two-thirds of Central Valley land. These farms measure approximately 20,000 or more acres, while Illinois farms, for example, average 600 to 1,000 acres. Water subsidies, and a long growing season, allow these larger California farmers to outproduce Eastern and Midwestern farmers. While federal dollars expand one part of the nation's economy, they lead to a contraction elsewhere.

THE LOS ANGELES STORY

"Whoever brings the water, will bring the people,"[39] said William Mulholland, the man who built the Los Angeles water system. He was right.

Bringing water to cities is not a partisan issue out West. Even those who normally object to government involvement in the economy are among the biggest supporters of water projects, for in the American West, water is the key to growth and the ability to live in a desert with a lifestyle modeled on the rainy parts of America. No city exemplifies these goals more than Los Angeles. It serves as a paradigm for urban water development in a desert landscape, and a model for other cities, and government agencies, in engineering large schemes designed to move water vast distances in the West. (See Figure 13-3.)

Although most Californians live by the water, they do not live by water they can drink. Most of California's urban water comes from snowfall high in the Sierras, which, upon melting, runs off into rivers and reservoirs. Unlike in the East, precipitation in California is highly seasonal, mostly falling during the winter months. During the peak summer water use period, there is little rainfall. Los Angeles does not have the same dense development patterns of eastern cities such as New York, Boston, or Chicago. Consequently, much of its settlement consists of sprawling residential neighborhoods, which greatly increases summer demand for watering yards. Many of Los Angeles's settlers in the 20th century arrived from the East, and they chose to live in the same manner as back East, with one-third of the precipitation they had been accustomed to. Attempts to live a humid area lifestyle in arid lands creates water management problems.

At one time Los Angeles took its water from local sources, such as groundwater, and small rivers, such as the Los Angeles River. For the better part of this century, however, it has engaged in efforts to bring water from Northern California and from the Colorado River, hundreds of miles away, which today serve as its main sources. (The cities in the San Francisco Bay Area are not much different—their water mostly comes from reservoirs in the Sierra Nevada Mountains over a

Figure 13-3

Water Projects in Southern California

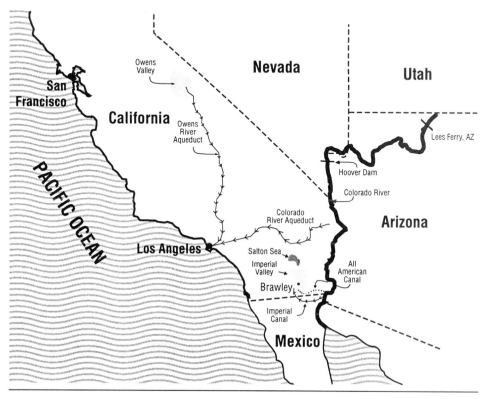

hundred miles away.) Los Angeles' search for water at the turn of the century was of greater significance than merely solving that city's water supply problem. Los Angeles' model of water acquisition, and the way water became tied to economic development, influenced not only other cities, but also the United States Bureau of Reclamation, which started its work concurrently with Los Angeles, and aided Los Angeles in the acquisition of water. The reasons and processes used by Los Angeles to acquire its water serve to elucidate the major force driving Western water policy: the need to accommodate economic growth.

Los Angeles began as a small town, with a poorly developed system of water supply. In the 1860s, Los Angeles granted a private company the franchise to provide water for the city. The newly formed Los Angeles City Water Company derived most of its water supply from the Los Angeles River and from groundwater. Although it was small, Los Angeles sought to grow. Railroad magnate Collis P. Huntington, who controlled the Southern Pacific Railroad, took advantage of the city's desire to grow and agreed to build his railroad to Los Angeles in exchange for 5% of the assessed valuation of Los Angeles County. After establishing this transportation link, the Southern Pacific promoted southern California as an agricultural Eden. California, after all, boasts one of the longest growing seasons in the United States; Los Angeles County often has its first frost in late December, and its last frost in early January. Los Angeles grew rapidly to become the largest city in southern California. Its rail connections, originally built to serve agriculture, made it an ideal outlet for agricultural products. The fact that rainfall in the area averaged only 13 inches per year—half of California's average precipitation— did not strike anyone as particularly vexsome. Presumably, somebody would get the water for the city.

Los Angeles would obtain that water through the efforts of a man whose rise in stature paralleled that of the city of Los Angeles: William Mulholland, the head of the Los Angeles Water Department. William Mulholland arrived in Los Angeles in 1877, as a seaman, and decided to stay. In 1878 he began maintaining irrigation ditches for the Los Angeles City Water Company. One day, while he was working, a man drove up in a carriage and asked Mulholland who he was and what he was doing. Mulholland told him that he was doing his work and his name was none of the man's damned business. When Mulholland's fellow workers informed him that the man he had spoken to was the president of the company, Mulholland went to collect his pay, expecting to be fired. Instead, admiring Mulholland's spirit, the president promoted him to foreman in charge of ditch maintenance. Mulholland devoted himself to the study of geology, hydrology, and engineering. Through diligence, and the application of his studies, by 1886 he had become superintendent of the water company's operations.

Mulholland was remarkably ahead of his time in terms of understanding the techniques needed to provide water in an arid region. He promoted metering of large users, and later residential users, at a time when many cities were still charging a flat rate for water use. He promoted planting trees as a way to conserve water, while conventional wisdom opposed such ideas. Mulholland favored storage of water in aquifers, knowing the toll that evaporation could take on a reservoir in a desert climate. During the 1890s, Mulholland worked to use available water in the Los Angeles basin in the most efficient manner. Ironically, because his success in making water supplies available made growth possible, that growth required even more water. In 1902, the city bought the privately held Los Angeles City Water Company. William Mulholland became the head of the new municipal agency. The city had little choice. There was no schematic depicting the system. All details, such as pipe location and pipe size, were all held in William Mulholland's prodigious memory.

Municipalization proved a great boon to the waterworks, because the city had the financial resources to back the expansion and improvement of the waterworks— something the private company had been reluctant to do. The city continued to grow, affecting the water company dramatically as the number of new hookups to the water system increased by 75% in 1903, and 25% in 1904. Mulholland realized that water was needed from outside the Los Angeles basin—a decision that eventually led to the construction of the largest municipal public works project in American history, and provided the backdrop for one of the most prominent movies of the 1970s: *Chinatown*.

Fred Eaton, formerly Mulholland's boss at the Los Angeles City Water Company, later city engineer, and then mayor of Los Angeles, told Mulholland of a new source of water, the Owens River in the Sierras. It was possible, through the use of siphons, for the water to flow to Los Angeles without pumping. Eaton also saw a way for himself to make money by buying up the rights to the water, and leasing those rights to the city of Los Angeles. One major factor stood in the way of realizing the project. The newly formed Reclamation Service, later renamed the Bureau of Reclamation, wanted to build a large irrigation project that would promote irrigated agriculture in the farmland of the Owens Valley. Such a project would preclude Los Angeles from tapping that water source.

The city of Los Angeles had a fortunate ally: Joseph Lippincott, regional director of the Reclamation Service, a highly qualified engineer, who kept his private engineering consulting practice. Lippincott was good friends with Eaton and Mulholland, and interested in their ideas about Owens Valley water. When two private power companies applied for the rights to build dams in the Owens Valley, Lippincott hired Eaton as a consultant to decide the case. Eaton used that consultancy to study deeds to both land and water rights, and stream flows, information to which he was not otherwise legally entitled. This was the information Los Angeles would need to purchase water rights to Owens Valley water.

Three days after hiring Eaton, Lippincott was hired as a consultant to the Los Angeles Water Department, to study the city's future water needs. Eaton started buying up land and the associated water rights which would be transferred to the city. Sellers assumed that because Eaton was working for Lippincott, that Eaton was buying the rights for the U.S. government, while in reality Eaton was purchasing the rights on behalf of the city of Los Angeles. One of the largest landowners in the valley, rancher Thomas Rickey, had a major financial interest in one of the hydropower firms that wished to build a plant in the valley. Eaton contacted Rickey and persuaded him to sell his land by showing how Rickey's firm could be granted the right to build its project, even though it was inferior to the competitors. In that way, Eaton secured the land and water rights that would block the Reclamation Service from going ahead with its irrigation project.

The city was ready, but it needed money. The problem was that the Los Angeles city charter limited its bonding power (legal ability to sell city bonds) to 15% of the city's net worth. Thus, the solution that easily presented itself was to increase the city's valuation by expanding the city. The ideal area for annexation was the then rural San Fernando Valley, because it would allow for storage of the excess water in underground aquifers that also would contribute to the flow of the Los Angeles River. Mulholland wanted to take as much water as possible from the Owens River, because according to western water law, users could only hold rights to water if they used it. This plan would open up the San Fernando Valley to development. Certain insiders took advantage of this information to buy up much of the San Fernando Valley, knowing that land prices would skyrocket once water was brought to the valley.

Although some politicians tried to highlight the land speculation in order to create opposition, in 1905 the city's voters overwhelmingly approved the bonds for the project. To ensure public support, Mulholland had predicted that without the project, Los Angeles could accommodate no more than 10,000 newcomers. He also manufactured a shortage by having water company employees drain water into the Pacific Ocean. Ironically, Los Angeles was able to accommodate 500,000 new citizens before the Owens River Aqueduct had delivered new water supplies to the city.

The only major obstacle left for the project was to acquire rights of way for the aqueduct over federal lands. The citizens of the Owens Valley, now fearing for their future, after willingly selling their water rights, started to oppose the project. Their congressman tried to effect a compromise that would allow both a Reclamation project and the city's water project. However, President Theodore Roosevelt, and the head of the Forest Service, Gifford Pinchot, a noted conservationist, believed that the nation would be better served by building a prosperous city on the West Coast, and the water would serve a higher value in Los Angeles. They prevented the Reclamation Service from developing its project, thereby saving Los Angeles. In addition, Pinchot enclosed most of the valley in the Inyo Valley National Forest to prevent any development that would compete with the city for the valley's water. The city was now ready to move ahead on the aqueduct project.

Construction on the aqueduct started in 1907, and concluded in 1913. At times as many as 6,000 workers were employed. The work was a major engineering accomplishment, tunneling through hard rock mountains, and traversing the Mojave Desert, where temperatures can fluctuate 80 degrees in a day. Mule teams were required to move piping, because no large earth moving equipment capable of functioning in the desert existed at that time. A large celebration was held when the aqueduct was completed, and Los Angeles was again ready for growth.

The aqueduct served Los Angeles well, but the mid-1920s were very dry years, and the city was still growing. The water department decided to buy more water rights, and fully exercise the rights it held to water in the river. This angered citizens of the Owens Valley, who saw that farms and their way of life would disappear if enough water were drawn from the valley. The city bought up senior water rights, and often would purchase enough of the rights along a cooperative irrigation ditch so that remaining owners were forced to sell because they could not or would not bear the expense of maintaining the ditch. This caused anxiety among merchants in the valley who were losing customers and an economic base. At no time, however, did the city "steal" water. It always paid for its rights, and even when it controlled a ditch, those who had prior rights always received their entitled allocation. In addition, the prices the city paid were nearly always above the market price for water in the valley.

Nonetheless, farmers saw that their way of life would disappear along with their water. Their resentment grew, fanned by two brothers, Mark and Wilfred Watterson, who ran the Inyo County Bank, to which most farmers in the valley were indebted. The Wattersons were friendly bankers who extended credit to farmers and often lengthened repayment periods on loans. They would have had a great deal to lose if agriculture left the valley and commerce declined. They led the opposition to the aqueduct, and appeared to finance that opposition. On November 16, 1924, the Wattersons and irate farmers actually seized the control gates that funneled water from the Owens Valley into Los Angeles' aqueduct, and routed the water onto the dry bed of Owens Lake. This lasted for three days, until in a meeting with Los Angeles bankers, the Wattersons arranged to have the city of Los Angeles buy up all remaining property in the valley at a price that included compensation for damage to property value caused by the water project. The deal fell through, however, and in the following year valley residents took the law into their own hands, dynamiting parts of the aqueduct. Local law enforcement was slow to act, and Los Angeles had to use its own police force to patrol the aqueduct.

The resistance ended when the Wattersons were tried and convicted of bank fraud. They had been using the funds in their bank, the savings of the very valley residents they were trying to help, to shore up their failing mining enterprises. Nonetheless, there were tears in the eyes of judge, juror, and prosecutor as the brothers were sentenced. The main business in the Owens Valley later became tourism, with much of the trade, ironically, coming from Los Angeles.

In the 1920s, Los Angeles needed more water due to its rapid growth. New industries—motion pictures and aviation—moved in to take advantage of its sunny climate and low rainfall (the city boasted of "350 flying days a year"). Discovery of oil in Southern California led to further growth from an energy industry with its concomitant water needs. Los Angeles grew to become the largest city in the West, not only in population, but also in area—all because of water. Nearby communities such as Venice, Watts, and nearly all of the San Fernando Valley with its large farms, chose to be annexed by Los Angeles in order to assure access to a supply of water as their populations expanded. Between 1913 and 1928, Los Angeles became the municipality with the greatest land area in the nation.

Unlike in major cities of the East Coast, land was not at a premium in Los Angeles. The low cost of land tended to promote sprawling development. A large proportion of the residences were single-family homes complete with lawns in a desert clime. This pattern of low-density development created more demand for water than the multi-family dwellings common in cities in the East, where water was abundant. Just as this rapid growth occurred in the 1920s, precipitation fell off in California, creating concern for future water supplies. William Mulholland decided that the Colorado River, the largest river in the Southwest, would provide a good supplement to the Los Angeles Aqueduct. Since the early part of the century, farmers in the Imperial Valley of California had been agitating for federal development of the Colorado River, in order to provide them with a stable supply of irrigation water. However, now Los Angeles had entered the picture, seeking to tap the Colorado River, more than 450 miles away from the city, and bring its water to California. As William Mulholland put it when he testified before Congress, "I am here in the interest of a domestic water supply for the city of Los Angeles, and that injects a new phase into this whole matter."[40]

This was no longer a struggle for water between California agricultural interests and the unpopulated, desert states of the Colorado Basin. Now the biggest, most powerful city in the region, which needed water to fuel its growth and had the reputation for getting what it wanted, had put in its claim for Colorado water. Getting that water with the agreement of seven states of the Colorado Basin—Wyoming, Colorado, Utah, New Mexico, Arizona, and California—might not be as easy, though, as wresting water from the farmers of the Owens Valley.

THE ERA OF BIG WATER WORKS PROJECTS

William Mulholland's comments to Congress significantly affected water policy by making the Colorado River the most disputed river in the Southwest to this day. It is a river that states depend on for economic growth. Marc Reisner, author of *Cadillac Desert*, says of the Colorado:

> The Colorado's modern notoriety. . .stems not from its wild rapids and plunging canyons but from the fact that it is the most legislated, most debated, and most litigated river in the entire world. If the Colorado River suddenly stopped flowing, you would have two years of carryover capacity in the reservoirs before you had to evacuate most of southern California and Arizona and a good portion of Colorado, New Mexico, Utah, and Wyoming.[41]

In the Southwest, the Colorado is the only water game in town. No other river in that area approaches it in terms of flows. It is the main surface water source for that region, which does not have five Great Lakes or an Ogallala Aquifer.

The Colorado River does not flow consistently, which early settlers of the Imperial Valley discovered as they tried to develop large-scale irrigation farming. In the early 1900s, private investors tried to set up an irrigation colony in the Imperial Valley that utilized the flows of the Colorado River. The California Development

Company, which was attempting to develop the land, built a canal in Mexico to connect the Colorado River with the bed of the Alamo River. The canal project enabled the company to sell land to farmers and set up a major agricultural center. Unfortunately, in the mid-1900s the Colorado flooded, inundated the Imperial Valley, and transformed the Salton Sink, a below sea-level depression, into the Salton Sea. The land company could not afford to keep up the battle against the flooding. However, E. H. Harriman, who had taken over the Southern Pacific Railroad following the death of Collis P. Huntington, had to protect the Southern Pacific's investment in rail service to the Imperial Valley. He took over the California Development Company, and the effort to contain the Colorado, in order to protect the railroad track that exported the Valley's agricultural produce.

However, Harriman's investments in levees and other controls along the river did not succeed in containing the Colorado. In addition, irrigators were unhappy with the fact that part of their irrigation canal ran through Mexico. The Mexican government was slow to assent to improvements to the canal and made life difficult at the border for Americans working to maintain the irrigation ditch—Mexican officials even charged customs tariffs on the workers' lunches. Around 1912, Mark Rose, a farmer, lobbied Congress to build an irrigation canal to provide a direct link to the Imperial Valley that did not go through Mexico. The route, coincidentally, also would be a marvelous source of water for his lands.

Rose and other farmers also lobbied the Bureau, which in turn saw a need for a dam on the Colorado River to regulate river water levels and prevent the swings in flows that were hampering growth of irrigation in the Imperial Valley. The two groups came to an understanding in 1919, when the Bureau of Reclamation and the Imperial Irrigation District, which governed irrigation water in the Imperial Valley, agreed to build an All-American Canal, in conjunction with a Colorado River dam. Word of the agreement soon spread. Other states in the Colorado River basin became concerned that if such a canal were built it would benefit California at their expense. These states were not putting their water to beneficial use (that is, using it on the land) so California, under the doctrine of prior appropriation, could rightfully claim as much Colorado River water as it was using. Given its soil and warmer climate, California had much more agricultural potential than a state such as Wyoming, where in 1919, growing seasons ranged from 110 to 152 days in length. (In comparison, Brawley, in the Imperial Valley, had a 276-day season.)

The Colorado Basin states tried, unsuccessfully, to negotiate a water agreement among themselves. Federal intervention came in the person of Herbert Hoover, Secretary of Commerce in the Harding administration. Hoover led 10 months of negotiations that resulted in the signing of the Colorado River Compact on November 24, 1922. The compact designated Lees Ferry, Arizona, as the dividing line between the Upper and Lower Basins of the Colorado River. Wyoming, Colorado, Utah, and New Mexico were designated as in the Upper Basin. Arizona, Nevada, and California were designated as in the Lower Basin. The developers of the compact used as the basis of their negotiations the Bureau of Reclamation's determination of the Colorado's average flow: 17.5 million acre-feet per year. The compact allocated 7.5 million acre-feet to the Upper Basin, and 7.5 million acre-feet to the Lower Basin, with 1.5 million acre-feet allocated to Mexico. The Lower Basin, in addition, was entitled to a one million acre-feet bonus from surplus flows above the 7.5 million acre-feet per year mark. The flow numbers, however, were based on statistics compiled during a wet period. Average flow, under normal conditions, was closer to 13 million acre-feet per year. The compact had allocated nonexistent water. The passage of the compact depended on ratification by six of the seven state legislatures.

For the next six years, the states of the lower basin, primarily Arizona and California, could not decide how to allocate the water between them. While each state was finding fault with the compact, Los Angeles was growing rapidly, and looking for its next major water source. In 1923, William Mulholland brought staff of the Los Angeles Department of Water and Power to the Colorado River near Las Vegas, and announced: "Well, here's where we get our water."[42] In 1924, he filed claims for one million acre-feet per year of Colorado River Water. Then, in 1925, the major cities of Southern California, including San Diego and Los Angeles, joined together to form the Metropolitan Water District of Southern California (MWD), in order to work together to bring Colorado River water to Southern California's urban areas. Both urban and agricultural interests agreed to support a Colorado River aqueduct, a large dam to regulate the flows of the river, and a public hydroelectric power plant at that site to subsidize the irrigation project.

In 1928, Congress passed the Boulder Canyon Project Act to build what would become Hoover Dam, the Bureau of Reclamation's largest project to that date. The Act also allocated the water in the lower basin, with California receiving 4.4 million acre-feet per year, Arizona receiving 2.8 million acre-feet, and Nevada receiving 300,000 acre-feet. The surplus of one million acre-feet was to be split evenly between Arizona and California. By the time the dam was completed in 1935, the era of large-scale water development had begun. Construction of large dams—Shasta, Grand Coulee, and Bonneville—boomed in the 1930s.

California's push for more water had stimulated the Bureau of Reclamation to begin work on big projects, and had stimulated water agencies throughout the country to investigate all sorts of water schemes, regardless of the cost. Southern California again had pushed water development further in the direction of large water projects. At the same time, in the waning days of the Hoover administration, Interior Secretary Ray Lyman Wilbur, a Californian, exempted the Imperial Irrigation District from the 160-acre limit. A program originally started to help small farmers settle the West now was going to provide subsidized water to large growers in what would become one of the most productive agricultural regions of the United States.

The Democrats, too, encouraged dam building and large land holdings. In the 1930s, the Roosevelt administration exempted lands in the service area of the Colorado-Big Thompson project from the 160-acre limitation. The Bureau of Reclamation, by this time, had changed its emphasis from irrigation to dam building. Although some projects were not feasible under reclamation law, building dams to subsidize these irrigation projects reduced scrutiny of the effectiveness of reclamation projects in promoting efficient irrigation. The Truman administration did attempt to enforce the acreage limitations. By the start of the 1950s, though, the Bureau again had drifted away from enforcing the law, even when it was clear to those involved that laws were being violated. The Bureau of Reclamation focused on building dams in order to support irrigation projects with questionable economics.

The mood was best summed up by Edmund G. "Pat" Brown, who was elected governor of California in 1958. He was convinced that in order to maintain its growth, California needed to bring water from the north of the state to the south. Brown believed that water development needed to be pursued at any cost. Of water projects he said, "... I don't think it [cost] has any validity because you need water."[43] Politicians and water industry leaders often promote water projects by projecting scarcity—a fear of drought and thirst. The reality in California, though, is that very little of this water goes to support human life. Instead it is used for agriculture, for crops that grow just as easily in the humid regions of the nation.

In 1960, Governor Brown promoted a California State Water Project that required the passage of a $1.75 billion bond issue, which was a known understatement of the project's cost. The project was economically justified as a water improvement by comparing it against the cost of desalinating seawater, the most expensive known method of water purification at that time. Brown also revealed another, more personal reason for building the State Water Project: "I loved building things. I wanted to build that goddamned water project. I was *absolutely determined* I was going to pass this California Water Project. I wanted this to be a monument to *me*."[44]

Brown's statement reveals how the passion for water development in the West can interfere with sound economic planning. Nonetheless, the bond issue passed and the project was implemented, even though it seems that the water was not badly needed by the cities. Taxpayers wound up subsidizing agricultural users who paid a fraction of the cost that urban dwellers paid. Upon commencing work at Oroville Dam, Governor Brown commented, "We are going to build a river 500 miles long. We are going to build it to correct an accident of people and geography."[45] The California State Water Project was to be one of the final glories of that expansive era of water development and public works, when planners rarely considered either cost or environmental impacts.

In the 1960s, the environmental movement emerged on the national scene. Many environmental initiatives originated in California. Public sentiment against large dams grew. People saw how those projects not only altered natural ecosystems, but often were based on questionable economics. Preservationists sought to keep California's few remaining free flowing rivers in an undeveloped state. In addition, the water industry was coming under scrutiny because of concerns over pollutants in water, which resulted in the passage of two federal laws, the Clean Water Act in 1972 and the Safe Drinking Water Act in 1974. The growing environmental movement helped elect Jerry Brown, Edmund Brown's son, to the governorship of California in 1974. It is ironic, though, that Governor Jerry Brown sought to expand the State Water Project by building a canal that would make it possible to tap into Northern California Rivers, and take that water around the San Francisco Bay-Sacramento Delta, thereby depriving a large, environmentally sensitive estuary and wetlands area of fresh water flows. Unlike the State Water Project, the bond issue for this project was badly defeated, revealing that the forces promoting growth were losing some of their support. Northern Californians vehemently opposed the loss of their water, and two large agricultural corporations that would have been hurt by the diversions allied themselves with environmentalists against the water interests of Southern California. Industry insiders were shocked by what they perceived as affronts to their growth machine. The Metropolitan Water District did not help its case when in public it promoted fear of shortages, and in private it assured potential purchasers of its bonds that it did not expect a shortfall for a long time, and that it had other alternatives to the expansion of the State Water Project.

The 1980s brought Ronald Reagan to the presidency. His administration spent less on water projects than previous administrations. Yet Southern California's population grew rapidly during that decade. Urban water agencies sought new ways to procure water without construction of large reservoirs. Irrigated agriculture, which used about 80% of California's water, seemed the ideal place to look for water. During drought periods in the early 1990s, the state of California diverted water from agriculture to domestic water users, because water for domestic use was considered a higher value use of water under California law. Urban interests began to question why agriculture should receive so much water. Could the water be transferred for urban use, even if that required paying the farmers for their heavily subsidized water? It appeared to be cheaper to buy water from farmers than to develop new sources of supply.

In fact, the Metropolitan Water District has entered into an agreement with the Imperial Irrigation District (IID), whereby the MWD has paid the IID to implement measures to conserve water in its district, and send the conserved water to the MWD. No land is fallowed, so farmers are not economically affected by the transfer. With the passage of the Omnibus Water Bill in 1992, transfers were allowed between agencies receiving Central Valley Project water and urban agencies. This bill was supposed to encourage a market in water rights, but the market, as of 1998, has not sprung up yet. (See Appendix B for further discussion of the Central Valley Project.) Although the MWD has arranged transfers on its own, it has recently sought to prevent one of its member agencies, the San Diego County Water Agency, from doing so. San Diego had sought to buy water directly from farmers in the IID and send the water through the Colorado River Aqueduct to its pipes. The MWD, however, balked at this, for reasons that are not clear. Some observers see the MWD as worried about losing revenues from one of its biggest customers, so it wishes to charge the San Diegans for much more than the cost of using the aqueduct if they wish to ship water—including all the costs of operating the whole MWD distribution system. Although at the time of this writing (1998) the issue has not been resolved, it seems, with increasing pressures on the San Diego water system to provide for growth, and little likelihood of building new supplies, that some sort of compromise will be worked out to transfer the water, ushering in an active market in water rights that harkens to the pre-reclamation days.

CONCLUSION

California, especially Southern California, has been in the vanguard of western water development, whether tapping the Owens Valley, promoting the building of Hoover Dam, or, more recently, promoting large-scale purchases of water from agricultural users. Other western cities, such as Denver and Phoenix, bring in water from great distances, and are constantly growing, and hunting for new water supplies in an area that does not have many. Holders of unused or under-used water rights see great value in selling rights to those cities, which will pay more for water than it is worth in farming. Some cities may not be able to pay what Los Angeles can for water. They could face a questionable future if they cannot provide the water to meet growth. The West still emphasizes growth. There is a lot of unused land, but not enough water. As the Southwest experiences rapid growth, its scarce water resources will become more important, and it seems likely that more and more agricultural water will move to the cities, and that indirectly, through the Bureau of Reclamation, the federal government will wind up as a major municipal water supplier, rather than as an aid to small farmers seeking to reclaim the West from the desert. The future seems to point to more urban growth in an area of low rainfall and precarious water supplies.

CHAPTER 14

Private Water Companies

A private company providing a public service is a separate power center and revenue source not subject to the control of city hall.[46]

— Gilbert Cross

In the United States, private enterprise controls almost all business activities. In the public utility sector, Americans have opted for private ownership of service providers, with an overlay of public regulation to assure adequate levels of service at reasonable prices, in order to protect the public. The provision of electricity, as vital to the operation of a modern economy as the provision of water is to public health, is firmly in the hands of the private sector. Government-owned utilities provide roughly 25% of electricity. Government-owned utilities furnish a lower percentage of natural gas and telecommunication services. But government-owned entities furnish about 85% of publicly supplied water and possibly 95% of publicly supplied sewer services. Furthermore, they have dominated the industry for over a century.

EARLY PATTERNS

America's first water utilities began as private enterprises. The Water Works Company of Boston, established in 1652, may have been the first. In 1755, Hans Christiansen instituted service at the first pumped public waterworks in America, in Bethlehem, Pennsylvania, which, incidentally, became the country's second water system. Providence, Rhode Island chartered two water companies in 1772. But, by and large, American cities of the time did not have real public water systems, besides public wells. Other than that, people requiring water dug their own wells, purchased water from entrepreneurs who sold it from wagons, or sent their servants or slaves to fetch water from the nearest body of water. The Revolutionary War put a stop to public improvements.

In the 1790s, the country expected private enterprise to bring clean water to cities and towns. In this period, state legislatures had to charter every new corporation. From 1791 through 1800, legislatures chartered 295 corporations, of which 29 were chartered to provide public water supply. Some admittedly had another principal purpose, with water supply of secondary importance. As an example, Pennsylvania's Delaware and Schuylkill Canal Company was chartered in 1792 both to build a canal and to provide water to Philadelphia. The most egregious example, though, was the Manhattan Company, supposedly established in 1799 as a water company with a banking arm, but quickly transformed into a bank reluctantly providing water.

From 1795 through 1800, Massachusetts chartered 18 waterworks companies, including Boston's Aqueduct Company in 1795, Pittsfield's supplier in the same year, four towns in 1796, six in 1797 (including the Salem and Danvers Aqueduct Company, which was still serving customers in 1859), four more in 1798, and two more in 1799-1800.

States chartered companies to serve other major cities: Hartford, Connecticut in 1797, Portsmouth, New Hampshire in 1798, Charleston, South Carolina and Morristown, New Jersey in 1799, and New London, Connecticut in 1800. From 1799 to 1820, New York State chartered 25 water companies. This is an impressive list for a rural country, largely wilderness, whose major cities had unpaved streets with pigs running through them.

In the first half of the 19th century, many of the growing cities chartered private water suppliers, but few remained private. The Baltimore Water Company, founded in 1804, survived through 1854, when the city bought out the company. The Cincinnati Water Company, founded in 1820, pumped water out of the Ohio River, and distributed it in wooden mains. The city bought the company in 1839. New Orleans, in 1833, brought in a private company to finish a project begun by the city. The Chicago Hydraulic Company, founded in 1836, used steam engines to pump water from Lake Michigan. The city bought the company in 1852. Buffalo, New York, late to the game, got its private water company in 1852. Elizabethtown Water, incorporated in 1854, still serves its namesake in New Jersey. Brooklyn's Nassau Water Company was established in 1855, and later bought out. In 1857-1860, Louisville, Kentucky made deals to allow several private water suppliers to operate.

In 1799, Winchester, Virginia constructed the first municipal water system. A few other cities set up their own systems in the next three decades. By 1860, private water systems still out-numbered the government-owned systems, but the municipally owned systems, however, supplied 12 of America's 16 largest cities. The four exceptions were New Orleans, Buffalo, San Francisco, and Providence. The privately owned companies held sway in the smaller cities and towns. By 1896, municipalities owned 15 of the 16 original water systems operating in 1800, and half the water systems in the country. By 1927, cities owned 70% of the urban water systems. (See Table 14-1.) The fall in the percentage of water suppliers in government hands subsequent to 1927 probably represents the increasing number of small real estate developments that entrusted service to private water companies, and the rise of the suburbs, in which private water suppliers took root. In 1976, however, government suppliers furnished water to 84% of the population that took water from community suppliers. That percentage dropped to 79% in 1994, probably reflecting the growth of the suburbs relative to the central city.

Table 14-1

Ownership of Water Systems
1800-1994

Year	Government Owned	Privately Owned	% Government Owned
1800	1	15	6
1810	5	21	19
1820	5	25	17
1830	9	35	21
1840	23	41	36
1850	33	50	40
1860	57	79	42
1870	116	127	48
1880	293	305	49
1890	806	1,072	43
1896	1,690	1,489	53
1927	6,860	2,940	70
1950	20,250	13,950	69
1976	19,390	15,240	56
1994	22,600	34,000	40

Sources:
Charles F. Phillips, Jr., *The Regulation of Public Utilities* (Arlington, VA: Public Utilities Reports, 1984), pp. 687, 688, 692.
U.S. Department of Agriculture, *The Year Book of Agriculture 1955* (Washington, D.C.: U.S. Govt. Printing Office, 1955), p. 651.
American Water Works Association Water Industry Data Base (1994 data).

The private sector fell to its insignificant position within the industry due to the rise of municipal socialism. So far, the private sector has shown little sign that it can recover its former dominance, despite the rapid increase in the number of private water companies. The government sector still serves most of the population.

MUNICIPAL SOCIALISM

Wherever large industrial firms had easy access to water, they did not need public water suppliers. They could locate their facilities on waterways, taking the water they wanted without aid of local governments. Farmers could do the same, or they could work together to create cooperative irrigation entities. People in small towns dug their own wells. The great crowded and dirty cities, however, required public water supplies and sewers. The municipalities, by and large, had handed the task to private companies. The private firms, though, desirous of making profits for their shareholders, expanded cautiously, unwilling to invest in projects unlikely to pay off economically. Those policies discouraged service to low-income areas and to sparsely populated neighborhoods. The private companies, therefore, inhibited the expansion of the city, because people avoided areas without water supply. The companies, moreover, had little economic incentive to provide service to where it was most needed for public health purposes, because the population in those areas was poor. The city governments of the day could have offered subsidies to the private firms to provide seemingly uneconomic services, but they did not. Nor did the government hand out welfare checks that enabled the poor to buy a necessary service at a price that covered a supplier's costs. If water and sanitation improvements were necessary for public health and safety, and if the private suppliers were unwilling or unable to do what was necessary, then the city felt that it had to take on the task directly. (Utility franchises usually had set lives. At the expiration of the franchise, the city might have the right to take the assets of the utility, which made it easier for the city to take over the business.) As Lewis Mumford observed:

> Hygiene demanded . . . resources that had hitherto been lacking. In time, this demand enforced municipal socialism, as a normal accompaniment to improved service. Neither a pure water supply, nor . . . disposal of . . . sewage, could be left to private conscience or attended to only if they could be provided for a profit.[47]

Mumford noted, too, that private companies might retain their franchises in small cities, as happened in the American water industry, but:

> in the bigger cities socialization was the price of safety; and so, despite the theoretic claims of laissez faire, the nineteenth century became . . . the century of municipal socialism. . .[48]

The improvements in public health that came with safe drinking water enforced the belief that the public, as a whole, gained from widespread use of water and public sanitation, leading to:

> the supply of city water to dwelling houses at less than cost. . . justified on the ground that a too liberal use of water is in the interest of community health.[49]

Obviously, no private water supplier could afford to offer below-cost water and stay in business. The private supplier had no way to monetize the public health benefits as an offset to the losses it would take when supplying the water at a price below cost.

The municipal reform movement affected more than ownership of water utilities. Between 1896 and 1906, the number of municipally owned electric systems tripled. The threat of wholesale municipalization, in fact, led the National Electric Light Association, in 1907, to make a deal with the National Civic Federation to propose regulation of utilities by states. The utility companies viewed regulation as the alternative to government takeover of properties. By that time, though, municipal government had long ago taken over the water systems of the major cities.

THE PRIVATE SECTOR PLAYERS

Despite the dominance of government-owned water utilities, private sector firms thrive. Some have operated for over 100 years. Thousands of small, local water and sewer companies serve real estate subdivisions, suburbs and a few large cities. In 1997 though, only two of America's 25 largest cities were served by private water companies. Fewer than two dozen water companies have regularly traded stock. Holding companies dominate the private sector. The two largest are American Water Works and United Water Resources, which together account for about 60% of the revenues of the top 10 private water companies.

American Water Works is the largest private sector firm. The holding company traces its origins to a partnership, Kuhn Brothers & Company, set up in 1882 by a Pennsylvania pipe manufacturer to build and run water companies. (United Gas Improvement, the first of the great utility holding companies, a model for all that followed, was established in 1882 as well.) In 1886, Kuhn Brothers organized American Water Works & Guarantee Company to build, operate, own and guarantee the principal and interest on water company bonds. Within two years, the company owned 18 waterworks throughout the East and Midwest. New Jersey, in 1889, changed its corporation charter laws to allow a corporation to own stock in other corporations. That meant that a New Jersey corporation need not buy all the assets of a company it wished to control. It could, instead, buy only enough stock to control the other corporation. Buying control of voting stock, instead of buying the entire business, allowed a corporation to take control for less money, which meant that it could use its resources to control more corporations. In 1891, American Water Works & Guarantee headed for New Jersey, in order to operate under that state's corporate law.

In 1909-1913, American spread its wings. It invested in irrigation and hydroelectric projects in Idaho, and irrigation projects in California. It purchased control of a coal company. It took control of West Penn Railways (the predecessor to Allegheny Power System) in 1910. Early in 1913, American owned water and electric utilities in 14 states, one of the largest trolley systems, the biggest bituminous coal producer in the United States, irrigation projects and a hotel. That same year, the seemingly prosperous company went bankrupt, as a result of having guaranteed $20 million worth of bonds of irrigation projects that failed.

Reconstituted with new management in 1914 as the American Water Works & Electric Company, the organization launched an expansion program, acquiring control of more electric and water utilities. By early 1936, the company controlled 44 water operations in 17 states and Cuba. Later in the year, the purchase of Community Water Service added 42 more companies and four more states to the collection. In that same year, Congress passed the Public Utility Holding Company Act, which decreed the dissolution of non-contiguous electric systems and the separation of electric service from other operations. The Act neither prohibited formation of nor decreed dissolution of water holding companies. Arthur Stone Dewing, the legendary finance professor, commented:

> The water holding company, consisting of widely scattered operating water companies, is permitted, as if water is less a public utility and less of an essential in our twentieth-century living, than either electricity or gas.[50]

The water holding company, presumably, had the same ability to control assets or evade regulation that caused Congress to kill off electric and gas holding companies. Perhaps, though, few people cared, because the water holding companies were relatively small, and because most of the water supply industry was already in public hands.

In 1947, a dozen years after passage of the Holding Company Act, American Water Works & Electric put its water operations up for sale. John Ware, a Pennsylvania entrepreneur who had amassed a fortune through acquisition and operation of small water companies, bought control, and dropped "Electric" from the corporate name. During the booming postwar years, American invested in its existing companies, and bought and sold properties. Selling properties to municipal governments, in fact, was a big business for private water companies. The municipalities often took control only after long disputes over value of the assets. Courts generally ruled that the municipalities could not condemn (take over) the properties for less than fair value, which normally was well above cost. The private water companies could earn hefty profits in disposal of properties.

John Ware, most of the time, stuck to small projects and small cities. Uncharacteristically, in 1955, he decided to build a $300 million reservoir and aqueduct to supply clean, but more expensive, mountain water to Pittsburgh. Four years later, after public opposition and numerous accusations, the project died. American Water Works, from then on, concentrated on buying water companies or water holding companies. Between 1960 and 1990, volume increased from 7,543 million gallons to 121,193 million gallons, and the customer count rose from 86,000 to 772,000. By 1996, American sold 247,300 million gallons to 1,884,000 customers.

United Water Resources, the second largest multi-state private water group, began in 1893 as New Jersey's Hackensack Water Company. In the 1950s and 1960s, the company purchased several small water companies, and in 1983 took on its present name. United made the big time in 1994 when it merged with GWC.

In 1942, Philadelphia financier Howard Butcher set up General Water Works (later GWC) to acquire 16 water companies in Arkansas from a utility holding company. By 1951, he controlled 29 water companies in 14 states plus five small telephone companies. In 1968, Butcher arranged for the merger of General into International Utilities (later IU International), a Philadelphia-based holding company. That conglomerate controlled utilities in Canada, General Water Works, a pump manufacturer, truckers, a shipping line, and was one of the largest shareholders in

Penn Central, before that railroad went bankrupt. Subsequently, IU sold half of General Water Works to an American subsidiary of the French giant, Lyonnaise des Eaux, to form GWC. In 1985, the French bought the rest of GWC. Then, in 1994, United Water Resources bought GWC, paying for the company largely with stock. As a result of the deal, Lyonnaise des Eaux became United's largest shareholder. At the end of 1996, United served 589,000 water customers in 13 states.

Of the top 10 private water utilities, only two serve one of America's 20 largest cities. SJW Corporation provides water in San Jose, California, the capital of Silicon Valley, and IWC Resources Corporation sells water in Indiana's capital, Indianapolis.

Rounding out the top 10 are two other California utilities (California Water Service Company and Southern California Water Company), a company serving the Phila-delphia suburbs (Philadelphia Suburban Corporation), a multi-state holding com-pany (Consumers Water Company), a New Jersey utility (Elizabethtown Water Company) and an old line Connecticut utility (Aquarion Company).

The revenues of all privately owned water and sewage providers in 1996 probably came to less than $7 billion out of a $55 billion total for the industry. The top 10 private water companies account for only $2 billion, and American Water Works, alone, shows close to $900 million of that total. (See Table 14-2.)

OPPORTUNITIES

Overall, water usage grows slowly. Private suppliers seem boxed in, with a small share of the market. Even the biggest companies have only a small percentage of the private water market. They obviously can grow by purchasing other privately owned utilities. They can invest abroad too, but they do not have the financial resources or experience of the major foreign water utilities.

As an alternative, they can participate in the privatization of government-owned facilities. Doing so in the past was difficult. Until an executive order issued by President George Bush in 1992, municipalities that sold assets that had been funded through grants from the federal government had to pay back those grants before retaining any of the proceeds from the sale. That procedure removed any incentive for the municipality to sell its water system because the municipality might receive little or nothing from the proceeds, after it had finished paying back the federal government. The allocation of proceeds instituted by President Bush changed the picture. If the municipality decides to sell facilities, it has first claim on the proceeds, taking out the amount that it has invested, before it has to distribute the balance to anyone else. Then the federal government can recover the grants that it has provided to the utility. Anything left over goes to the municipality. Thus, municipalities now have an incentive to sell properties if a private operator can run them a better. The Internal Revenue Service (IRS), how-

Table 14-2

Ten Largest Private Water Companies
1996

Company	Utility Revenues[1]	Net Utility Plant[1]	Sales[2]	Customers[3]	Utility Revenue per Customer	Sales per Customer[4]	Net Plant per Customer	States Served	Other
American Water Works	$875	$3454	247.3	1884	$467	131	$1833	21	Ware family controls over 12% of stock
Aquarion	82	304	24.1	136	603	177	2235	2	—
California Water Service	183	444	105.1	376	487	280	1181	1	SJW owns 8.5%
Consumers Water	94	404	23.4	228	411	103	1775	6	Générale des Eaux owns 22%
Elizabethtown Water Company	110	560	48.0	196	561	245[5]	2857	1	Kean family owns 6%
IWC Resources	78	310	46.9	235	332	200	1319	1	NIPSCO owns 100%
Philadelphia Suburban	120	503	34.4	284	423	103	1771	1	Générale des Eaux owns · 4%
SJW	103	235	48.4	209	488	232	1124	1	Moss brothers own 32%
Southern California Water	140	330 E	59.4	241	581	246	1369	1	—
United Water Resources	294	1082	82.8	615	478	135	1759	13	Suez-Lyonnaise des Eaux owns 26%

[1] $ millions—water and sewer only
[2] Billion gallons in year
[3] Thousands, water and sewer
[4] Thousands of gallons—as computed by company when available
[5] 117 for own system retail
E—Estimated

ever, had created its own obstacle to another form of privatization: the operating contract, whereby a private enterprise would take over operation of and make improvements on a government-owned facility. The IRS had ruled, since the 1986 tax law, that contracts to serve projects financed through tax-exempt municipal bonds could not have terms greater than five years. Five years, however, did not give the private firm enough time to depreciate the investment it would make to improve the facility. The alternative was to replace tax-exempt with taxable debt, which reduced the potential savings to consumers. In 1997, the IRS agreed to stretch the allowable contract period to 20 years. Thus, privatization of one sort or another—either through outright purchase or outsourcing of services—now constitutes a realistic business opportunity that could enable the private water suppliers to break out of their circumscribed market.

CONCLUSION

Private water companies started first out of the gate, but soon lost the lead. They could not function simultaneously as a profit-making company, developer of new neighborhoods, protector of public health and safety, and income redistribution agent. The big cities took over the privately owned operations, leaving a small private sector water industry. Now, government-owned utilities are under pressure to reduce capital spending, cut operating costs, repair aging infrastructure, and meet all the new environmental rules. The private sector might get a second chance, if it proves more capable of meeting the challenges more efficiently than public sector entities.

CHAPTER 15

Water and Health

Drunkards and filthy, wicked people ... are swept away ... as if the Holy God could no longer bear their wickedness ... The cholera is not caused by intemperance and filth, in themselves, but it is a scourge ... in the hand of God ...[51]

— Editorial in *Western Sunday School Messenger*, Sept. 1, 1832

In 1789, Benjamin Franklin's will warned that well water in the cities would become unfit to drink. How did people, in those days, determine what water was fit to drink? In 1798, as an example, Dr. Joseph Browne of New York, tested the wholesomeness of water by taste, by whether it came from a clear running source, and by whether soap dissolved in it. Meanwhile, the health experts explained how washing down the streets prevented disease, and the moralists declared that epidemics represented the wrath of God.

CONTAMINATION

In 1831, the New York Lyceum of Natural History claimed that local water had a high mineral content due to contamination from nearby graves and privies. The learned authors of the report did not know whether the minerals were dangerous to the health of the citizenry, but they did connect the high mineral content to sewage contamination.

Governments of the day realized the danger of pollutants. In 1803, Philadelphia set fines for dumping trash or filth into the water basin. In 1832, the city added excrement, carrion, and noxious matter to the list of substances one should not drop into the river. In 1808, Baltimore enacted fines for water polluters. In 1817, the city took steps to protect springs from the pollution seeping in from cesspools and privies. New York City, in 1842, imposed fines on those who bathed or threw stones into the Croton Reservoir or Aqueduct. The preventive measures, though, were only partially effective, because people believed that running water had the power to cleanse itself. As a result, the public health authorities worried about pollution near the water intake, but not elsewhere in the body of water that supplied the water system.

Health experts did not know what effect chemicals in the water had on human health. Nor did they know what to make of living organisms visible in the water supply (referred to as "animalcules"). The Boston authorities debated the matter in 1834. One water commissioner, Nathan Hale, said that "The only remedy against them is to avoid too curious a search.''[52] Another Bostonian claimed that animalcules could live only in clean water, so their appearance was a good sign. It seems to have occurred to no one to filter the water to remove foreign matter.

CHOLERA AS A CASE STUDY

Three frightening cholera epidemics spread across North America in 1832-1834, 1848-1849, and 1866. Within three decades, public health authorities learned the connection between cholera and water supply, and how to control the disease, and they did all this before they had discovered the cause of cholera.

In 1831, the disease spread from Russia and Poland to England. Americans prepared for the worst. New York City, as the principal port of entry, should have expected to feel the brunt of the disease earliest, but the city took no precautions. The Board of Health had rarely met in its 10 years of existence. The city had only three health professionals on its payroll. Pigs roamed the streets. People piled rubbish on the streets and the corrupt trash haulers left it there. The quality of the local water supply was notoriously bad. The Medical Society recommended that the city run water through its streets, disinfect cesspools with chloride of lime, and tell everyone to wash. That was the full extent of the preventive measures. Cholera struck its first victim, an Irish immigrant, on June 26, 1832. Anyone who could afford to, fled the city. The Special Medical Council, set up for the emergency, declared that, "the disease in the city is confined to the imprudent, the intemperate, and to those who injure themselves by taking improper medicines."[53]

Doctors believed that while atmospheric miasmas caused cholera, bad habits predisposed people to the disease. The doctors warned people not to sleep in drafts, nor drink alcoholic beverages, nor drink cold water if overheated, among other preventive remedies. Most victims were poor, often immigrants, those who had to drink New York City's noxious water because they could not afford anything better, people who opposed rapid burial of the disease's victims, and those who refused to go to hospitals. The epidemic ended in New York by August. It then swept into Chicago, and the West and South in 1833.

John L. Riddell, at the Cincinnati Medical College, as early as 1836, suggested that some type of reproducing, living organism produced cholera. Most doctors disagreed. Those who did not favor the miasma theory spoke about a ferment of miasma or of dirt as the disease's cause.

Another cholera epidemic spread from the Ganges to the rest of the world in 1848. Americans began preparations in the fall of that year. On December 1, the ship *New York* dropped anchor in New York Harbor, with cholera victims on board. The city quarantined the 300 passengers, but half of them escaped. The epidemic began in New York in May 1849. The city had to force its negligent sanitation contractors to clear the streets. They dumped the garbage in the river.

Pigs and filth in the street remained commonplace in most American cities. Ships brought the disease to ports in the American South. The disease spread to the Midwest, carried by immigrants on boats that dropped human waste and dead bodies into the waterways. The gold seekers heading to California carried the disease with them. Cholera hit hardest at the cities with the greatest immigrant populations, St. Louis, New Orleans, Cincinnati and New York.

John Snow, a London physician, in 1849 published a pamphlet entitled *On the Mode of Communication of Cholera*. In it, he speculated that cholera was caused by a poison that reproduced within the victims. The vomit and wastes of the victims carried the poison. Those substances contaminated the water supply, which then spread the disease. Of course, others had theories of cholera, and Snow had no proof. When cholera broke out in London in 1854, Snow found proof. Two water companies served London. The Lambeth company took its water supply from the Thames upriver from London. The Southwark and Vauxhall company had its source downriver from London's sewage discharge point. Cholera struck the latter company's customers more frequently. Contaminated water had to be the source of the disease, Snow reasoned, and he published that conclusion in 1855. Snow also traced a local outbreak of cholera to the Broad Street pump at Golden Square, which nearby privies had contaminated. He removed the pump handle (thereby preventing its use) and the outbreak ended. Max von Pettenkofer, a noted public health expert in Munich, took up the cudgels for Snow's theory, and he, too, warned of the dangers of a contaminated water supply.

The next epidemic of cholera struck the United States in 1866. By then, public health officials had remedies at hand. They disinfected the houses and bedding of victims, boiled water and cleaned privies. By that time, too, large cities had improved their water supplies. Death rates fell to a fraction of that of the previous epidemic. That was the last cholera epidemic in the country.

In 1883, German bacteriologist Robert Koch discovered the *Cholera vibrio*, the microorganism that causes the disease. That put to rest the miasmic and fermentation theories.

FILTRATION

Europeans began to filter water early in the 19th century. John Gibb installed the first filter in Paisley, Scotland, in 1804, and Glasgow and Greenock followed the example. London installed filters in 1829. Albert Stein, a German-American engineer, attempted the first American filtration system in Richmond, Virginia in 1832, but the filters could not deal with James River water. Frederich Erdmann, in 1846, suggested filters for the Philadelphia water supply. That leading waterworks' board turned down the idea in 1846, 1849, 1853, and 1854. The Croton Aqueduct's board said no to filters in 1849.

In 1855, Elizabeth, New Jersey installed a filter. Saint Louis city fathers hired James P. Kirkwood to investigate the European use of filters in 1869, but subsequently decided not to filter the city's water. Kirkwood, in 1872, did install a slow sand filter at Poughkeepsie, for use on Hudson River water. The real impetus for filtration however, came from the Massachusetts State Board of Health, established in 1869. That body, in 1878, sent Prof. William Ripley Nichols to Europe to study water purification. In 1887, the Board set up the Lawrence, Massachusetts, Experiment Station, installing a filtration station there in 1892.

Hiram F. Mills of Lawrence, Massachusetts and J. J. Reincke of Hamburg, Germany, in 1893-1894, made studies that showed that the death rate fell after introduction of purification of water in both cities. This was the so-called Mills Reincke phenomenon. Then in, 1904, Allen Hazen tested the hypothesis using data from other cities. He wrote that, "where one death from typhoid fever has been avoided by the use of better water, a certain number of deaths, probably two or three, from other causes have been avoided."[54]

Philadelphia's actions, however, demonstrate the slowness to install filters. In 1853, the city turned down filtration. By 1860, the city's Bureau of Health reported water shortage in the summer. Water was needed to clear the streets, to flush sewers, and for personal hygiene. But the water supply was polluted. In 1861, the Bureau of Health complained of pollutants of all sorts in the water: sulfate of iron from coal mines, refuse from factories, and city sewage. Yet the city did not begin to install filters until 1902. It did so, water district by water district, through 1909. The typhoid epidemic of 1905-1906 did not affect inhabitants of the two districts that installed filters in 1902 an 1904. Typhoid ceased in the next district after installations of a filter in 1907. Once all districts had filters in place, typhoid epidemics ended. As historian Paul Starr observed:

> The isolation of the organisms responsible for major infectious diseases lead public health officials to shift . . . to more focused measures . . . . Those new efforts made a . . . notable difference in the control of waterborne diseases . . . . Sand filtration of the water supply . . . was far more effective . . . than was earlier sanitary reform . . .[55]

SEWAGE

For early 19th century public sanitation experts, the simplest method to dispose of sewage was to dump it into the nearest river. Water purified the wastes, they believed, although it was not considered prudent to have the water supply intake too close to the sewer outlet. In Europe, though, city governments often piped the sewage to farms, thereby providing natural fertilizer. The waste water, filtering through the soil, would eventually reach a state of natural purity. Berlin and Paris had such farms. London, on the other hand, dumped the sewage into the Thames, thereby upsetting parliamentarians who worked near the outflow pipes.

In the United States, public authorities favored piping the raw sewage into a local body of water, without regard to who was using the water elsewhere. After all, they believed the body of water purified the sewage.

Eventually, the development of the trickling filter allowed the separation of the waste water from the organic matter. In 1912-1915, the British developed the activated sludge process to more effectively separate the organic material from the waste water. Finally, the sewage industry turned to chemical treatment of waste, something already tried in the 19th century but rejected due to cost.

Treatment of sewage, as opposed to dumping it raw into rivers, not only creates a cleaner environment, but it also makes it easier to furnish a safe water supply from those same bodies of water.

CHEMICAL SOLUTIONS

Karl Eberth of Germany discovered the typhoid bacillus in 1880. His countryman, Robert Koch, isolated the cholera-causing microorganism in 1883. In a pamphlet entitled *The Dangers from the Domestic Use of Polluted Water*, published in 1883. Dr. Morton Prince, of Boston, pointed to diseases carried in polluted water, and declared, "No water supply should be contaminated with the slightest amount of sewage or polluted with organic matter of any kind."[56]

Obviously, water suppliers could no longer ignore microorganisms in the water. As a first step, they installed filters, dramatically reducing disease. Then public health authorities began to consider disinfectants: chemicals that would kill the pathogenic organisms in the water. In 1893, B. Krohnke proposed using cuprous chloride in Hamburg, Germany. Louisville, Kentucky experimented with electrically produced chlorine gas in 1896. Jersey City, in 1908, began to use sodium hypochlorite to disinfect water. In 1908-1910, water suppliers began to use liquid chlorine as a disinfectant. Philadelphia was one of the first American cities to do so. (New York City, in contrast, decided the right preventive remedy was to keep the watershed clean.) Chlorinated water was many times cleaner than filtered water. The disease rate from water-borne diseases fell dramatically.

Ozone is a form of oxygen with the formula O_3. Christian Schönbein, a German scientist, discovered ozone in 1840. The gas is unstable. One of the three oxygen atoms in the ozone molecule splits off. Those atoms splitting off destroy bacteria and oxidize substances. In 1893, Oudshoorn, in the Netherlands, put into service the first commercial ozone disinfecting system for drinking water. Baron Tindal planned an ozone disinfecting system for Paris, which was put into use in France and Belgium in 1898. Ozonation of water supply became a standard practice in many European countries. Whiting, Indiana, became the first American city to apply ozonation to drinking water, in 1940.

Chlorination produces byproducts that may be harmful to consumers. Chlorination does not kill a number of pathogenic organisms in the drinking water, including such villains as *Escherichia coli, Salmonella, Giardia,* and *Cryptosporidium.* In 1991, the Environmental Protection Agency (EPA) said that ozone was "the most effective primary disinfectant available for drinking water."[57] Ozone is more effective against the newest pathogenic invaders, and its greater oxidation ability allows it to attack odors, colors, and harmful organic compounds in the water. Since 1996, the EPA has been collecting data on microbes that resist chlorine and on chlorine by-products in the water supply, for possible promulgation of new water treatment regulations. The rules could increase the number of water treatment facilities using ozonation from the present level of over 200.

In 1945, public health officials decided that water need not just be safe. Water could improve public health. Researchers had noticed that people living in areas whose water supply contained fluorides had fewer cavities. Therefore, why not add fluoride to the water supply in order to prevent cavities? The American Dental Association advocated fluoridation, even though doing so would reduce visits to dentists. Adding chemicals to the public water supply irked many people who felt that those who wanted fluoridation could add fluoride to their water at home. As noted by Pat Kendall:

> Opponents have long argued that fluoridation violates individual rights, certain religious beliefs that ban medications. . . . They also claim that it promotes a variety of ills. . . . Proponents counter that fluoridation is not a form of medication, but an adjustment of an essential nutrient to a level favorable to health.[58]

By 1989, though, 70% of cities with a population over 100,000 had begun to fluoridate their water supplies. Tooth decay has fallen dramatically after the introduction of fluoridation.

WATER-RELATED DISEASES

Water carries numerous diseases in various ways. While these diseases are most prevalent in less-developed countries, some have struck in areas with supposedly safe water. Table 15-1 lists these diseases and the means by which they are spread, using a classification devised by Steiner, Thielman and Guerrant. While tropical diseases dominate the list, water drinkers in northern climates cannot ignore some of the listed diseases.

NOT YET PERFECT

In the 1970s, Congress passed two laws that affected water quality. The Clean Water Act of 1972 regulated discharges into the waterways, and put the Environmental Protection Administration (EPA) in charge of regulating water standards. The Safe Drinking Water Act of 1974 focused entirely on drinking water standards. Both acts have been amended or reauthorized by subsequent Congresses. Both have brought about enormous improvements in water quality at a cost that may be in excess of $100 billion to participants.

Table 15-1

Water-Related Diseases

Classification	How Disease is Contracted	Disease
1. Waterborne	Drinking contaminated water.	Cholera, typhoid fever, cryptosporidiosis
2. Water-carried	Accidental drinking of or exposure to contaminated recreational water.	Giardiasis, cryptosporidiosis, Pseudumonas dermatitis
3. Water-washed	Inadequate water for washing hands or utensils. Passes disease onto others.	Shigellosis, hepatitis A, cryptosporidiosis
4. Water-based	Disease causing organism spends part of its life cycle in water.	Schistosomiasis, dracunculiasis
5. Water-vectored	Disease carried by insects that either bite or breed close to or in water.	Yellow fever, malaria, dengue fever, African trypanosomiasis

Source:
Ted S. Steiner, MD, Nathan M. Thielman, MD, and Richard L. Guerrant, MD, "Protozoal Agents: What are the Dangers for the Public Water Supply?" *Annual Review of Medicine 1997* (Palo Alto, CA: Annual Review, 1997), p. 330.

But, between 1986 and 1996:

> 116 significant outbreaks of disease have resulted from contaminated water. . . according to the Natural Resources Defense Council about 45 million Americans drink tap water that is contaminated with cryptosporidium. In addition, about 400,000 Americans become ill from drinking contaminated water each year.[59]

Steiner, Thielman, and Guerrant catalogued "129 water-associated disease outbreaks occurring among over 425,000 individuals in the United States from 1991 through 1994."[60] Several of the disease-causing organisms are resistant to chlorination.

Cryptosporidiosis is a disease caused by a protozoan parasite, *Cryptosporidium parvum*. Symptoms include vomiting and severe diarrhea. No effective medical treatment exists. Healthy people normally recover, but the disease is especially dangerous to those with impaired immune systems. Researchers documented the first case in humans in 1976. Thereafter numerous cases have been reported worldwide, including in areas with state-of-the-art water treatment facilities. Chlorination does not kill the organism in the water supply. In 1993, thanks to contamination of the water supply system of Milwaukee by cryptosporidium, 403,000 people contracted the disease. The Milwaukee water system was in compliance with all federal standards, but that did not prevent the outbreak of the disease.

Given its resistance to chlorination, eradicating the cryptosporidium may require additional or modified flocculation and filtration, or some other method of killing the organism. Yet, "it may well be that. . . we cannot afford to bring all household water up to the standards required for drinking. . ."[61]

In addition, the water supply that comes out of the tap contains numerous chemicals. Lead, for instance, can cause brain damage and raise blood pressure. Its impact is greatest on small children. Water, in nature, contains little lead. Soft water, however, will leach lead out of the water pipes and plumbing. The Environmental Protection Administration has set in motion measures to reduce lead content of water. Nitrates, naturally occurring or caused by contamination from farms or septic tanks, can affect the oxygen transporting activity of blood. Sulfates in the water, a natural occurrence, may have a laxative effect. Organic chemicals, such as pesticides, may damage human health. Radon in the water also poses a threat to health. Major water suppliers, however, process the water to remove radon, so the problem appears limited to private well water and water furnished by small water systems.

The EPA has failed, in the past, to establish standards for drinking water contaminants on its mandated schedule, leaving many groups to speculate about the possible harmfulness of what comes out of the tap, and encouraging the spectacular growth of home water treatment and bottled water sales. Ironically, as Pat Kendall comments, "In terms of bacterial content, it is questionable as to whether bottled water is better than municipal tap water."[62] More stringent water requirements, in the future, will not only tax the resources of the water suppliers, but also strain the EPA's ability to enforce the rules.

CONCLUSION

In the early days of the 19th century, water suppliers in the United States deserved their reputations as purveyors of a foul, disease-carrying product. Today, the country has one of the cleanest, most reliable water systems in the world. But if bottled water sales are an indicator, many people do not believe that it is good enough. And, if medical investigators are correct, they may be right.

CHAPTER 16

Federal Regulation

It is . . . both cheaper and more effective to purify the water and to allow the sewage to be discharged without treatment, so far as there are not other reasons for keeping it out of the rivers. . .$1 spent in purifying the water would do as much as $10 spent in sewage purification. . .

The water works man therefore must, and rightly should, accept a certain amount of sewage pollution in river water, and make the best of it.[63]

— Allen Hazen, Boston water supply expert, 1914

Purposeful discharge of pollutants cannot be tolerated on the premise that a downstream drinking water plant can remove it. It should not be dumped into the water supply in the first place . . . We are not ready to accept the responsibility of removing the myriad of contaminants which are present in most major water sources.[64]

— Richard Moser, American Water
Works Service Company of New Jersey, 1980

In most people's minds, the water supply system begins with the intake of fresh water into a treatment plant and ends with the discharge of sewage into a body of water. But it might be wise to remember that the endpoint of this process for one community marks the beginning point for the community downstream.

Two major pieces of federal legislation regulate the water supply and sanitation industry. The Safe Drinking Water Act (also known as the Public Health Service Act) sets maximum levels for pollutants in drinking water, and the Clean Water Act (also known as the Federal Water Pollution Control Act) governs the discharge of pollutants into the nation's waterways. The Environmental Protection Agency (EPA) is the federal body given the task of enforcing these laws.

The effects of these two acts, although taking place at different ends of the water process, are in fact very closely tied together. The effluent guidelines enacted under the Clean Water Act, though costly to implement, can help water companies by cleaning up the water that they wish to treat for drinking. This is especially true of the effluent regulations imposed on industrial dischargers and on urban runoff, because the toxic chemicals they bring into the waterways are among the most difficult for drinking water treatment plants to remove. Watershed management is the buzz phrase in policy circles now, and it is quite possible that at some point in the future we could see market systems implemented in watersheds, in which drinking water suppliers might find it worth their while to pay for measures to reduce pollution. In a rudimentary way, this is already happening in places like New York, where New York City is buying up land in its source watersheds in order to stop development and the pollution that development would cause in its reservoirs.

There are a number of governmental checks in place to prevent the EPA from writing regulations willy-nilly without regard to cost. The EPA is required to take into account "economic achievability" of its regulations, which is to say it must estimate the impact of its regulation on the industry in question and certify that the impact is not excessive. Usually this involves some sort of cost-benefit analysis, although assigning a monetary value to environmental and public health benefits is more an art than a science at this point. In addition, since regulatory compliance costs tend to be relatively large for small businesses, the EPA must make special effort to provide "regulatory flexibility" for small businesses. Usually this comes in the form of some sort of exemption for small businesses, or a variance allowing them to reach a lower level of compliance than large businesses.

WASTE WATER TREATMENT REGULATIONS

The Clean Water Act of 1972 and its amendments (the CWA) is the primary piece of legislation governing sewage discharges (as well as industrial wastewater dischargers). It is concerned with the protection of surface waters only, not groundwater. At the time of its passage, the CWA represented an important shift to a more aggressive approach to combat water pollution, keeping with the growing level of environmental concern in the United States. However, it was far from the first law passed by the federal government to deal with water pollution.

The Refuse Act of 1899 represented the first step towards controlling water pollution. It banned dumping or discharging refuse into any navigable water body. In theory, this would apply to most water bodies in the nation, since most streams and lakes eventually drain into a navigable water body. In practice, however, the law was almost entirely ignored.

As urban areas grew in the succeeding decades, friction began to develop between states where sewage from one state was polluting the water bodies of a neighboring state. In 1908, New York State sued New Jersey to stop construction of a sewer that would dump raw sewage into Upper New York Bay, on the basis that it would constitute a health menace to New York. (At the time, however, New York was already dumping seven times as much raw sewage into the Bay!) The U.S. Supreme Court ruled to allow construction to proceed, but conflicts such as this eventually prompted the formation of an interstate commission with the power to set and enforce sewage treatment standards, which generally amounted to installation of primary treatment, in the New York-New Jersey-Connecticut tri-state area. The three states vested in the Interstate Sanitation Commission (ISC) the power to enforce its mandates in the courts of those three states. A similar compact was formed among states in the Ohio River drainage basin in the 1940s. Some regions tried a different type of interstate agreement, based on voluntary compliance of member states with standards written by the interstate commission. This system was tried in the Delaware River and Potomac River basins.

Although an important step, these interstate commissions were not always so effective. The voluntary type of interstate compact, in particular, was prone to some member states dragging their feet and falling behind the others. However, a more general problem suffered by both types of compacts was that governmental agencies often move very slowly until the public takes notice of the problem in question, and in the matter of water pollution, there was little public outcry for action. As the Interstate Sanitation Commission remarked, rather dryly, in its 1947 report, "the entire subject of constructing sewage treatment works and providing pollution abatement is not of a popular nature."[65] A 1949 pamphlet by the Citizens Union Research Foundation lamented this lack of public interest, noting that in 1937 the waters under the jurisdiction of the ISC received enough raw or partially treated sewage to cover Central Park to a depth of six feet in one day, and remarked that "It would be an act of cruelty to post figures of this sort in beach areas, but it might be an effective way of stimulating pollution-abatement programs in regions where stimulus is needed."[66]

The federal government stepped into this scene with its first in a series of water pollution acts. The Federal Water Pollution Control Act of 1948 charged the Surgeon General of the Public Health Service with the task of preparing pollution reduction programs and provided some funding for construction of treatment plants. It also gave the federal government the authority to take the case to court in interstate matters. Since the act was based on the federal government's power to regulate interstate commerce, the federal government could only take action on intrastate matters at the behest of the governor of that state. At any rate, the act was not well funded, and in 1956 Congress passed a second act, which provided more funding. This act also recognized that sewage treatment was needed for more than just public health reasons, although the task of enforcing the act remained with the Public Health Service. The 1961 amendments increased the funding levels even further, as the initial grants had not encouraged enough construction. By 1965, it was apparent that there were still not enough funds being provided. Construction was just barely keeping pace with growth, but not eliminating the backlog of treatment facilities that needed to be built in order to treat all of the nation's sewage. Thus, in 1965, Congress again amended the act to increase funds. For the first time, these amendments called for the establishment of water quality criteria for interstate waters in order to set standards for how much pollution a given water body could absorb. (The previous legislation merely had as its goal the construction of primary treatment facilities, without regard as to whether that was too little or too much for a given body of water.) The amendments also created enforcement provisions for federal action against polluters, and created a separate agency within the Department of Health, Education, and Welfare to administer the act.

All of this was not occurring in a vacuum. The American public was showing greater concern as the condition of the nation's waterways visibly deteriorated in the 1960s. As early as the 1960 presidential campaign, water pollution was a topic of discussion, when John F. Kennedy called water pollution a "national disgrace" and criticized the Eisenhower administration for lack of action.[67] A number of water pollution problems, some of which were due to industrial wastewater rather than municipal sources, caught the public's attention even as the environmental movement gained strength. An increasing number of fish kills were being reported, from 6 million in 1960 to 15 million in 1968 to 41 million in 1969. The Nashua River in Massachusetts literally ran red with dye from paper mills. Beach closings due to untreated sewage in the water were commonplace. Many bodies of water were unsafe for fishing due to contamination in the fish—when there were even fish to be caught. The dramatic finale came in 1969 when the Cuyahoga River in Cleveland burst into flames from the oil and industrial waste floating on it. It was clear that the "cleansing" effect of flowing water had reached capacity.

Moreover, it was clear that as the country grew and urban areas expanded, the problems were only going to get worse, and existing legislation was not sufficient. Funding was not adequate and federal enforcement powers too limited. The abatement requirements set by the 1965 amendments were found in practice to be vague. A typical directive might be to install "secondary treatment or its equivalent," with the precise meaning of that for a given plant open to a wide range of interpretation by state officials and plant engineers. Precise limits on the pollutants the plant could discharge were not set. In addition, enforcement was inconsistent and ineffective. In an address to the American Bar Association, an EPA attorney complained that prior to the formation of the EPA in 1970, "No sanctions were imposed for default, except for the possibility of adverse publicity. Every day of delay saved the polluter money. . .default in meeting abatement requirements was so commonplace it was not even considered blameworthy."[68]

In 1971, Ralph Nader issued a report called *Water Wasteland* that detailed many of the problems America's waterways were facing. The report relied more on anecdotes than on comprehensive surveys, but it served to galvanize public awareness even further. Water pollution was now an issue that Americans wanted to confront head-on. They wanted to be able to swim without fear at their swimming holes and to be able to eat the fish they caught in their rivers.

In this context Congress passed the Clean Water Act of 1972. This act took a more aggressive approach than its predecessors and set up a legal and regulatory framework for consistent enforcement. The stated goals of the legislation were to achieve "fishable and swimmable waters" by 1983 and eliminate the discharge of pollutants into American waterways by 1985 (the "zero-discharge" goal).[69] It mandated secondary treatment in all municipal treatment facilities by 1983, and provided construction grants for that purpose. It introduced tough new penalties for noncompliance, ranging up to $25,000 per day.

Learning from the past, the act authorized the fledgling EPA to set national standards for maximum levels of discharges from sewage treatment plants (and industrial polluters). These standards are presented in the form of numerical limitations for pollutants. These standards are then used to write discharge permits for individual facilities. This system is known as the National Pollutant Discharge Elimination System, or NPDES. It is illegal to discharge into navigable waters without a NPDES permit. States are given most of the responsibility for implementing the NPDES. The NPDES permits are generally written by state agencies, states are responsible for monitoring water quality, and states develop programs to meet water quality standards. It is important to note that the EPA standards only represent the minimum water quality standards that states can use in writing permits. States are allowed to set stricter standards and write permits based on those. Ironically, the permit program was built on the foundations of the unenforced permit program of the Refuse Act of 1899.

Enforcement is likewise often delegated to state environmental protection departments. For instance, New York State took New York City to court for its inability to get some of its treatment plants up to the secondary treatment requirements of the Clean Water Act by 1988, under authority delegated to the state by the EPA. As a result, the city was forced to sign consent decrees with compliance schedules for upgrading the treatment plants. The city cannot change those schedules without negotiating with the state for permission.

The Clean Water Act has had mixed results. On the one hand, many of the most visible problems have been dealt with, especially from the industrial point of view. The Nashua River now looks like a pretty country stream, the Cuyahoga River is no longer a fire hazard. In general, industrial pollution has been decreased more successfully because industrial polluters have been pursued more aggressively by the government. On the municipal sewage treatment plant side of the issue, in only 13 years after passage of the act, the percentage of the U.S. population served by treatment plants increased from 42% to 74%, and the EPA estimates that the annual release of organic wastes was reduced 46% as a result.

However, only two-thirds of the municipal treatment plants met the 1983 deadline for installation of secondary treatment, and even now an estimated 13% of existing facilities are still out of compliance. A Public Interest Research Group study estimated that over an 18-month period, more than 20% of treatment plants were out of compliance.[70] The "fishable and swimmable" goal has not yet been met: the EPA estimates that more than 22% of lakes and rivers are still unsafe for fishing and swimming. In 1992, there were still 2,600 beach closings or no-swimming advisories, and the acreage where shellfishing was banned due to contamination actually *increased* by 6% from 1985 to 1990. Finally, the "zero-discharge" goal is still far from reality.

Some of these figures may reflect increased awareness of the situation by health authorities rather than a worsening of the actual situation. However, from the point of view of enforcing the law, it does not matter whether the problem was simply not noticed before. The point is that the law's water quality goals have not yet been met.

Unfortunately, it is also apparent that many of the future removals will come from sources that are even more difficult to deal with. Four hundred fifty million pounds of toxic chemicals are released into public sewers every year, and these are much more difficult and expensive to remove than organic waste. More than half the chemical pollutants entering the waterways now come from non-point sources such as polluted urban and rural runoff. Rural runoff includes sediments, pesticides, and fertilizers washed off farms, logging areas, and construction sites. Urban runoff washes oil, grease, road salts, and heavy metals from road surfaces into waterways. Furthermore, a typical city block generates nine times as much runoff as a woodland area of the same size because there is no exposed ground to soak up water. Although rural runoff is not the domain of municipal treatment systems, urban runoff collected in storm sewers is.

To address non-point sources pollution, Congress amended the CWA in 1987 to establish the Non-Point Source Pollution Management Program. This program provides grants to states to implement non-point source pollution controls. By 1995, the program already had provided $370 million in grants. In addition, storm sewer systems serving populations of 100,000 or more are regulated by the NPDES permit program. Communities of less than 100,000 are currently covered under the Coastal Zone Act Reauthorization Amendments (CZARA) of 1990. This piece of legislation helps states and territories voluntarily develop programs to protect coastal waters, and only applies to 29 states and territories. However, EPA is considering developing its own regulations for storm sewer systems serving populations of less than 100,000.

In a national water quality assessment, EPA determined that urban runoff is the leading source of water quality impairments to the surveyed estuaries and the third-largest source for surveyed lakes. In certain areas, this potentially can be a cause for not just environmental damage but also damage to drinking water sources. For instance, the tiny Waukegan River near Chicago has suffered from expanded development along its banks in recent years, causing an increase in toxic hydrocarbons and solid waste in the river. It also empties into Lake Michigan only 6,000 feet from Chicago's freshwater intake. It is very likely that in the future many cities will find it necessary to treat their stormwater before discharge.

In addition, sewage treatment systems are facing some large expenses in the next 20 years in order to come into, or stay in, compliance with the Clean Water Act. A 1992 EPA study estimates the cost at $137 billion for federal, state, and local governments in order to stay in compliance for the next 20 years.

Several factors are driving these estimates. One of these is the difficulty of dealing with combined sewer overflows, or CSOs. Combined sewers are systems in which storm drains empty into sewer lines, so that storm water is carried to the sewage treatment plant with sewage. On the face of it, it might seem that this could be an environmentally friendly approach that would remove the pollutants in stormwater before it is discharged. In reality, combined sewers are a nightmare for sewage system engineers because, during a storm, sewage plants cannot handle the increased volume of incoming water to treat. As a result, much of the water is simply passed through the plant untreated. This event is what is termed the combined sewer overflow. CSOs were once thought to be relatively harmless, since it was reasoned that although raw sewage was being emitted, it was sufficiently diluted by stormwater as to be acceptable. However, it has since been shown that, in fact, CSOs are a major problem, often resulting in closings of beaches and shellfish beds. For example, New York City still has a "wet weather advisory" at several beaches that bans swimming within 12 hours of a heavy rain. That represents a significant improvement over the period prior to 1993, when the advisory was a 48 hour ban that was in effect for three times as many beaches. Most people probably would be horrified to know that swimming was still such risky business.

CSOs are expensive to deal with. The three options for a city with combined sewers are to separate the storm drains from the sewer system, to build treatment plants with enough capacity to handle all the stormwater (typically several times the normal sewage flow), or to build storage facilities to hold stormwater until it can be treated. Costs to correct the CSO problem are estimated to be $100 billion to $200 billion nationwide in the long run. More than 1,100 communities have combined sewers, mostly in the Northeast, Midwest, and Great Lakes region. In addition, it is likely that at some point municipalities will have to treat their stormwater anyway, because stormwater carries enough polluted runoff to make it a significant pollution source on its own.

Another problem faced by sewerage systems is the rising cost of sludge disposal. Cities often disposed of sludge in the past by ocean dumping, burial in municipal landfills, or other low-cost methods. However, sludge contains toxins, and, in 1994, EPA developed treatment rules to set standards for sludge disposal. The estimated cost of compliance is $157 million per year, with one-third of U.S. sewage treatment plants affected. Oddly enough, stricter enforcement of the Clean Water Act can actually benefit sewage treatment plants, when it comes to sludge. Many industrial facilities send their wastewater through sewage systems. Under the Clean Water Act, "pretreatment" standards regulate what pollutants industrial facilities must remove from the wastewater before discharging it to the sewage treatment plant. Therefore, tighter control over pretreatment standards can actually reduce the toxins in the sewage treatment plant's sludge and allow it to use a cheaper disposal method.

Given the enormous costs of compliance, where will the money come from? The Clean Water Act authorizes funding for construction of sewage treatment plants, but it turns out this will only provide a small portion of the funds. In the 1970s the money was provided in the form of construction grants, at the rate of about $6 billion to $7 billion per year, but by 1986 this had dropped to $2.4 billion per year. The 1987 amendments replaced the direct grant system with money made available to state revolving funds (SRFs). States also add their own money to the SRFs. The SRFs are used to make low-interest loans to communities to finance wastewater treatment plant construction. By 1994, the federal government was only contributing $1.2 billion in SRF funds.

Undoubtedly, much of the funding will have to come from price hikes paid by users. According to the American Water Works Association, sewage fees have already been rising at twice the rate of inflation since 1988. Some sewage agency officials claim that household water use fees will rise from the current $150 per year to $1,700 per year within 20 years.

DRINKING WATER LEGISLATION

Interestingly, drinking water has a less-substantive history of regulation at the federal level than wastewater. Municipalities took an interest in the quality of their drinking water long before their wastewater, because they realized its importance from a public health perspective. Indeed, filtration and disinfection by chlorination were quickly adopted in the early 1900s when public health officials realized that typhoid epidemics were spreading through the water systems. Ironically, the presence of typhoid in the drinking water was due to a large extent to the contamination of drinking water sources by sewage. However, the general attitude prevalent at the time was that it was vastly cheaper to treat drinking water than to treat sewage water.

In 1914, the Public Health Service published a set of water quality standards with the aim of preventing the interstate spread of disease. The standards, which were revised in 1925, 1942, 1946, and 1962, actually only applied to interstate water carriers and other systems subject to federal quarantine regulations. However, the standards were accepted by the American Water Works Association (which encompasses most water systems, municipal and private) and by most state health departments as criteria for systems outside the scope of federal control. That was one reason the federal government felt no need to pass legislation giving it more authority over standards.

Another reason was that, quite simply, the problem of drinking water quality appeared to be licked. Drinking water was not seen as an area of public health that needed to be improved. Filtration and chlorination were enough to stop the typhoid epidemics, and once those ended public health officials saw no signs that any diseases were getting through the systems.

Several things changed this perception enough to lead to passage of the Safe Drinking Water Act in 1974. Health officials generally relied on coliform bacteria counts as a measure of the quality of the water, but a 1965 episode of *salmonellosis* in the drinking water in Riverside County, California, showed the fallibility of that measure. The presence of this pathogen is not registered by coliform counts, and as a result, an epidemic of the disease spread throughout the community's youth for many days before health officials traced it back to the water system. Suddenly public health officials around the country were shocked into the realization that they did not really know what was in their supposedly "clean" water.

At the same time, a series of incidents demonstrated that water treatment systems were fairly laxly run. A 1968 epidemic of gastroenteritis in Angola, New York, turned out to be from a failed disinfection system. Even worse, during the 1969 football season the entire Holy Cross University football team was bedridden with infectious hepatitis that was traced to a water fountain that had been misconnected so that its water bypassed the town treatment plant. A 1969 survey by the U.S. Public Health Service discovered widespread neglect on the part of city and state inspectors, with some treatment plant operators unable to remember the last time they had been visited by an inspector. A large proportion of systems were found to be violating the federal guidelines.

However, these problems were not serious enough to get legislation passed. By 1974, proposed legislation had been languishing in Congress for four years. The final impetus to take action came from a study released by the Environmental Defense Fund that year. That study linked consumption of Louisiana water with incidence of cancer of the digestive tract, with the culprit presumed to be the large collection of chemical plants along the Mississippi. This in turn led to the discovery of toxic chemicals in drinking water around the nation. The standard water treatment of the time would do nothing to keep toxic chemicals from reaching the tap. On the heels of these revelations, Congress passed the Safe Drinking Water Act of 1974.

The SDWA, together with its 1977, 1986, and 1996 amendments, gives the EPA the power to set standards for natural and man-made substances in drinking water, known as maximum contaminant levels (MCLs), and to require monitoring for these. Like the CWA, much of the administration of the act is done by the states. In order to have "primacy," or primary enforcement responsibility, a state must adopt standards at least as stringent as the EPA's. There is some flexibility in the time frame of this requirement: the state has two years to adopt these standards (or four years if it is granted an extension), so that water systems in some states will likely have some time before they feel the brunt of the costs of compliance. To be granted primacy, the state also must pass legislation giving itself the authority to levy fines on systems that are out of compliance, at a minimum of $1,000 per day per violation for systems serving more than 10,000 people. Primacy requirements often have been a headache for states, because many of them lack the staffing needed to enforce the provisions of the SDWA. In 1992, for instance, EPA began proceedings to remove primacy from Maine because it lacked the administrative staff necessary for enforcement, and the following year Florida informed the EPA that it wanted to end its primacy. Unfortunately, the EPA, to whom responsibility reverts for states that do not have primacy, does not have the necessary staff either. To some, the SDWA is a prime example of an unfunded mandate.

Unlike the Clean Water Act, the SDWA in its original form did not provide significant funding for construction of the mandated treatment works. At the time, it was thought it would only take a few years to get the nation's water systems into compliance. But in 1976, Alexander Kalinski, head of the National Association of Regulatory Utility Commissioners, admitted that "Only 15 states even pretend to meet the current drinking water standards," and that water suppliers were not spending nearly enough money to ensure safe water.[71] The situation has improved tremendously since then, but still more than one-quarter of the nation's water systems were in violation of EPA standards at least once during the period from 1993-1994.

The 1996 amendments address the funding issue by providing $1 billion per year through 2003 for state revolving funds (SRFs). In order to be eligible, states must retain primacy and develop operator training and certification programs for water system workers. They also have to add to the fund an amount equal to 20% of the federal contribution. In addition, states are allowed to transfer up to one-third of the money to the Clean Water Act SRF, and vice versa.

One of the more interesting requirements of the 1996 amendments is a right-to-know provision. This requires water systems to send to its consumers an annual "consumer confidence report" detailing the contaminants in its drinking water, and the possible health effects of any violations that may have occurred. In addition, consumers must be notified of serious violations within 24 hours of the event, and the water system must explain the possible health effects resulting from the violation, what is being done about it, and what the consumers should do to protect their health. Among other things, this provision will probably prove a boon to the home purification and bottled water markets. Whether it spurs water systems to greater compliance will depend on how responsive water companies are to customer complaints.

The 1996 amendments also repeal an earlier amendment that required that the agency regulate 25 additional contaminants every three years. That provision had originally been passed in response to the slow pace with which the EPA was writing regulations for contaminants already identified in water systems. It proved to be unpopular because its rigidity tended to result in the regulation of contaminants at high costs without determination if any significant public health benefits might result. The new mandate requires that the EPA publish a list every five years of unregulated contaminants known, or anticipated, to occur in public water systems. Every five years, the agency must determine whether or not to regulate five contaminants on that list.

To cushion the impact of the regulations on small systems that would otherwise have to incur very large fixed costs relative to their size, EPA must identify affordable technologies for systems with fewer than 10,000 customers. Where it cannot identify such a technology, it must identify "variance technologies" that get as close to the EPA standards as possible while still being affordable. States can then grant variances to systems serving up to 3,300 customers if they are unable to afford compliance with and they install this variance technology. Variances can be granted for systems up to 10,000 people with EPA approval. In addition, in order to reduce monitoring costs, states can adopt looser monitoring requirements for small systems that can show that the monitored contaminant has not been found in their system before and is unlikely to show up in the future.

The SDWA required that all drinking water drawn from surface supplies be filtered. However, water systems can bypass this provision if they can control development in their watershed and can show that this is as effective in removing pathogens as filtration and chlorination. The prime example of a system trying this route is the New York City system, which in fact received special funding in the 1996 amendments to try this as a "demonstration" project. The city has embarked on a land acquisition program around its sources to stop development. The cost of filtration for New York City is estimated to run to about $4 billion to $8 billion, so it is worthwhile for the city to set aside $250 million to acquire land around its watershed. On the other hand, it is now being sued for $10.5 billion by property owners in the upstate watersheds, on the claim that the program is reducing their property values.

Compliance costs with the SDWA are expected to be large, with estimates of $21 billion to $49 billion through the year 2000 alone. However, these costs are actually fairly small compared to the cost of replacing the aging infrastructure of America's water systems. In a water system, treatment costs are typically only about 10% of the system's costs, whereas distribution accounts for a whopping 65%. Given the age and poor condition of the distribution systems in the U.S., it is not surprising that the EPA estimates repair and updating of water systems in large cities will cost $150 billion over the next 20 years.

These costs are likely to affect the water industry in a number of ways. Many analysts expect to see consolidation within the industry in the coming years, because large water companies will find it easier to raise the necessary capital. Capital needs could be particularly intense for small water systems, for whom SDWA compliance costs could be very large. However, the severity of the impact on small systems will actually depend on how much leeway they are given under the variance system put in place by the EPA. Besides the benefits consolidation and regionalization bring in terms of economies of scale in source development, water treatment, and general management, it may be encouraged by the government as a way of implementing a more holistic approach to watershed management. Past policies tended to treat every polluter or drinking water plant as a separate case, but more recently it has been recognized that more can be accomplished by regarding all the sites within a watershed as part of one system.

Increasing privatization may be another result. Privatization has occurred extensively in Britain and France. In the U.S., some evidence suggests that private operators may run water systems at lower costs than governmental operators: for instance, one study claimed that government-owned water systems cost an average of $547 per connection versus $426 per connection for private services.[72] Until recently, privatization of entire systems was greatly complicated by rules pertaining to repayment of federal funds after the sale of facilities (since most were financed with federal grants and loans and the sales of public bonds). In 1992, however, President Bush signed an executive order easing repayment requirements on federal funds, simplifying the whole process. On a simpler level, government-owned systems may find it cheaper to contract out to private firms to run their systems for them.

Privatization could have other policy implications as well. The EPA tends to enforce the law more strictly, and demand faster compliance, against private entities than government entities. (Witness the Clean Water Act: by 1980, no less than 90% of major industrial polluters had achieved compliance versus one-third of cities and towns). In part this is because federal enforcers know local governments are often strapped for cash, whereas for-profit companies are expected to live up to their obligations to earn their profit. And of course there can be more pressure from legislators to give their district a break to keep local taxes down. It may turn out that privatization would benefit the public health.

However, advocates of deregulation should step with caution. Janice Beecher and Patrick Mann point out that legislators are reluctant to deregulate an industry while prices are rising, feeling that this is precisely when some sort of regulatory control is needed. "Deregulation has primarily occurred when real prices were declining,"[73] they point out, whereas water prices are most definitely on the rise. They have been rising faster than inflation since 1984, and since 1990 they have been rising from 10% to 12% every two years. Water cost, on average, 93 cents per 1,000 gallons in 1980, $1.74 per 1,000 gallons in 1990, and $3.11 per 1,000 gallons in 1995. Although the blame is commonly thrown on the cost of complying with federal and state drinking water standards and rehabilitation of infrastructure, much of it is probably due to underpricing of water in the past, something that water systems can no longer afford to do.

Conclusion

The CWA and SDWA undoubtedly have accomplished a great deal in cleaning up the nation's waterways and drinking water. The two acts also have undoubtedly cost many billions of dollars for compliance. If we are to believe the estimates cited in this chapter, they will cost many billions more in the near future. This leads to the obvious question: Just how accurate are these estimates of the costs of compliance? Looking at past history is not heartening. In 1972, the EPA estimated the cost of installing secondary sewage treatment at $12.6 billion, versus the $160 billion actually spent between 1972 and 1981. But there are many other industries in which costs of complying with EPA regulations have turned out to be much less than anticipated. For example, the sulfur dioxide permitting program for electric utilities introduced by the EPA in 1995 has resulted in compliance costs one-half to one-fourth of the EPA cost estimates (and, less surprisingly, cost one-fourth to one-eighth of industry cost estimates.)[74] Why this difference? Much depends on whether firms find more efficient ways to achieve compliance (EPA compliance costs are almost always estimated on the basis of existing technology). According to Goodstein and Hodges, "When an industry is required to lower pollution output, it usually doesn't just slap a new filter on an existing process; it often invents new technology. Frequently the technology turns out to have higher productivity benefits, which help to offset the cost of the regulation."[75] In part this is because rather than retrofit existing equipment, firms tend to buy completely new capital equipment. More often than not, the new equipment, incorporating the latest technology, is more productive than what it replaces. Often this merely represents a capital investment that would have taken place eventually to modernize equipment.

The question, then, is that of whether or not the water business is capable of innovating in a search for the least-cost method of production. Unfortunately, there are several factors that may limit the level of innovation in this industry. Both government and privately owned water systems have little incentive to take chances on innovation. For private systems, regulators will give the benefits of cost reductions to customers, not the water company. On the other hand, in the event of failure, regulators will most likely make the water company soak up the costs. In government-owned water companies, the risk of dead-ending one's career by taking chances with the public's health tends to promote conservative policies. Moreover, few systems are large enough to really innovate.

In an era of complex and difficult-to-comprehend international environmental problems such as global warming and the thinning ozone layer, "fishable and swimmable" surface waters and clean drinking water seem like simple goals to aim for. Environmental problems of the 1990s do not seem to have such direct public health impacts. The scale of the Milwaukee cryptosporidia epidemic pales in comparison to the 27,000 person death toll from typhoid fever in 1900. The CWA and SDWA grew out of very basic environmental and public health problems, in an era where these problems were both extremely visible and also seemingly solvable—why else include a provision mandating zero-discharge in only 13 years? The technology to solve them existed then and exists today. All that is required is the money and the will to implement them fully.

CHAPTER 17

Summary

The most striking thing about modern industry is that it requires so much and accomplishes so little.[76]

— E. F. Schumacher

The structure of the water supply industry has remained almost unchanged since Roman times. In urban areas, vast enterprises collect water, transport it to the city, and then distribute it. Sewers collect the wastewater and dispose of it. Population in the countryside obtains its own water, individually, and takes care of its own sewage. Today, those with enough money contract for a private water supply, in bottles, just as people bought water from carters when they judged the public supply undrinkable, two hundred years ago.

The government plays an unusually important role in the industry. It sets health standards for water and sewage. It regulates the profits of privately owned water suppliers. On the federal level, it owns or subsidizes vast water projects. On the municipal level, it owns the local water or sewage supplier. In the West, the government's policies helped to develop the region, but also created incentives for the enormous waste of water.

Clean water plays a key role in the maintenance of public health. Ignorance of that role encouraged the spread of water-borne diseases. Many of the municipal water utilities that were established because the city governments did not want to entrust the public health to profit-making companies have proven conservative in their willingness to accept new means of protecting public health. After a while, even the most progressive of entities seems to turn into a self-protecting bureaucracy.

Today, water suppliers may need more flexibility in order to serve the public well. Public-private partnerships might allow entities to raise capital more easily, and run more efficiently. Market-based trading practices and pricing that makes users aware of costs should encourage greater efficiency in the use of water.

Environmental regulations have added to cost of service. Clean water does not come cheap. Several decades after the passage of the precedent-setting federal water laws, although water is cleaner than before, the water suppliers have even more work to do.

So far, no groundswell of support has arisen to deregulate the water business. Water suppliers act as they have acted for decades. The industry's sales grow slowly. The structure of the business remains unchanged. Yet the public water suppliers still have to deal with huge capital expenditures, changing rules, and questioning customers. Some of today's discussions sound as if they could have taken place in the 19th century.

NOTES

1. Luis de Camões, *Os Lusíadas* (Rio de Janeiro: Edições de Ouro, no date), p. 517, Canto VII, 520.

2. Richard Shelton Kirby, Sidney Withington, Arthur Burr Darling, and Frederick Gridley Kilgour, *Engineering in History* (New York: Dover, 1990), p.16.

3. *Tanakh: A New Translation of the Holy Scriptures According to the Traditional Hebrew Text* (Philadelphia: The Jewish Publication Society, 1985), p. 603, (Kings 20:20).

4. Herodotus, *The Histories*, translation by Aubrey de Selincourt (Harmondsworth, Middlesex: Penguin Books, 1954), pp. 199-200.

5. Kirby, *Engineering in History*, p. 66.

6. Last will and testament of Benjamin Franklin. Quoted in Nelson Manfred Blake, *Water for the Cities: A History of the Urban Water Supply Problem in the United States* (Syracuse: Syracuse University Press, 1956), p. 4.

7. Blake, *Water for the Cities*, p. 18.

8. Ibid., p. 6.

9. Ibid., p. 46.

10. Ibid., p. 51.

11. Ibid., p. 130.

12. Ibid., p. 140.

13. Tom Andersen, "Hearings to open on site for water filtration plant," *Tarrytown Daily News*, Feb. 4 1998, p. 1A.

14. Blake, *Water for the Cities*, p. 175.

15. Ibid., p. 177.

16. Ibid., pp. 211-212.

17. Ibid., p. 228.

18. Ibid.

19. Ibid., p. 229.

20. Ibid., p. 233

21. Louis P. Cain, "Raising and Watering a City: Ellis Sylvester Chesbrough and Chicago's First Sanitation System," in Judith Walzer Leavitt and Ronald L. Numbers, eds., *Sickness and Health in America* (Madison: University of Wisconsin Press, 1985), p. 440.

22. Cain, "Raising and Watering a City," p. 442.

23. Ibid., p. 443.

24. Ibid.

25. Barry Goldwater, quoted in Robert Gottlieb, *A Life of its Own: The Politics and Power of Water* (San Diego: Harcourt Brace Jovanovich, 1988), p. 272.

26. Glenn T. Trewartha, "Climate and Settlement of the Subhumid Lands," in *Climate and Man: Yearbook of Agriculture 1941* (Washington, D.C.: United States Department of Agriculture, 1941), p. 171.

27. Trewartha, "Climate and Settlement of the Subhumid Lands," p. 168.

28. Ibid., p. 170.

29. C. Warren Thornthwaite, "Climate and Settlement in the Great Plains," in *Climate and Man: Yearbook of Agriculture 1941* (Washington, D.C.: United States Department of Agriculture, 1941), p. 178.

30. Marc Reisner, *Cadillac Desert: The American West and Its Disappearing Water* (New York: Viking, 1986).

31. William A. Green, Harry A. Steele and Mark M. Regan, "Public Development of Resources," in *The Yearbook of Agriculture 1958* (Washington, D.C.: United States Department of Agriculture, 1958), p. 542.

32. Reisner, *Cadillac Desert.*

33. Jack Hirshleifer, James C. DeHaven, and Jerome W. Milliman, *Water Supply: Economics, Technology, and Policy* (Chicago: University of Chicago Press, 1960).

34. Terry L. Anderson, *Water Crisis: Ending the Policy Drought* (Washington, D.C.: Cato Institute, 1983).

35. United States General Accounting Office, *Reclamation Law: Changes Needed Before Water Service Contracts are Renewed* (Washington, D.C.: General Accounting Office, 1991).

36. Garald G. Parker, "The Encroachment of Salt Water into Fresh," in *The Yearbook of Agriculture 1955: Water* (Washington, D.C.: United States Department of Agriculture, 1955), p. 617.

37. C. A. Bower and Milton Fireman, "Saline and Alkali Soils," in *The Yearbook of Agriculture 1957: Soils* (Washington, D.C.: United States Department of Agriculture, 1957), pp. 282-283.

38. Bower and Fireman, "Saline and Alkali Soils," p. 288.

39. Remi A. Nadeau, *The Water Seekers* (Santa Barbara: Peregrine Smith, 1974), p. 4.

40. Ibid., p. 192.

41. Reisner, *Cadillac Desert*, pp. 125-126.

42. Nadeau, *The Water Seekers*, p. 192.

43. Reisner, *Cadillac Desert*, p. 361.

44. Ibid., p. 361.

45. Nadeau, *The Water Seekers*, p. 257.

46. Gilbert Cross, *A Dynasty of Water: The Story of American Water Works Company* (Voorhees, New Jersey: American Water Works, 1991), p. 24

47. Lewis Mumford, *The City in History* (New York: Harcourt, Brace & World, 1961), p. 476.

48. Ibid.

49. James C. Bonbright, *Principles of Public Utility Rates* (New York: Columbia University Press, 1961), p. 56.

50. Arthur Stone Dewing, *The Financial Policy of Corporations* (New York: The Roland Press, 1953), p. 1005.

51. Charles E. Rosenberg, *The Cholera Years* (Chicago: The University of Chicago Press, 1987), p. 44.

52. Blake, *Water for the Cities*, p. 252.

53. Rosenberg, *The Cholera Years*, p. 30.

54. Gretchen A. Condren, Henry Williams, and Rose A. Cheney, "The Decline in Mortality in Philadelphia from 1870 to 1930: The Role of Municipal Services," in Leavitt and Numbers, *Sickness and Health in America* (Madison: University of Wisconsin Press, 1985), p. 428.

55. Paul Starr, *The Social Transformation of American Medicine* (New York: Basic Books, 1982), p. 135.

56. Blake, *Water for the Cities*, p. 261.

57. Leslie Lamarre, "A Fresh Look at Ozone," *EPRI Journal* 22 (July/August 1997), p. 8.

58. Pat Kendall, "Drinking Water Quality and Health," Colorado State University Cooperative Extension Service, The National Agriculture Safety Database (NASD), 1992, p. 3.

59. Leone T. Young, *Pollution Control Monthly: Water Treatment* (New York: Smith Barney, December 1996), p. 3.

60. Ted S. Steiner, MD, Nathan M. Thielman, MD, and Richard L. Guarrant, MD, "Protozoal Agents: What Are the Dangers for the Public Water Supply?" *Annual Review of Medicine 1997* (Palo Alto, Calif:: Annual Reviews, 1997), pp. 330-331.

61. Steiner, Thielman and Guerrant, "Protozoal Agents," p. 338.

62. Kendall, "Drinking Water Quality and Health," p. 5.

63. John R. Sheaffer and Leonard A. Stevens, *Future Water: An Exciting Solution to America's Most Serious Resource Crisis* (New York: William Morrow and Company, Inc., 1983), p. 35.

64. Ibid., p. 79.

65. Samuel D. Smoleff, *Compacts For Clean Waters: A Study of Methods of Interstate Cooperation in Combating Water-Pollution* (New York: Citizens Union Research Foundation, Inc., 1949), p. 3.

66. Ibid., p. 6.

67. James M. Quigley, "New Frontiers in Water Pollution Control," 17th Purdue Industrial Waste Conference, Lafayette, Indiana, 1 May 1962.

68. John R. Quarles, Jr., "Water Pollution and the Rule of Law," The American Bar Association National Institute, New York City, 26 October, 1972.

69. U.S. Environmental Protection Agency, "Clean Water Anniversary: Celebrating 25 Years of Progress," from *Brief History of the Clean Water Act*, accessed 26 September 1997 online at the Clean Water Act Web site, http://www.epa.gov/owow/cwa/history.html.

70. "Wastewater Treatment," *Smith Barney Pollution Control Monthly*, January 1997, p. 5.

71. T. Ward Welsh, "NAWC Centennial: 1970-1995," *Water* (Fall 1995), p. 7.

72. "Water Treatment," *Smith Barney Pollution Control Monthly*, December 1996, p. 7.

73. Janice A. Beecher and Patrick C. Mann, "Real Water Rates on the Rise," *Public Utilities Fortnightly*, 15 July 1997, p. 46.

74. Eban Goodstein and Hart Hodges, "Polluted Data: Overestimating Environmental Costs," *The American Prospect*, November-December 1997, p. 68.

75. Ibid., p. 67.

76. E. F. Schumacher, *Small is Beautiful* (New York: Harper & Row Perennial Library, 1975), p. 118.

Part IV

*Regulation, Pricing,
and Economics*

CHAPTER 18

The Development of Public Utility Regulation

The concept of a public utility is essentially a creation of legislation, but social scientists have endeavored to rationalize legislative procedure by identifying the intrinsic common characteristics which our lawmakers have set aside for special "public utility" treatment . . .[1]

— Joe S. Bain

Historical and legal precedents for the regulation of business existed before most of the industries that are commonly called public utilities. The laws and court decisions that define our concept of the public utility were more a product of anti-business thinking in the time of the Grangers, trustbusters, and muckrakers, than the result of a careful study of natural monopoly, declining cost curves, and all the other supposed characteristics of a public utility.

EARLY REGULATION

Historically, the governments of Great Britain and the American colonies regulated some prices and services. Regulated businesses, rarely monopolies, provided important services to the public. Ferrymen, bakers, innkeepers, and common carriers were regulated. In 1820, Congress permitted the City of Washington to set the prices of bread, sweeping chimneys, and wharfage. In 1839, Rhode Island established a regulatory commission. Other New England states followed. Usually, the commissions were advisory and dealt with railroads. In 1885, at the behest of the gas utilities, Massachusetts instituted a regulatory board. Congress, in 1887, established the Interstate Commerce Commission, the most important regulatory body of the day. New York and Wisconsin, in 1907, created the first state regulatory agencies of the modern type. By 1910, state regulators could no longer deal with the burgeoning interstate long-distance telephone service, so Congress placed that traffic within the jurisdiction of the Interstate Commerce Commission. By 1920, two-thirds of the states had utility regulatory agencies.

The regulatory agencies followed concepts established by the courts. Landmark cases defined what a regulator could or should do. *Munn v. Illinois*[2] was the first major decision. In 1871, the Illinois legislature had enacted a law to fix the rates charged by grain elevators. Chicago elevator owners went to court, pointing out that they had established their businesses before enactment of the law. They claimed that the law had deprived them of their rights under the Fourteenth Amendment ("nor shall any State deprive any person of life, liberty, or property, without due process of law").[3] Chief Justice Waite wrote the Supreme Court's majority opinion in the case. The Chief Justice delved into the history of price regulation, even quoting Britain's Lord Chief Justice Hale (1609–1676) on public interest along the way, as he concluded:

> Looking, then, to the common law, from whence came the right which the Constitution protects, we find that when private property is 'affected with a public interest, it ceases to be *juris privati* only'. . . . Property does come clothed with a public interest when used in a manner to make it of public consequence, and affect the community at large. When, therefore, one devotes his property to a use in which the public has an interest, he, in effect, grants to the public an interest in that use, and must submit to be controlled. . . . He may withdraw his grant by discontinuing the use. . . .

> Common carriers exercise a sort of public office, and have duties to perform in which the public is interested. . . .

> Their business is, therefore, 'affected with a public interest,' within the meaning of the doctrine which Lord Hale has so forcibly stated.[4]

The Court noted that grain from seven or eight states had to pass through Chicago. A few people owned the Chicago warehouses. They set rates together, indicating "a virtual monopoly."[5] If the state can regulate ferrymen or innkeepers, it certainly can regulate grain elevators: "They stand, to use again the language of their counsel, in the very 'gateway of commerce,' and take toll from all who pass."[6] The Court then set forth the theory of legislative ratemaking. The plaintiffs argued that the Court should set a return on their property:

> It is insisted, however, that the owner of property is entitled to a reasonable compensation for its use . . . and what is reasonable is a judicial and not a legislative question.

> As has already been shown, the practice has been otherwise. In countries where the common law prevails, it has been customary . . . for the legislature to declare what shall be a reasonable compensation. . . . The controlling fact is the power to regulate at all. If that exists, the right to establish the maximum charge, as one of the means of regulation, is implied. . . .

> We know that this is a power which may be abused; but that is no argument against its existence. For protection against abuses by legislatures the people must resort to the polls, not to the courts.[7]

The decision in the *Munn* case upheld the right of the state to regulate the prices charged to the public by a business "affected with a public interest." The decision also proposed a philosophy of regulation that, if adhered to, would have prevented the development of healthy, privately owned utilities. The legislature would have set prices and the owners would have had no recourse of appeal to the courts. During a period of inflation, businesses would encounter difficulties because of rigidities of price. Justice Fields dissented, saying, "If this be sound law . . . all property and all business in the state are held at the mercy of a majority of its legislature."[8]

FAIR VALUE

Fortunately, the regulation of price moved beyond the concept set forth in the *Munn* decision. As early as 1679, an English court had held that a common carrier was entitled to a reasonable payment.[9] Determining reasonableness, though, can turn into more of a theological than economic or legal argument. The Supreme Court tried its hand at the question in 1898, producing *Smyth v. Ames*.[10] Although in some ways a monument to judicial confusion about finance, the decision revolutionized thinking about regulation and put an end to the absolute right of legislatures to fix rates as they pleased.[11]

Nebraska, in 1893, had established a Board of Transportation to fix railroad rates. The railroads challenged the rates set. The issues were rate base and whether the railroads had been deprived of property without due process of law—that is, reducing the earning power of the business is equivalent to the confiscation of property. The railroads had been built during and after the Civil War boom period. Subsequently, prices fell. The railroads wanted their assets valued at original cost. The State of Nebraska (represented by the silver-tongued orator of Platte, William Jennings Bryan) wanted the properties valued at reproduction cost, which was lower than original cost.

The Supreme Court affirmed the right of a state to set rates as long as the rates provided "just compensation."[12] The Court then defined "proper compensation":

> We hold . . . that the basis of all calculations as to the reasonableness of rates . . . must be the fair value of the property. . . . And, in order to ascertain that value, the original cost of construction, the amount expended in permanent improvements, the amount and market value of its bonds and stock, the present as compared with the original cost of construction, the probable earning capacity of the property under particular rates prescribed by statute, and the same required to meet operating expenses, are all matters for consideration, and are to be given such weight as may be just and right in each case. We do not say that there may not be other matters to be regarded in estimating the value of the property. What the company is entitled to ask is a fair return upon the value of that which it employs for the public convenience.
>
> On the other hand, what the public is entitled to demand is that no more be exacted from it for the use of a public highway than the services rendered by it are reasonably worth.[13]

How did that confused judicial laundry list set ratemaking doctrine for more than 40 years? Present costs and original costs are contradictory terms. The market value of securities depends on earning power, but earning power in turn is what needs to be determined. Therefore the reasoning is circular. The Supreme Court concluded by saying: consider everything. For the next 20 years, regulators and utilities battled over the choice of rate base: fair value or original cost.

A quarter of a century after *Smyth v. Ames*, Justice Brandeis, with Justice Holmes concurring, wrote a scathing denunciation of regulatory practices. That dissenting opinion, written in the 1923 *Southwestern Bell*[14] decision, was ahead of its time.

> The so-called rule of Smyth v. Ames is . . . legally and economically unsound. The thing devoted by the investor to the public use is not specific property, tangible and intangible, but capital embarked in the enterprise. Upon the capital so invested the federal Constitution guarantees to the utility the opportunity to earn a fair return.
>
> The investor agrees, by embarking capital in a utility, that its charge to the public shall be reasonable. His company is the substitute for the state in the performance of the public service, thus becoming a public servant. The compensation which the Constitution guarantees an opportunity to earn is the reasonable cost of conducting the business. Cost includes not only operating expenses, but also capital charges. Capital charges cover the allowance, by way of interest, for the use of the capital, whatever the nature of the security issues therefore; the allowance for risk incurred; and enough more to attract capital. The reasonable rate to be prescribed by a commission may allow an efficiently managed utility much more. But a rate is constitutionally compensatory, if it allows to the utility the opportunity to earn the cost of service as defined. . . .
>
> The experience of the twenty-five years since Smyth v. Ames was decided has demonstrated that the rule there enunciated is delusive. . . . The rule of Smyth v. Ames sets the laborious and baffling technique of finding the present value of the utility. It is impossible to find an exchange value for a utility, since utilities, unlike merchandise or land, are not commonly bought and sold in the market. Nor can the present value of the utility be determined by capitalizing its net earnings, since the earnings are determined, in large measure, by the rate which the company will be permitted to charge. . . .
>
> Under the rule of Smyth v. Ames . . . each step in the process of estimating the cost of reproduction involves forming an opinion. . . . It is true that the decision is usually rested largely upon the records of financial transactions, on statistics and calculations. But . . . 'every figure . . . that we have set down with delusive exactness' is speculative.
>
> The conviction is widespread that a sound conclusion as to the actual value of a utility is not to be reached by a meticulous study of conflicting estimates of the cost of reproducing new the congerie of old machinery and equipment, called the plant, and the still more fanciful estimates concerning the value of the intangible elements of an established business. Many commissions . . . have declared . . . that 'capital honestly and prudently invested must . . . be taken as the controlling factor in fixing . . . rates.'[15]

The Brandeis dissent laid the groundwork for changes in regulation that would take place years later. It did not influence the Supreme Court of the period. The *Bluefield*[16] decision of 1923 set aside a decision in which a company's estimate of reproduction cost was disregarded. Then followed *McCardle v. Indianapolis Water Co.*,[17] a decision which was, to quote Wilcox, "the high-water mark of reproduction cost valuation. . . ."[18]

Bluefield is better known to regulators for another reason, a paragraph that sets forth the standards for rate of return:

> The return should be reasonably sufficient to assure confidence in the financial soundness of the utility and should be adequate, under efficient and economical management, to maintain and support its credit and enable it to raise the money necessary for the proper discharge of its public duties.[19]

MODERN RATEMAKING

The Roosevelt era's Supreme Court backed away from an insistence on the fair value rate base, although some states were still battling about fair value in the 1970s. The decision in the *Hope Natural Gas Co.*[20] case of 1944 marked the beginning of a new era of regulation. The Federal Power Commission disregarded estimates of the fair value of Hope's properties in setting a rate of return. Hope appealed the decision. Justice Douglas wrote:

> ... that 'fair value' is the end product of the process of ratemaking, not the starting point.... The heart of the matter is that rates cannot be made to depend on 'fair value' when the value of the going enterprise depends on earnings under whatever rates may be anticipated.

> We held ... that the commission was not bound to the use of any single formula ... in determining rates.... And when the commission's order is challenged in the courts, the question is whether that order 'viewed in its entirety' meets the requirements of the act. Under the statutory standard of 'just and reasonable' it is the result reached, not the method employed, which is controlling. It is not theory, but the impact of the rate order which counts. If the total effect of the rate order cannot be said to be unjust and unreasonable, judicial inquiry ... is at an end.... Moreover, the commission's order ... is the product of expert judgment which carries a presumption of validity....

> From the investor or company point of view it is important that there be enough revenue not only for operating expenses, but also for the capital costs of the business. These include service on the debt and dividends on the stock. By that standard the return to the equity owner should be commensurate with returns on investments in other enterprises having corresponding risks. That return, moreover, should be sufficient to assure confidence in the financial integrity of the enterprise so as to maintain its credit and to attract capital....[21]

The case of *Munn v. Illinois* ushered in a period of legislative ratemaking. *Smyth v. Ames*, in a sense, heralded a period of judicial ratemaking (in which lawyers fought before courts over the methodology of the rate case), and the *Hope* case brought forth the age of the regulatory commission. The advent of competition and dissatisfaction with old regulatory methods has reduced the importance of the regulatory agency in all but the water sector and has caused regulators to seek new methods of meeting their goals. But the agencies still judge the efficacy of new methods by the reasonableness of the return earned.

CHAPTER 19

What Is a Public Utility?

As with other important terms . . . a definition is, at best, too general to be useful and, at worst, mere legal pedantry. To say that a public utility is a business affected with a public interest is to include piggeries and mortuary parlors. To say that a public utility supplies a service necessary to our present stage of economic life . . . is to include the United States Steel Corporation. . . . The legalistic descriptions are equivocal. . . . As a practical matter, a public utility . . . is a private enterprise over which the . . . government attempts to determine the prices received for its services rather than to allow the prices to be determined by the free play of economic forces. In the end, economic forces will dominate every situation, but temporarily and through the perspective of a short period of time, and within the myopic intelligence of the politically minded bureaucrats, they can be thwarted or measurably controlled by administrative or judicial decrees. . .[22]

— Arthur Stone Dewing

Electric, gas, telephone, and water companies have been classified as public utilities. What distinguishes those regulated industries from the insurance, milk, or stock brokerage industries, all of which are or have been regulated in various ways? The standard characteristics of and rationalizations for public utility designation—"rationalizations" because it is doubtful how well the standards hold true today for many of the still regulated firms and if they ever held true in the textbook sense—include:

The franchise or the designation of a service area. In the past, when a utility served only a municipality, it had to seek a franchise for its operations in the area. The franchise gave the public utility privileges such as use of the streets for its facilities. In return, the utility agreed to pay certain taxes, possibly to set rates at particular levels, and to provide a given measure of service. Usually, the franchise ran for a specific period and granted the utility a monopoly in the municipality. Eventually service areas developed, with their boundaries set by state agencies. The regulatory agency, by and large, granted the public utility the exclusive right to provide a particular service to the public within a geographic area. That monopoly, though, was one only in the sense that the water or wastewater utility had the exclusive right to act as public supplier. Obviously, people could drill wells, and use septic tanks to the extent allowed by local health ordinances, and buy bottled water, as well.

Obligation to serve. The consumer within a service territory cannot choose between suppliers of a utility service. The utility cannot choose to serve some customers and not others. Nor can it discriminate unduly between customers. An unregulated industry can turn away customers for reasons of poor profitability. The utility has to serve those customers. The utility could seek rate relief from all customers to cover the additional costs caused by the unprofitable customers. The utility might not receive the rate relief requested, but still would have to serve the customers.

Necessity of the service to the public. The utility provides a service that is necessary, widely used, and for which good substitutes are not available. These concepts, derived from Bain, take a static view of the industry, not considering that an outsider might develop an adequate substitute, if the price for the utility's service were sufficiently high.[23] Arthur Stone Dewing, a student of history and an active participant in bankruptcies and reorganizations, did not have any illusions about the permanence of monopoly. Bonbright said, "What must justify public utility regulation . . . is the necessity of the regulation and not merely the necessity of the product."[24] (That comment qualities as sophistry unless one takes a static view of the world. The product is a necessity, the laws of supply and demand are suspended, and no substitute will develop if the monopolist takes advantage of the situation.) More to the point, why does the government regulate one service (public water supply) and not another (bottled water) when both provide identical output, such as a drink of water? What makes one service a necessity and not another? So far, though, nobody has developed an adequate substitute for public water and wastewater services to urban areas.

The service provided is a natural monopoly. The term "natural monopoly" requires interpretation. Some experts have argued that a utility exhibits diminishing unit costs as scale increases. If so, customers will be served at a lower cost by one large system of a monopoly than by several smaller, less efficient, competing facilities. Monopoly also prevents needless duplication of plant and equipment. Bonbright made two points on the natural monopoly. He said that natural monopoly "is due . . . to the severely localized and hence restricted markets for utility services—markets limited because of the necessarily close connection between the utility plant on the one hand and the consumers' premises on the other."[25] A manufacturing plant can have the whole country or world for its market. A utility distribution system serves a limited area. "Were it compelled to share its limited market with two or more rival plants owning duplicate distribution networks, the total cost of serving the city would be materially higher."[26] Bonbright then declared that the declining cost characteristic of utilities had been overstressed and was not a prerequisite for a natural monopoly because "even if the unit cost of supplying a given area with a given type of public utility service must increase with an enhanced rate of output, any specified required rate of output can be supplied most economically by a single plant or system."[27]

So far, water and wastewater firms still fit the definition of public utilities.

CHAPTER 20

The Purposes and Drawbacks of Regulation

Regulation was . . . a substitute for competition. Where competition was impossible, its purpose was to bring the benefits that competition would have brought.[28]

— Clair Wilcox

This is the basic premise: the utility is a monopoly. In the United States, to monopolize, or attempt to monopolize, is illegal under antitrust laws. The textbooks tell us that competition breeds efficiency and innovation: competition is a force that weeds out the unfit producer and protects the consumer from exploitation. "The essence of regulation," according to Kahn, "is the explicit replacement of competition with governmental orders as the principal institutional device for assuring good performance."[29]

Regulators, then, must assure that the customer receives reliable service from the utility because the customer has no choice among suppliers. Regulators, in theory, should apportion fairly the costs of service so that no group of customers is charged unduly. They may attempt to set rates, on the other hand, in a way to assure that certain groups of customers can afford service, with other customers paying more in order to cover the costs of the subsidized class. Finally, regulators must set the overall level of revenues at a point where the utility can earn a return similar to that earned in competitive industries. Practically, regulators do not concern themselves with quality of service unless the quality is obviously bad. The big issues in rate cases are the overall level of revenues and the apportionment of revenue sources among customers.

Regulation has been attacked from all sides. Some believe that the regulators have sold out to the utilities, and others think that the regulators are too politically oriented to treat utilities fairly. Many economists accept the concept of regulation, but quarrel with the methods used by the regulators. The complaints, too numerous to cover fully, include three fundamental objections to regulation.

The public utility's "monopoly status . . . is an illusion."[30] Competition clearly exists in the telephone industry. Gas companies fight fiercely to protect markets from other fuels. The natural monopoly status no longer prevails in electric generation because of the seeming end of economies of scale. Before, the utilities would not have exploited customers because it was not in the interest of the utilities to do so, people might have said. Now, critics might argue, the utility no longer has the ability to exploit the customer. So far, as noted before, nobody has come to the scene with plans to duplicate or replace public water and wastewater utilities. What may be true about the disappearance of monopoly power in other utility sectors is not yet true for the water and wastewater utilities.

Cost of service regulation provides little encouragement for efficient operations. Many experts believe that standard regulation bails out bad management while offering no reward to good management. Reducing costs, furthermore, might involve the utility in innovation and risk taking. If the measures taken fail, regulators might penalize the company. Regulators clearly believe that the old style of regulation is inappropriate to some regulated sectors, though. They have replaced cost-of-service regulation with mechanisms that encourage efficiency.

Public utilities supply vital services and, therefore, should not be run on a profit basis, but should be socialized, in which case regulation would be unnecessary. In the United States, most water and wastewater firms are government-owned and unregulated for those reasons. Whether they actually perform better is a matter of dispute.

Sooner or later, regulators have to reevaluate their activities, decide what sectors of the market still require regulation, determine what sort of regulation is best, choose whether to rush to deregulation or to get the industry structure right first, and lead the effort to assure that universal service requirements are met in the most efficient possible manner. The old drawbacks of regulation are evident, but it is not yet evident how regulators will accomplish their new purposes. The fact that the water industry remains a monopoly may assure the continued presence of regulation, but that does not mean that existing forms of regulation do assure good performance.

CHAPTER 21

Setting the Rate of Return

The regulatory commissions do not fix rates so as to guarantee that they will yield a rate of return. The commission's function is simply to determine a rate which will have that result of permitting a utility to earn a fair return, if the utility's earning power and other economic circumstances . . . so . . . permit . . .[31]

— Francis X. Welch

Rate making in theory is a relatively simple process. To the cost of producing the service furnished is added a reasonable return to the investor. The making of public utility rates requires four basic determinations:

1. *what are the enterprise's gross utility revenues under the rate structure examined;*

2. *what are its operating expenses, including maintenance, depreciation, and all taxes, appropriately incurred to produce those gross revenues;*

3. *what utility property provides the service for which rates are charged and thus represents the base (rate base) on which a return should be earned; and*

4. *what percentage figure (rate of return) should be applied to the rate base in order to establish the return (wages of capital) to which investors in the utility enterprise are reasonably entitled . . .*

Simple as this formula sounds, the task of the rate maker is more often than not extremely difficult.[32]

— Maine Supreme Judicial Court

Surely rate-of-return ratemaking is obsolete. Business people valuing enterprises do not use the method. Financial theorists do not go through rate-of-return exercises like those of the regulatory agencies. Telecommunications regulators already have moved off the method, seemingly, as they seek more flexible, more incentive-oriented methods of regulation for those parts of the business in which competition will not flourish. If not yet obsolete, competition will make it obsolete, along with other forms of regulation, many would argue. Is an examination of rate-of-return regulation akin to a class in medical school on how to bleed patients? Doctors no longer bleed patients. What they did to George Washington belongs in a class on the history of medicine. Having said all that, regulators, utility executives, investors, and consumers have to face up to the implicit or explicit presence of rate-of-return regulation. To begin with, the courts have set standards by which to judge the results of regulation, and return earned is one of them, although the courts may not quarrel with new methods of reaching the desired result. Regulators may eschew explicit rate-of-return regulation, as they have done in the United Kingdom, while retaining closet rate-of-return regulation. That is, they may not discuss rate of return, but they may set prices in a way to produce an acceptable rate-of-return range. They will judge the results of new methods of regulation by the rates of return produced. Investors, too, still assess whether the utility has succeeded by ratios that are part of rate of return analysis. Probably the best way to put it is this: until the market changes in such a way as to destroy monopolistic domination of the market, regulation will remain in place, and the regulators will take into account—covertly or overtly—rate-of-return analysis. How does this century-old system work? This is the answer in a nutshell.

RATE OF RETURN

The regulator attempts to set revenues that allow the utility to cover operating costs plus earn an acceptable level of profit. Usually, that profit is stated as a given return on investment in utility plant, or as a return on rate base. The system is called "cost of service ratemaking." Return on the capital invested in the business is, therefore, just one more cost. The regulator examines a utility's results for a test period to determine if the utility is earning a proper return. The regulator uses the following calculations:

> Revenue
> *less* Operating expenses
> *less* Taxes
> *equals* Operating income, or net operating revenue, or earnings available to meet fixed charges, or to provide a return on capital invested in business (interest on debt plus a profit for shareholders)

and $\dfrac{\text{Operating Income}}{\text{Rate Base}}$ = Rate of Return

Regulatory agencies do not necessarily accept company figures. They adjust revenue and operating expense figures for abnormal and even theoretical conditions. The regulators, generally, want to consider "normal" conditions. Sometimes a regulatory agency bases its decision on estimated results for a future test year on the ground that rates are being set for the future and, therefore, should respond to projected conditions at the time that the rates will go into effect. When an estimated test year is used, the utility and its opponents may disagree in their estimates of revenue and expenses. The company and the regulators also may differ on estimates of rate base. Small differences add up:

		Company Projection	Commission Projection
	Revenues	$1,000	$1,010
less	Expenses	500	495
less	Income taxes	250	255
equals	Operating income	250	260
divided by	Rate base	4,000	3,990
equals	Rate of return earned	6.25%	6.52%

With so many figures subject to adjustment, one cannot always determine if the rate order was designed to produce the allowed rate of return or if the revenues and expenses cited in the decision were adjusted to produce a return on paper that in fact, will not be realized.

Income taxes constitute a significant part of the utility's expenses. Rates charged must cover those tax costs, as well as other operating costs, even before compensating owners of capital. Businesses, however, employ strategies to reduce taxes in the current year, by deferring payment to a future year. Should the regulator allocate both the current tax payment plus the deferred tax payment to the expenses of the current year? Both do derive from the activities of the year. Or should the regulator declare that the current payment is real, and that determination of a future payment is sheer speculation? Doing so would let current ratepayers pay for current taxes and let future ratepayers worry about future taxes.

Consider a simplified situation. A utility uses a tax strategy that will reduce taxes by $50 in the first year, but will cause the utility to pay $50 more in the second year. Regulators have set a 13% rate of return for the utility.

Line	Year 1	Year 2
1. Rate base	$1,000	$1,000
2. Pretax income	200	200
3. Regular income taxes	70	70
4. Tax (reduction) or increase due to tax strategy	(50)	50
5. Income taxes paid (3 + 4)	20	120
6. Net income (2 − 5)	180	80
7. Rate of return (6/1)	18%	8%

In the first year, the utility earns more than its allowed return because of the tax savings. The regulator could require the utility to reduce its prices to bring return down to 13%. In the second year, the utility has to pay back the tax savings, so it will not earn the allowed 13% return. Regulators could raise prices in the second year to bring return up to the allowed level. If the tax saving is included in income for ratemaking purposes, as shown above, then the savings are "flowed through" to customers. Most regulators, though, did not want price of utility service to fluctuate because of temporary tax savings. Neither did Congress, which prohibited the procedure in the 1980s. Utilities now set aside a reserve for tax savings to be used when taxes must be paid. Because the taxes must be paid eventually, the setaside is called "deferred taxes." Using the same example as before, we have:

Line	Year 1	Year 2
1. Rate base	$1,000	$1,000
2. Pretax income	200	200
3. Income taxes paid	20	120
4. Tax deferred to reserve or (withdrawn) from reserve set aside from savings	50	(50)
5. Regular income taxes (3 + 4)	70	70
6. Net income (2 − 5)	130	130
7. Rate of return (6/1)	13%	13%

Note that when tax savings are deferred the effect of the swing in taxes is averaged out and the taxes shown in the income statement are as if no tax savings had been realized.

Having determined the tax bill for regulatory purposes and subtracted that amount and the operating expenses from revenues, the remainder is available to compensate the suppliers of capital.

CALCULATING RETURN ON RATE BASE

Regulators set a return on rate base. To do so, they have to decide what constitutes return and what constitutes rate base. If the regulatory agency defines rate base as plant in service, it will define the income available to pay capital as operating income, because that is the income earned from current operations using existing plant in service. The regulator, however, might choose to include plant under construction in rate base, in which case the regulator might decide to define return differently, as well. Regulators have many variants with which to work:

1) *Net original cost rate base.* The rate base is determined by the original cost of the properties, less depreciation.
2) *Fair value.* The cost of the plant is adjusted to account for at least some of the additional cost now required to duplicate the plant. Several states claim to be fair value jurisdictions, but most of the rate orders differ little from those of other jurisdictions.
3) *Average rate base.* The test year encompasses the operating results of an entire period. The rate base at one point in that period may not be representative of the investment throughout the test period. Many regulators, as a result, will determine an average of the rate base throughout the year and will use that average in the case.
4) *End-of-period rate base.* The rate order considers not only the experience of the past test year, but also what may occur in the future. If a utility has been adding plant at a rapid pace, the average rate base may not be representative of plant investment at the time the rate order goes into effect. Thus, the utility is unlikely to be able to earn the allowed return on the enlarged rate base. Many regulators attempt to reduce that attrition in return by using an end-of-period rate base.

5) *Used-and-useful rate base.* Should current consumers be required to pay a return on plant that is not yet in service? In a number of jurisdictions, the regulators include in rate base only plant that is actually serving customers.

6) *Construction work in progress (CWIP) in rate base and allowance for funds used during construction (AFUDC) included in income.* In this approach, the regulators do not distinguish between useful and incomplete plant. Nor do they distinguish between income derived from the sale of a service and income created by a bookkeeping credit in the income statement.

7) *Construction work in progress in rate base.* In this case, the regulator agrees to have the customers bear the current burden of construction work in progress for the following reasons:

a) The plant will, in the main, serve current customers.

b) The plant will be completed in the near term. To hand down a rate order excluding the particular plant would be to regulate for the past rather than for the future. Moreover, the utility would have to file for another rate hike immediately after the new plant is placed in service.

c) The utility has a serious cash flow problem because of the size of its capital expenditure program and cannot finance the completion of the plant additions unless it can generate more cash from operations. Charging the current consumer for the capital costs of the construction program will help cash flow.

d) Making consumers pay in advance for assets that will serve them later sends a price signal about future costs to consumers, who can then begin a process of adjusting their demands to the new price level.

Here is a simple example of some of the many returns that can be derived from the same set of numbers. In an actual case, rate base also includes some amount for working capital.

Revenues	$600
Operating expenses and taxes	400
Operating income (OI)	200
Allowance for funds used during construction (AFUDC)	10
Income before interest charges (IBIC)	$210

Beginning of year net plant in service	$2,000
End of year net plant in service (End NPIS)	2,200
Beginning of year construction work in progress	50
End of year construction work in progress (End CWIP)	100
Working capital in all periods (WC)	50

The above numbers will produce various rates of return, as shown below.

1) Rate of Return $= \dfrac{OI}{\text{Average NPIS} + WC} = \dfrac{200}{2,100 + 50} = 9.3\%$

2) Rate of Return $= \dfrac{OI}{\text{End NPIS} + WC} = \dfrac{200}{2,200 + 50} = 8.9\%$

3) Rate of return on fair value (where fair value equals 150% of the end-of-period net original cost of plant in service)

$$= \dfrac{OI}{\text{Fair Value Rate Base} + WC} = \dfrac{200}{3,300 + 50} = 6.0\%$$

4) Rate of Return $= \dfrac{IBIC}{\text{End NPIS} + \text{End CWIP} + WC}$

$$= \dfrac{210}{2,200 + 100 + 50} = 8.9\%$$

5) Rate of Return $= \dfrac{OI}{\text{End NPIS} + \text{End CWIP} + WC}$

$$= \dfrac{200}{2,200 + 100 + 50} = 8.5\%$$

6) Rate of Return on rate base that includes some construction work in progress without an AFUDC offset (assumes half of year-end CWIP goes into rate base) and year-end plant

$$= \dfrac{OI + \frac{1}{2}\,AFUDC}{\text{End NPIS} + \text{End CWIP} + WC}$$

$$= \dfrac{200 + 5}{2,200 + 50 + 50} = 8.9\%$$

7) Rate of Return that includes all CWIP in denominator and only some AFUDC in numerator either by specifying a lower rate for AFUDC or including only part of AFUDC (assumes half of AFUDC)

$$= \dfrac{OI + \frac{1}{2}\,AFUDC}{\text{End NPIS} + \text{End CWIP} + WC}$$

$$= \dfrac{200 + 5}{2,200 + 100 + 50} = 8.7\%$$

As can be seen in the above examples 1) and 2), rate of return is lower when a year-end rate base is used, and the company, as a result, can justify more rate relief. As can be seen from 2) and 3), the utility may report a low return on a fair value rate base in comparison with that on an original cost rate base. Do not conclude from the examples, however, that a company using fair value can now justify a greater amount of rate relief because of the low return. Most fair value jurisdictions have tended to allow lower returns on the higher fair value rate bases. Examples 4) and 5) demonstrate that a utility might allow better returns by capitalizing credits on construction funds at a higher rate than the company can earn on plant in service, and, unfortunately, that higher return on paper may not be a good substitute for cash. Examples 6) and 7) give halfway measures that could be used by regulators who do not want to unduly encourage construction, but want to aid cash flow.

AFUDC AND CWIP: A RECAPITULATION

To summarize, when plant is not in service and when the utility is not allowed a current return on that plant by the regulators, the company will capitalize the financing costs of the facility (allowance for funds used during construction or AFUDC) and will add those costs to the total cost of the plant. When the plant is completed, the rate base will then include both the actual expenditures on construction and the capitalized financial charges.

The utility depreciates the total cost, including the AFUDC, and earns a return on the total cost. Therefore, the consumer actually pays on the basis of total cost during the life of the plant. When the construction period lasts for several years, however, the utility has to advance large sums for financing charges, while it collects no cash from the consumer. That can create a serious cash drain for a utility with a big capital spending program. Therefore, utility investors should be concerned about the treatment of construction work in progress, or CWIP, by the regulators.

The problem can be handled in several ways. (Keep in mind that there are partial solutions, too, such as adding some CWIP to the rate base.) In some jurisdictions, the plant under construction is included in the rate base, and the current consumer pays a high bill to provide a return on CWIP. In other jurisdictions, CWIP may be included in the rate base, but the rate of return is calculated to include the allowance for funds used during construction (see the following examples). In still other jurisdictions, no CWIP is permitted in the rate base, and the utility capitalizes construction costs by using AFUDC. Because AFUDC is a non-cash credit, from a cash flow standpoint, including CWIP in the rate base (RB) without the offsetting AFUDC is the preferred conservative method. A simplified example is on p. 182.

Note that in Case A, the utility collects $80 from operations, but in Cases B and C, it collects only $64 from operations and the balance of the income before interest charges of $80 is a $16 bookkeeping credit (AFUDC).

In addition, regulators generally include in rate base a sum for working capital. They may not allow a return on an unnecessary facility and may subtract from rate base costs of construction that they consider to be excessive. They may also reduce rate base by the amount that has been financed by cost-free income tax

Line	Case A CWIP in RB No AFUDC in Allowed Income	Case B CWIP in RB and AFUDC in Allowed Income	Case C No CWIP in RB and No AFUDC in Allowed Income
1) Operating Income	$ 80	$ 64	$ 64
2) AFUDC (8% rate)	0	16	16
3) Income Before Interest Charges	80	80	80
4) Plant in Service	800	800	800
5) CWIP	200	200	200
6) Total Plant	1,000	1,000	1,000
7) Rate Base—See Line	6	6	4
8) Allowed Income—See Line	1	3	1
9) Rate of Return Formula—See Lines	1 ÷ 6	3 ÷ 6	1 ÷ 4
10) Rate of Return	8%	8%	8%

deferrals, or by advances and contributions for construction, because none of these items has any cost of capital. They all represent cost-free advances to the utility.

TRENDS IN RATE OF RETURN

Determining the rate base and the actual earnings are two important steps in the regulation process. The next step is to set the proper return to be allowed. In the early days of regulation, when great emphasis was placed on finding the fair value of the rate base, allowed rates of return stayed in a relatively narrow range.

A phrase often repeated in a study of rate cases from 1915 on was, "The Commission gave no indication how the rate of return was established."[33] The Arthur Andersen compilation of rate cases from 1915 to 1960 indicates that the current method of determining cost of capital, which was pioneered by the Federal Power Commission (FPC), was first used in the Safe Harbor Water Power decision of October 25, 1946.[34] By 1949, several regulatory agencies appear to have adopted the FPC method.

The allowance for rate of return seems to have gone through phases. Between 1915 and 1929, regulators granted returns in the 6% to 8% range, perhaps using level of business and interest rates as a basis. In the early years of the Depression, both interest rates and allowed returns drifted down. By the mid-1930s, returns settled in at 6% and remained there until the mid-1960s. Then, because of strong business conditions, inflation, and sharply rising interest rates, rate of allowed return rose dramatically through the early 1980s. From that point, returns have gradually declined in line with the fall in interest rates and inflation. (See Figures 21-1 to 21-5.)

The need for substantial rate relief from the 1960s on may have forced regulators to do more than arbitrarily choose a rate of return above interest rates. They had to pay greater attention to calculating a utility's overall cost of capital from the cost of each of the components of capital. Tables 21-1 to 21-6 show the trends in rates of return, return on equity, and money market costs from 1915 to 1996.

Figure 21-1

Allowed Rates of Return and Interest Rates
1915-1996

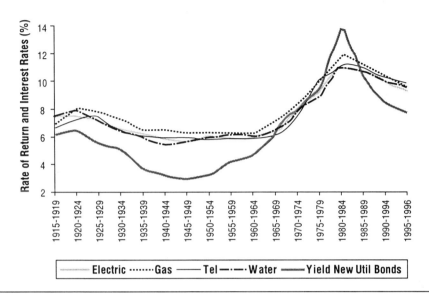

Figure 21-2

Allowed Rates of Return and Interest Rates
1968-1992

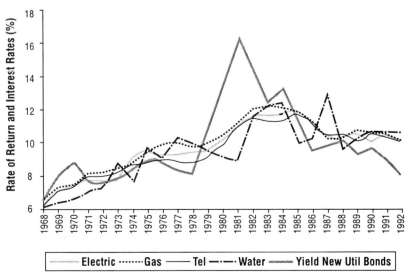

Figure 21-3

Allowed Returns on Equity, Stock Valuation, and Interest Rates
1973-1992

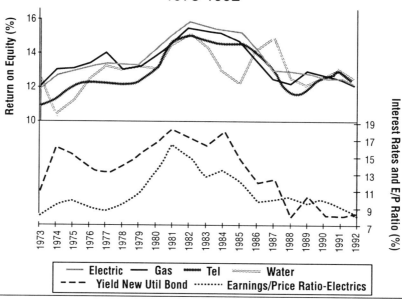

Figure 21-4

Allowed Rates of Return and Interest Rates
1985-1996

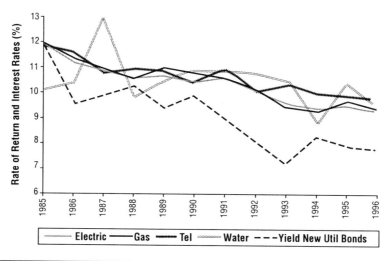

Figure 21-5

Allowed Returns on Equity, Stock Valuation, and Interest Rates
1985-1996

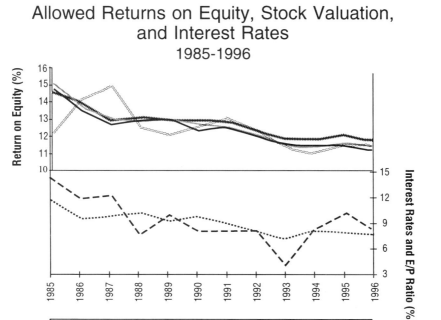

Regulators, in determining the cost of common equity, must assess the business and financial risk inherent in the business venture, and then determine what constitutes a reasonable return on equity, taking into account then-current market conditions. During periods when capital costs are high, as indicated by high interest rates, regulators normally allow higher returns, and, conversely, usually lower allowed returns when capital costs are low. Those trends show in the figures. One would expect regulators to adjust returns for the added risk that comes about as the industry faces structural change, and for taking added risk by utilizing financial policies that could lower costs to consumers, but the prevailing determinant of return on equity may still be overall capital market rates.

CALCULATING THE RATE OF RETURN

The arithmetic needed to calculate cost of capital is simple. For example, a utility borrows $500 at a cost of 7%, raises $500 of common equity, and puts the entire $1,000 into assets that serve the customer. The regulatory agency believes that cost of equity is 12%. Thus, cost of capital is:

Capital Component	$ Amount		Cost		Weighted $ Cost
Debt	$ 500	×	0.07	=	$35
Common Stock	500	×	0.12	=	60
Total	$1,000				$95

185

Usually, the commission determines the cost of each segment of the capital structure and adds the results to determine the overall cost of capital, or rate of return. Determining the cost of debt and preferred stock is fairly easy because the required interest charges and dividends are fixed. Determining the return on common equity, however, is a long, complicated, and subjective process. In many states, the commission will allow a utility to earn a high return on equity if the utility has a low equity ratio, on the theory that greater financial risk requires greater compensation. Regulators should also take into account the business risk level of the company, but they rarely attempt to quantify that factor of the decision.

Basically, the money that goes into the rate base that serves the consumer comes from four sources. Debt is borrowed money that earns a predetermined interest rate. Preferred stock is a special class of stock that collects a predetermined

Table 21-1

Estimated Average Rates of Return Granted in Rate Cases and Indicators of Costs of Capital (%)

	1915–1930	1931–1940	1941–1950	1951–1960	1961–1970	1971–1980	1981–1990	1991–1996
	(1)	(2)	(3)	(4)	(5)	(6)	(7)	(8)
Return Granted on Rate Base								
Electric	7.5	6.5	6.2	6.2	6.4	8.9	11.2	9.6
Gas	7.4	6.5	5.9	5.9	6.5	9.4	11.3	9.7
Telephone	7.2	5.9	5.7	6.1	6.7	8.8	11.0	10.1
Water	7.1	6.1	5.7	5.8	6.1	8.9	11.0	10.1
Return Granted on Equity								
Electric	—	—	—	9.2	11.1	12.9	14.2	11.7
Gas	—	—	—	9.1	10.6	13.0	13.9	11.6
Telephone	—	—	—	9.6	9.6	11.9	13.7	12.1
Water	—	—	—	—	10.2	12.1	13.5	11.8
Indicators of Utility Cost of Capital								
Bond Yields	6.0	4.1	3.0	4.0	5.8	9.2	11.7	8.0
Earnings/Price Ratio	—	5.7	8.1	6.7	6.0	13.1	13.4	7.8

Notes:
Bond yields are all for newly issued utility bonds. Earnings/price ratio of Moody's Electric Utility Average. Simple averages of annual modal values (1915–1961) for return granted. Simple average of unweighted annual means (1962–1996) for return granted.

Sources:
Francis X. Welch, *Cases and Text on Public Utility Regulation, Revised Ed.* (Washington, D.C.: Public Utilities Reports, Inc., 1968), pp. 480–481.
Merrill Lynch Regulatory Data Base.
Moody's Public Utility Manual.
Return Allowed in Public Utility Rate Cases (Arthur Andersen & Co., 1960 ed.)
"Major Rate Case Decisions—January 1995–December 1996 Supplemental Study," *Regulatory Focus* (Jersey City, NJ: Regulatory Research Associates, January 16, 1997.)
PURbase CD-ROM (Vienna, VA: Public Utilities Reports, 1997)

Table 21-2

Regulatory Data
1915–1961

Year	Modal Rate of Return (%) (Andersen)				Cases Reported (Andersen)				Long-term Interest Rates and Earnings Yield (%) (Moody's)	
	Electric	Gas	Telephone	Water	Electric	Gas	Telephone	Water	Newly Issued Utility Bonds	Electric Average Earnings/ Price Ratio
	(1)	(2)	(3)	(4)	(5)	(6)	(7)	(8)	(9)	(10)
1915	7.0	6.0	—	6.5	6	1	0	1	5.80E	–
1916	8.0	7.5	8.0	6.1	3	4	2	1	5.70E	—
1917	7.0	8.0	8.0	7.0	3	2	1	5	6.00E	—
1918	7.5	6.0	6.7	6.2	6	4	2	3	6.65E	—
1919	8.0	6.0	7.4	7.0	5	4	2	3	6.60E	—
1920	8.0	8.0	7.0	8.0	6	8	5	4	7.40E	—
1921	7.5	8.0	8.0	7.5	7	13	6	1	7.31	—
1922	8.0	8.0	7.0	7.0	5	7	3	5	6.02	—
1923	8.0	8.0	7.5	7.0	8	9	1	6	5.98	—
1924	8.0	7.6	8.0	7.0	3	4	6	5	6.03	—
1925	7.5	8.0	8.0	8.0	2	7	6	1	5.61	—
1926	7.7	8.0	7.2	7.5	2	6	7	4	5.50	—
1927	7.0	7.5	7.0	7.0	1	3	2	4	5.26	—
1928	6.0	7.5	6.5	7.5	1	5	3	1	5.20	—
1929	7.0	7.0	7.0	7.5	3	1	7	5	5.21	3.80
1930	—	7.5	7.0	7.0	0	3	4	4	5.20	4.26
1931	7.0	8.0	7.7	6.0	3	1	1	2	4.71	5.43
1932	7.0	7.0	5.7	6.0	5	3	2	4	5.74	6.33
1933	6.0	6.0	6.5	6.0	5	7	3	4	4.98	4.55
1934	6.0	6.5	6.0	6.0	8	4	5	2	4.86	4.39
1935	6.7	7.0	6.0	6.0	8	5	3	3	3.84	5.65
1936	6.5	6.0	6.0	6.0	7	2	5	2	3.55	5.00
1937	6.0	6.0	—	6.0	4	4	0	3	3.55	6.21
1938	6.0	6.5	5.5	—	4	2	1	0	3.46	5.85
1939	6.0	6.2	6.0	—	6	2	1	0	3.46	6.49
1940	6.1	6.2	5.2	7.0	5	2	3	1	3.08	7.04
1941	5.5	6.2	5.0	5.5	1	2	1	1	3.07	8.77
1942	—	6.5	6.0	5.5	0	6	1	1	3.26	10.87
1943	6.0	6.5	5.2	—	3	6	3	0	3.26	8.20
1944	6.0	6.2	5.8	5.4	6	6	1	1	2.98	8.40
1945	5.5	6.5	5.5	—	4	5	1	0	2.85	6.54
1946	5.0	6.0	—	—	4	4	0	0	2.73	6.45
1947	6.0	6.0	5.5	—	3	5	10	0	2.79	7.30
1948	6.0	6.0	5.5	—	6	10	10	0	3.09	8.13
1949	5.7	6.0	6.0	6.0	9	9	20	5	3.07	8.33
1950	6.5	6.0	6.0	6.1	4	3	20	1	2.85	8.40
1951	6.0	6.0	6.0	5.1	7	6	26	1	3.29	7.52
1952	5.7	6.2	6.0	5.7	18	14	26	4	3.38	6.94
1953	6.0	6.2	6.0	—	13	17	21	0	3.77	7.35
1954	5.7	6.2	6.0	6.0	10	15	19	5	3.17	6.62
1955	5.8	6.0	6.0	5.6	6	17	18	6	3.33	6.54
1956	5.8	6.2	6.0	6.0	11	10	22	6	3.86	6.76
1957	6.1	6.0	6.1	6.0	10	19	23	13	4.74	6.90
1958	6.0	6.2	6.1	6.0	16	19	29	12	4.21	6.25
1959	5.8	6.2	6.5	6.0	16	16	18	7	4.97	5.75
1960	6.0	6.0	6.8	6.0	14	29	16	7	4.84	5.92
1961	5.5	6.2	6.3	6.0	6	22	5	10	4.70	4.78

Source:
Arthur Andersen & Co., *Return Allowed in Public Utility Rate Cases* (Vol. I, 1915–1954 and Vol. II, 1955–1961). No date or place of publication.

E = estimated.

Table 21-3

Regulatory Data
1935–1992

Year	Average Rate of Return (%) (Welch)				Average Rates of Return (%) (Merrill Lynch)				Cases Reported (Merrill Lynch)				Long-term Interest Rates and Earnings Yield (%) (Moody's)	
	Electric	Gas	Telephone	Water (Andersen & PUR)	Electric	Gas	Telephone	Water (PUR)	Electric	Gas	Telephone	Water (PUR)	Newly Issued Utility Bonds	Electric Average Earnings/ Price Ratio
	(1)	(2)	(3)	(4)	(5)	(6)	(7)	(8)	(9)	(10)	(11)	(12)	(13)	(14)
1935	7.0	6.7	6.0	6.0									3.84	5.65
1936	6.0	6.5	6.0	6.1									3.55	5.00
1937	6.0	6.0	5.6	6.0									3.55	6.21
1938	6.7	6.0	5.4	—									3.46	5.85
1939	6.2	6.0	5.3	—									3.46	6.49
1940	6.2	6.2	5.2	7.0									3.08	7.04
1941	6.2	5.4	5.0	5.5									3.07	8.77
1942	6.5	6.0	5.3	5.5									3.26	10.87
1943	6.5	6.0	5.3	—									3.26	8.20
1944	6.2	6.0	5.7	5.4									2.98	8.40
1945	6.4	5.5	5.5	—									2.85	6.54
1946	6.0	5.4	6.1	—									2.73	6.45
1947	6.0	6.0	5.6	—									2.79	7.30
1948	6.0	6.0	5.6	—									3.09	8.13
1949	6.0	5.8	6.0	5.8									3.07	8.33
1950	6.0	6.4	6.0	6.1									2.85	8.40
1951	6.0	6.0	6.0	5.1									3.29	7.52
1952	6.3	5.8	6.0	5.8									3.38	6.94
1953	6.3	6.0	6.0	—									3.77	7.35
1954	6.3	5.8	6.0	5.9									3.17	6.62

Table 21-3 *continued*

Year	Average Rate of Return (%) (Welch)				Average Rates of Return (%) (Merrill Lynch)				Cases Reported (Merrill Lynch)				Long-term Interest Rates and Earnings Yield (%) (Moody's)	
	Electric	Gas	Telephone	Water (Andersen & PUR)	Electric	Gas	Telephone	Water (PUR)	Electric	Gas	Telephone	Water (PUR)	Newly Issued Utility Bonds	Electric Average Earnings/Price Ratio
	(1)	(2)	(3)	(4)	(5)	(6)	(7)	(8)	(9)	(10)	(11)	(12)	(13)	(14)
1955	6.0	5.8	6.0	5.8									3.33	6.54
1956	6.3	5.8	6.0	5.9									3.86	6.76
1957	6.0	6.2	6.0	5.6									4.74	6.90
1958	6.1	6.0	6.1	6.2									4.21	6.25
1959	6.2	5.8	6.1	5.6									4.97	5.75
1960	6.0	6.0	6.2	5.8									4.84	5.92
1961	5.9	6.0	6.2	5.9									4.70	4.78
1962	5.8	6.0	6.2	5.8									4.44	5.18
1963	5.9	6.1	6.3	5.9									4.39	4.85
1964	6.0	6.2	6.4	6.2									4.56	4.98
1965	6.2	6.1	6.4	5.7	6.00	6.88	6.57	5.72	2	5	1	16	4.68	5.05
1966	6.5	6.6	6.7	6.0	6.43	6.50	6.38	5.97	2	1	1	22	5.61	6.13
1967					—	—	7.25	5.82	0	0	1	21	6.01	6.54
1968					6.44	6.67	6.19	6.24	4	10	10	22	6.72	6.76
1969					7.24	7.43	7.23	6.39	6	8	13	32	7.99	7.30
1970					7.53	7.54	7.44	6.59	29	31	17	39	8.85	8.70
1971					7.81	8.20	8.10	7.20	42	40	26	46	7.71	8.47
1972					7.77	8.27	8.08	7.34	84	48	59	38	7.46	9.62
1973					7.82	8.58	8.25	8.83	69	54	50	2	7.88	10.64
1974					8.55	8.82	8.80	7.70	106	58	45	2	9.21	15.87

Table 21-3 continued

Year	Average Rate of Return (%) (Welch)				Average Rates of Return (%) (Merrill Lynch)				Cases Reported (Merrill Lynch)				Long-term Interest Rates and Earnings Yield (%) (Moody's)	
	Electric	Gas	Telephone	Water (Andersen & PUR)	Electric	Gas	Telephone	Water (PUR)	Electric	Gas	Telephone	Water (PUR)	Newly Issued Utility Bonds	Electric Average Earnings/ Price Ratio
	(1)	(2)	(3)	(4)	(5)	(6)	(7)	(8)	(9)	(10)	(11)	(12)	(13)	(14)
1975					8.88	9.61	8.85	9.73	133	67	64	3	9.76	15.15
1976					9.32	10.03	9.10	9.16	112	47	55	2	8.80	13.51
1977					9.33	10.10	8.98	10.40	100	41	56	3	8.38	12.82
1978					9.47	9.81	8.82	10.00	94	67	33	3	9.22	13.52
1979					9.58	9.90	9.31	9.52	84	44	27	4	10.64	14.85
1980					10.24	10.47	9.90	9.15	114	36	53	2	13.09	16.38
1981					11.06	11.16	11.14	9.04	137	39	68	1	16.30	18.33
1982					11.73	12.10	11.63	11.61	123	80	65	3	14.56	17.15
1983					11.71	12.31	11.44	12.30	105	46	81	2	12.53	16.05
1984					11.83	12.22	11.32	12.53	79	32	42	1	13.33	17.80
1985					11.99	11.94	11.81	10.03	54	24	43	3	11.78	14.39
1986					11.22	11.37	11.21	10.28	44	18	18	3	9.45	11.87
1987					10.54	10.26	10.48	12.90	28	9	5	1	9.75	12.26
1988					10.59	10.42	10.66	9.69	19	18	6	2	10.19	7.70
1989					10.72	10.86	10.13	10.44	24	28	16	5	9.27	10.10
1990					10.10	10.69	10.55	10.78	38	30	10	3	9.83	8.02
1991					10.52	10.61	10.44	10.76	41	33	20	4	9.03	7.92
1992					10.07	10.18	10.14	10.74	48	29	7	9	8.04	8.05

Sources:
Columns 1–4, from Francis X. Welch, *Cases and Text on Public Utilities Regulation* (Washington, D.C.: Public Utilities Reports, 1968).
Columns 5–7, 9–11, from Merrill Lynch Regulatory Data Base.
Columns 4–12, from Andersen, *Return Allowed in Public Utility Rate Cases*, and Public Utilities Reports.
Columns 13–14, from *Moody's Public Utilities Manual*.

Note:
Unweighted averages.

Table 21-4

Regulatory Data
1965–1992

Year	Average Rate of Return on Equity (%) (Merrill Lynch)			(PUR)	Cases Reported (Merrill Lynch)			(PUR)	Long-term Interest Rates and Earnings Yield (%) (Moody's)	
	Electric	Gas	Tele-phone	Water	Electric	Gas	Tele-phone	Water	Newly Issued Utility Bonds	Electric Average Earnings/Price Ratio
	(1)	(2)	(3)	(4)	(5)	(6)	(7)	(8)	(9)	(10)
1965	11.31%	—%	8.57%	9.25%	1	0	1	—	4.68%	5.05%
1966	11.27	11.70	—	—	2	1	0	—	5.61	6.13
1967	—	—	9.00	—	0	0	1	—	6.01	6.54
1968	8.85	9.10	10.09	—	1	4	6	—	6.72	6.76
1969	12.00	10.51	10.52	12.50	4	4	11	—	7.99	7.30
1970	11.89	11.02	10.78	—	23	24	13	—	8.85	8.70
1971	12.07	12.15	11.39	10.00	33	35	20	—	7.74	8.47
1972	12.08	11.89	10.91	—	78	42	45	—	7.46	9.62
1973	11.80	11.96	10.85	12.50	56	48	35	1	7.88	10.64
1974	12.69	13.09	11.33	10.31	97	50	36	2	9.21	15.87
1975	12.95	13.10	12.14	11.20	128	65	56	3	9.76	15.15
1976	13.21	13.44	12.26	12.63	109	40	51	2	8.80	13.51
1977	13.41	13.96	12.34	13.33	104	44	57	3	8.38	12.82
1978	13.26	13.08	12.18	12.98	93	58	28	3	9.22	13.52
1979	13.34	13.23	12.34	13.31	92	37	25	4	10.64	14.85
1980	14.08	13.78	13.07	13.10	117	32	50	2	13.09	16.38
1981	15.13	14.74	14.65	14.40	139	37	79	1	16.30	18.33
1982	15.76	15.53	15.06	15.22	125	70	61	3	14.56	17.15
1983	15.46	15.26	14.77	14.40	106	48	87	2	12.53	16.05
1984	15.37	15.22	14.49	13.00	82	36	48	1	13.33	17.80
1985	15.16	14.70	14.64	12.23	59	32	43	3	11.78	14.39
1986	14.09	13.56	14.22	14.08	45	16	13	3	9.45	11.97
1987	12.99	12.52	12.88	15.00	29	10	4	1	9.75	12.26
1988	12.86	12.19	11.57	12.46	24	20	8	4	10.19	7.70
1989	12.83	12.89	11.73	12.09	27	32	15	8	9.27	10.10
1990	12.54	12.73	12.67	12.52	41	31	13	5	9.83	8.02
1991	12.58	12.45	12.92	13.12	44	30	18	5	9.03	7.92
1992	12.06	12.06	12.28	12.38	48	31	8	11	8.04	8.05

Sources:
Columns 1–3, 5–7, Merrill Lynch Regulatory Data Base.
Columns 4, 8, Public Utilities Reports.
Columns 9–10, Moody's.

dividend, and nothing more. Regulators determine cost of debt and preferred capital by looking at the loan agreements or the dividend rate set on the preferred stock. The third source of capital is the common stockholder, who earns whatever is left over after the expenses, interest, and preferred dividends are paid. The common stockholder works without a contract. Determining what the stockholder requires as a return on investment is a complicated procedure. The fourth source

Table 21-5

Average Rates of Return Allowed in Rate Cases
1985–1996

	Average Rate of Return (%)				Cases Reported				Long-term Interest Rates and Earnings Yield (%) (Moody's)	
									Newly Issued Utility Bonds	Electric Average Earnings/ Price Ratio
Year	Electric	Gas	Telephone	Water	Electric	Gas	Telephone	Water		
	(1)	(2)	(3)	(4)	(5)	(6)	(7)	(8)	(9)	(10)
1985	11.84	11.89	11.76	10.03	56	38	40	3	11.78	14.39
1986	11.09	11.34	11.45	10.28	51	26	19	3	9.45	11.87
1987	10.75	10.80	10.74	12.90	49	28	11	1	9.75	12.26
1988	10.54	10.45	10.94	9.69	32	28	10	2	10.19	7.70
1989	10.61	10.85	10.80	10.44	24	31	14	5	9.27	10.10
1990	10.39	10.67	10.30	10.78	42	30	6	3	9.83	8.02
1991	10.45	10.52	10.85	10.76	44	35	17	4	9.03	7.92
1992	10.01	10.10	10.04	10.74	46	29	6	9	8.04	8.05
1993	9.46	9.44	10.26	10.43	30	41	12	8	7.10E	4.03
1994	9.29	9.21	9.91	8.78	30	32	12	15	8.20	8.38
1995	9.44	9.64	9.81	10.28	30	16	8	14	7.75	10.27
1996	9.21	9.25	9.65	9.41	20	23	2	10	7.65	8.05

Sources:
Regulatory Research Associates Data Base, except for columns 4 and 8 (PUR) and columns 9 and 10 (Moody's)

---

of money is deferred taxes of various sorts, and advances or contributions from customers who give money to the utility for specific purposes. The government has devised, over time, numerous schemes that allow corporations to put off paying taxes until years in the future. In a sense, that tax deferral is like an interest-free loan from the government. The federal government has instructed regulators to look at some of those tax savings as if the money were part of stockholders' equity and therefore deserving of the same type of return as stockholders' equity. Other deferred taxes get no special treatment, and regulators look upon them as the equivalent of a loan with a zero-interest cost. The same treatment may apply to advances and contributions. That is, regulators may not allow the water company to earn a return on money that costs it nothing, so they may provide a zero return on that part of rate base financed by deferred taxes and advances or they may deduct both from the rate base. (In the examples that follow, "deferred credits" is shorthand for deferred taxes, advances, and contributions.)

Table 21-6

Average Returns on Equity Allowed in Rate Cases
1985–1996

	Average Return on Equity (%)				Cases Reported				Long-term Interest Rates and Earnings Yield (%) (Moody's)	
Year	Electric	Gas	Telephone	Water	Electric	Gas	Telephone	Water	Newly Issued Utility Bonds	Electric Average Earnings/ Price Ratio
	(1)	(2)	(3)	(4)	(5)	(6)	(7)	(8)	(9)	(10)
1985	15.20	14.75	14.59	12.23	58	34	40	3	11.78	14.39
1986	13.93	13.46	13.93	14.08	49	25	18	3	9.45	11.87
1987	12.99	12.74	12.85	15.00	57	29	13	1	9.75	12.26
1988	12.79	12.85	13.13	12.46	33	31	13	4	10.19	7.70
1989	12.97	12.88	12.97	12.09	27	31	15	8	9.27	10.10
1990	12.70	12.37	12.91	12.52	44	31	9	5	9.83	8.02
1991	12.55	12.46	12.89	13.12	45	35	16	5	9.03	7.92
1992	12.09	12.01	12.27	12.38	48	29	7	11	8.04	8.05
1993	11.41	11.35	11.83	11.34	32	45	12	7	7.10E	4.03
1994	11.34	11.35	11.81	10.99	31	28	11	15	8.20	8.38
1995	11.55	11.43	12.08	11.50	33	16	8	15	7.75	10.27
1996	11.39	11.19	11.74	11.36	22	20	4	12	7.65	8.05

Sources:
Regulatory Research Associates Data Base, except for columns 4 and 8 (PUR) and columns 9 and 10 (Moody's).

Here are some sample calculations of how regulators might set the allowed rates of return for two companies:

a) Both companies have the same capitalization ratios. Both have a 12% cost of equity. One company has higher debt and preferred costs than the other.

			Company X					Company Y	
			Amount	Cost				Amount	Cost
Debt	@	5%	$ 50	$2.50	Debt	@	6%	$ 50	$3.00
Preferred	@	5%	10	0.50	Preferred	@	6%	10	0.60
Common	@	12%	30	3.60	Common	@	12%	30	3.60
Deferred Credits	@	0%	10	0.00	Deferred Credits	@	0%	10	0.00
Total			$100	$6.60	Total			$100	$7.20
				or a 6.6% return					or a 7.2% return

b) Both companies have the same cost of preferred stock and debt. One company, however, has a higher equity ratio and lower cost of equity than the other.

| | | | Company X | | | | | Company Y | |
			Amount	Cost				Amount	Cost
Debt	@	5%	$ 40	$2.00	Debt	@	5%	$ 50	$2.50
Preferred	@	5%	10	0.50	Preferred	@	5%	10	0.50
Common	@	11%	40	4.40	Common	@	12%	30	3.60
Deferred Credits	@	0%	10	0.00	Deferred Credits	@	0%	10	0.00
Total			$100	$6.90	Total			$100	$6.60
			or a 6.9% return					or a 6.6% return	

c) Regulators decide to readjust the return for Company X set in example b). They allow a 7.67% return on deferred credits (which is the weighted cost of all components of capital other than deferred credits). The order, in effect, raises the return on equity, as is shown below in the recalculation on the right.

| | | | | | | Return on Deferred Credits Is Added to Return on Common Equity | | | |
Company X			Amount	Cost				Amount	Cost
Debt	@	5%	$ 40	$2.00	Debt	@	5%	$ 40	$2.00
Preferred	@	5%	10	0.50	Preferred	@	5%	10	0.50
Common	@	11%	40	4.40	Common	@	12.925%	40	5.17
Deferred Credits	@	7.67%	10	0.77	Deferred Credits	@	0%	10	0.00
Total			$100	$7.67	Total			$100	$7.67
			or a 7.67% return					or a 7.67% return	

The utility's calculated cost of capital does not remain static. For instance, Company A, which decides to maintain its capitalization ratios at 50% and 50% equity, has to borrow additional funds at a higher rate than the rate previously paid in order to build new plant. The regulators leave the cost of equity unchanged at 12%.

Utility A Expands
Capitalization and Cost of Capital Before Expansion

	Amount		Cost	
Debt	$ 500	@	5%	$25
Common Equity	500	@	12%	60
Total	$1,000			$85
			or 8.5% cost of capital	

Securities Offered to Finance Expansion

	Amount		Cost	
Debt	$ 500	@	8%	$40
Common Equity	500	@	12%	60
Total	$1,000			$100
			or 10.0% cost of new capital	

Capitalization and Cost of Capital After Expansion

	Amount			Cost
Old Debt	$ 500	@	5%	$25
New Debt	500	@	8%	40
Common Equity	1,000	@	12%	120
Total	$2,000			$185
				or 9.25% cost of capital

In another example, utility B, similar to A in all other respects, had borrowed a great deal of money at a high interest rate in the past. The company wants to improve its financial situation by calling in some of the debt and replacing the high-cost debt with common stockholders' equity. After the recapitalization, however, the regulators decide that the common stockholders no longer take as much risk as before and therefore should accept a lower return on their equity investment.

Utility B Recapitalizes and Allowed Return Is Reduced
Capitalization and Allowed Rate of Return Before Recapitalization

	Ratio	Amount			Cost
Debt	70%	$ 700	@	8%	$56
Common Equity	30%	300	@	14%	42
Total	100%	$1,000			$98
					or 9.8% rate of return

Capitalization and Allowed Rate of Return After Recapitalization

	Ratio	Amount			Cost
Debt	50%	$ 500	@	8%	$40
Common Equity	50%	500	@	10%	50
Total	100%	$1,000			$90
					or 9.0% rate of return

The conclusion that two identical firms have different costs of capital might, rightly, perturb financial theorists. (They might be just as upset when told that the same company can have different costs of capital depending on how the firm alters its capitalization.) They might argue that the firm's inherent cost of capital, at any time, is based on the firm's business risk and the cost, at that time, of risk-free capital. In other words, if risk-free capital (such as a U.S. government bond) pays 6%, and a formula determines that the firm requires 4% over the risk-free rate, the firm has a cost of capital of 10%. If risk-free rates go to 10%, then the firm's cost of capital is 14%. Two firms with the same risk levels should have the same costs of capital at any time.

The problem, basically, is that cost of capital can have two different meanings. Business people need to know cost of capital in order to make decisions for the future. What capital cost in the past is not relevant to what it will cost now or in the future. If cost of capital was 9% last year, and is now 11%, the business will not make a new investment that produces a 9% return. But regulators do not view the matter in that way. They have a way of calculating cost of capital that combines historic information on the cost of debt and preferred stock with a judgment about the present cost of common stockholders' equity. As a result of this mispricing of capital, they may set prices that encourage demand when the price of the service does not cover its present or future costs and discourages demand when the price more than covers costs of capital in any real business sense.

Regulators assert that common equity is the most expensive component of capitalization, so the regulated firm should use as little of it as possible. Admittedly, the firm might have to pay a higher interest rate on the debt and a higher dividend on the preferred, because of the increased risk to the senior securities brought about by having a smaller cushion of common equity. Also, the return on common stock would have to go higher, too, due to the increased risk to that security. After all, so much of the income is tied up paying the debt and preferred that, if anything goes wrong, nothing might be left for the common shareholder. So they do deserve a return that takes into account the greater risk. Nevertheless, say the regulators, the customer will gain from the higher leverage, because interest payments are deductible for tax purposes, and the regulated firm will save more in taxes than the higher cost of capital brought about by increased risk. Of course, the regulators do not want the firm to borrow too much money, or increase its financial risk too much. Just enough to benefit consumers. Simple arithmetic demonstrates how, according to this view of cost of capital, the regulated firm needs less revenue to cover its costs, even though the price of all components of capital is higher. First calculate cost of capital (the cost of each component of capital was chosen, arbitrarily, for the example to produce equal weighted costs of capital):

	$ Capital	% Capital		Cost (%)		Weighted % Cost of Capital	$ Cost of Capital Components
Company A							
Debt	$ 300	30%	@	8.0%	=	2.40%	$24.00
Preferred	100	10	@	8.0	=	0.80	8.00
Common	600	60	@	12.0	=	7.20	72.00
Total	$1,000	100%				10.40%	$104.00
Company B							
Debt	$ 600	60%	@	9.0%	=	5.40%	$54.00
Preferred	100	10	@	9.0	=	0.90	9.00
Common	300	30	@	13.66	=	4.10	41.00
Total	$1,000	100%				10.40%	$104.00

Now determine how much revenue the utility needs to collect from customers before tax in order to earn those capital costs, using a 35% tax rate for convenience of calculation:

	Company A	Company B
Revenue required	$197.08	$180.92
Operating expenses	− 50.00	− 50.00
Pretax operating income	147.08	130.92
Interest expenses	− 24.00	− 54.00
Pretax net income	123.08	76.92
Income tax	− 43.08	− 26.92
Net income	80.00	50.00
Preferred dividends	− 8.00	− 9.00
Net income for common stock	$72.00	$41.00

Note that in the above example, customers have to pay 8.9% more for the same service to the company that uses less debt. Regulators and financial executives might have a hard time calculating the real costs of the components of capital with differing capitalization ratios, but they would work on the assumption that consumers benefit if the company uses more debt, although at a certain point, too much debt makes the company financially unstable, so nobody wants the regulators to go that far.

CAPITALIZATION

Everyone should agree on the capitalization used in calculating rate of return, one would think. After all, the numbers are right there to see on the firm's balance sheet. Unfortunately, that is not the way it works. The regulators, for instance, might argue that the firm's capitalization is not optimal. They might want to substitute a hypothetical capitalization for the real one. For example, a company has a 100% equity ratio (no debt). The state normally allows a 14% return on equity for a utility with the usual capitalization ratios. Should the state allow the equivalent of a 14% return on all capital just because the company in question has no debt? The state cannot force the firm to sell debt, but the state may not force consumers to pay the price for the firm's excessive conservatism. The regulators decide to derive a rate of return from a hypothetical capitalization of 50% debt (at a 9% cost because that is the prevailing rate) and 50% equity (at a 14% cost). Although the rate order states that the regulators have granted a 14% return on equity (based on the hypothetical capital structure), in reality, they have granted an 11.5% return ($115 for $1,000) on the actual equity:

	Capitalization (%)	Amount ($)			Cost ($)
Hypothetical					
Debt	50%	$ 500	@	9%	$45
Common equity	50	500	@	14%	70
Total	100%	$1,000			$115
Actual					
Debt	0%	$ 0	@	—	$ 0
Common equity	100	1,000	@	11.5%	115
Total	100%	$1,000			$115

Note that the regulators decided that the firm could earn $115. They left it to the company to decide whether to allocate that sum between debt and equity or just to equity.

Sometimes the company sells securities that change capitalization and cost of capital after the close of the rate case or after the test period. If regulators set rates for the future, they should base the rate order on capitalization and cost of capital during the time when the rates will be in effect, not on history. Regulators, though, often will not accept projections of capitalization or of cost of capital. They may simply refuse to consider anything after the test period. Thus, the regulators may base decisions on a capitalization that is already out of date.

Determination of capitalization and cost of capital becomes complicated when the regulated firm, the operating utility, is owned by still another firm, called the parent or holding company. As an example, Operating Company (OC) is wholly owned by Parent Company (PC). Wholly owned means that PC owns all the common stock of OC. For this example, PC has no subsidiaries other than OC, and all the money that it raised through borrowing or through selling common stock was applied to buying the common stock of OC. Both OC and PC have borrowed money at a 6% rate. The OC, PC, and consolidated capitalizations are:

	OC		PC		Consolidated	
	$	Ratio	$	Ratio	$	Ratio
Debt	$ 300	30%	$490	70%	$ 790	79%
Common equity	700	70	210	30	210	21
Total	$1,000	100%	$700	100%	$1,000	100%

Keep in mind the concept of consolidation shown here. The Parent Company sold $210 to shareholders and borrowed $490 from bondholders. The Operating Company receives an infusion of that $700 raised by the parent. That infusion buys $700 of common stock, which Parent Company now owns. The Operating Company, however, needs a total of $1,000 to begin its operations, so it borrows $300 from bondholders. Note that a total of $1,000 is all the money that the two companies have raised. The two companies, together, have borrowed a total of $790 from bondholders. At some point, they will have to pay this money back. The total assets owned by the group consists of $1,000. Since $790 of that money came from borrowing, the $210 balance had to come from shareholders. And it did. That was the sum raised by the Parent Company from shareholders. The consolidated statement, which reflects the financial position of this family of companies, cannot be produced by adding together the totals of the individual components of the group, because that would produce a sum greater than the actual assets held. The consolidated statement eliminates the double counting of holdings within the group, adds up all the debt owed to outsiders, and shows the actual amount of money that shareholders have put in. (Note that if PC had lent money to OC, instead of investing in the stock of OC, that amount could have been eliminated from the consolidated debt. Counting it would have been like saying that your left hand owes money to your right hand.)

How do the regulators calculate the return for OC? What capitalization should they use? The easiest answer is to ignore who owns the stock of OC or how the investment in OC was financed. The regulator decides that OC's shareholders are taking little financial risk, as evidenced by the high equity ratio, so they deserve only a 10% return on equity. Rate of return works out to 8.8%:

	Portion of Capitalization		Cost of Capital Component		Weighted Cost of Capital
Debt	0.30	×	6.0%	=	1.8%
Common equity	0.70	×	10.0	=	7.0
Total	1.00				8.8%

Some regulators would argue that they should examine the sources of and cost of the equity investment. In this case, the parent only raised $210 of equity, and the rest of the capital came from borrowed money. They would claim that the real capitalization ratios (using what is called the double leverage method) is 21% equity and 79% debt:

Debt of OC	$ 300	30%
Debt of PC used to purchase equity in OC	490	49
Common equity of PC used to purchase equity in OC	210	21
Total	$1,000	100%

Now comes the problem. The regulator has to set a higher return on the lower equity ratio, because the equity holder is taking greater risk. In order to reach that same 8.8% rate of return, the regulator has to grant a 19.33% return on the newly calculated double leverage equity.

	Portion of Capitalization		Cost of Capital Component		Weighted Cost of Capital
Debt of OC	0.30	×	6.00%	=	1.80%
Debt of PC	0.49	×	6.00	=	2.94
Common equity	0.21	×	19.33	=	4.06
Total	1.00				8.80%

Most regulators, however, would hesitate to grant so high a return. They might decide that 15% is generous enough. Yet a 15% return on equity, using the double leverage method of calculation, produces only a 7.89% rate of return:

	Portion of Capitalization		Cost of Capital Component		Weighted Cost of Capital
Debt of OC	0.30	×	6.0%	=	1.80%
Debt of PC	0.49	×	6.0	=	2.94
Common equity	0.21	×	15.0	=	3.15
Total	1.00				7.89%

What is worse, the return actually earned on the equity investment in OC now falls to 8.70%, based on OC's capitalization:

	Portion of Capitalization		Cost of Capital Component		Weighted Cost of Capital
Debt	0.30	×	6.00%	=	1.80%
Common equity	0.70	×	8.70	=	6.09
Total	1.00				7.89%

Note that the regulators never said that 8.70% was an appropriate return on equity for OC. That number falls out from the arithmetic. Presumably, if the regulators were consistent, and OC were an independent company with thousands of shareholders, they would have to find out how each of those shareholders financed their investments in OC. Double leverage allows regulators to grant different returns to identical companies that have different ownerships. Perhaps because the holding company is often from out-of-state, and the share owners are far away, double leverage practices really represent a form of regulatory populism.

Sometimes, regulators will conclude that it is impossible to completely disentangle the finances of the local subsidiary from that of the holding company. Therefore, they decide to use the consolidated capitalization of the holding company system as the capitalization of the local operating subsidiary. That procedure, of course, creates another set of problems. Should the regulators calculate the cost of capital for the consolidated system, and superimpose those costs on the operating company in question, or should they try to make calculations with subsidiary cost of capital and then apply those figures to holding company capitalization? Probably the only consistent procedure would be to apply both consolidated capitalization and capital costs to the subsidiary.

Once regulators determine capitalization, they must set the proper return for each component of capitalization. It should be easy to determine the costs of debt and preferred stock, because contracts between the company and the holders of the securities set them. A problem could arise, though, when the regulated firm or the regulatory agency tries to estimate the costs of issues not yet sold to the public. On the whole, though, setting the costs of senior securities presents the least difficulty.

RETURN ON COMMON EQUITY

The regulator now faces the most difficult question: what is the proper return on common equity? No contractual relationship exists between the corporation and the equity holder specifying the required return. The regulators developed several methodologies that purport to discover the requirements of the stockholders. Over time, three methods dominated the regulatory scene.

The *comparable earnings method* probably owed its popularity over a period of time to the Supreme Court's judgment in the *Hope* case that the "return to the equity owner should be commensurate with returns on investments in other enterprises having corresponding risks."[35] Many rate-of-return experts interpreted that dictum to make as the point of reference the return on the book equity of comparable enterprises. What is a comparable enterprise, though? Some practitioners took the terms literally: a comparable enterprise is another utility of the type in question. That approach solves one problem but it creates another. To some extent, what a utility earns is a function of what the regulators allowed in the last rate case. If every regulatory agency followed a policy of allowing the same return as every other regulator, the procedure becomes circular. Rate of return allowed in a rate case should represent the agency's judgment of returns currently required by investors if the utility is to have the ability to raise money at reasonable terms, which regulators cannot determine by looking at what utilities are or were earning as a result of past regulatory decisions.

Could regulators avoid the problem of circularity by examining the returns earned on book equity by unregulated firms that have characteristics similar to those of the regulated firm? Unfortunately, picking the comparable firms or industries is not an easy task, and requires subjective judgment. Even after coming up with a list, the regulator has to deal with additional complications.[36] For instance, the industrial firms that have the steadiness of growth and profitability might be found in monopolistic or oligopolistic industries. Their returns might be attributable to monopoly power. Few would argue that the safe, regulated water company is entitled to a monopolistic rate of return. Also, accounting procedures do not allow true comparisons of value of assets, due to timing and method of purchase. Some accounts prove unstable due to fluctuations in the value of foreign currencies. We might try to construct a list of comparable firms by omitting obviously oligopolistic firms, those with large foreign holdings, those that put little into fixed assets, as well as those having other characteristics unlike those of water companies, and then use analyses of the risk of investing.[37]

Unfortunately, both inflation and technology have changed the picture since *Hope*. That decision, by basing the procedures on the audited books of large corporations, seemed to provide a more solid foundation than those methods that tried to read the minds of investors. But the Supreme Court wrote *Hope* in 1944, before the postwar inflation. In fact, wholesale prices in 1944 were at about the same level as in 1864, when prices were little higher than in 1814. In 1944, the judges had no reason to think that prices would break out of a pattern of wide swings around a slightly rising trend line. Since then, the distortions introduced into financial statements by inflation reduce the meaningfulness of inter-company or inter-industry comparisons. In addition, due to the rapid introduction of new technology, some of the assets on the books may be worth far less than shown, because they cannot accomplish what new assets could. Looking exclusively to the accounts of corporations may provide poor clues to what current investors want.

The *discounted cash flow technique* gained popularity because regulators hesitated to use the comparable earnings approach, ostensibly because of the difficulty of coming up with an acceptable sample of comparable companies. Witnesses using the comparable earnings approach had a tendency to be selective in their choice of comparable firms. Regulators objected that the witnesses had selected companies that would produce a desired answer. Given the adversarial nature of the regulatory process, that objection was reasonable.

Rate-of-return experts then developed alternative methods of finding a fair return on equity. Those methods "purport to give the objective judgment of the market place as to what is the cost of capital."[38] The discounted cash flow (DCF) technique is now one of the two prevailing popular approaches.

Theorists believe that the price of a common share equals the present value of the sum of all future income to be received from the share.[39] Assuming that the dividend payout ratio, earnings price ratio, and growth rate remain constant, in perpetuity, then (all numbers in decimals):

$$k = \frac{d}{p} + g$$

where:

k = expected return on investment in stock
d = dividend per share
p = price of stock
g = expected annual growth in dividend or market price of stock

To complete the analysis:

$$g = br$$

where:

b = the earnings retention rate ($1 -$ payout ratio)
r = expected return on book equity.

The formulas resemble those used by many investors. Unfortunately, the stated assumptions present practical problems, and the assumption that the stock price must remain at book value could invalidate the calculations. The basic formula also is circular. "The variable g . . . is affected by r and in some cases by the expected ratio of market value to book value. The term r is the result of regulatory action and the market-to-book ratio is influenced by regulatory action. This results in independent variable g being dependent on dependent variable k of the formula, which is circular."[40]

The market-to-book ratio affects the calculation in several ways. For example, when the market-to-book ratio is more than 100%, and the utility must sell stock for financing, the stock's growth in earnings and dividends per share (g) will be faster than if the stock sold at or below book value. Thus, if the market-to-book ratio differs for two utilities, the same k applied to the two stocks will produce different realized returns. To complicate matters further, the application to the book value of a return derived from the market value when book value differs from market value may be invalid.[41] As Alfred Rappaport noted in his pioneering book on shareholder value:

> Despite the fact that investors and managers both use the same discounted cash flow (DCF) model to estimate prospective returns, the rate of return that must be earned by corporate is ordinarily significantly higher than the investor-required rate itself.[42]

The following examples show the effect of price on growth in earnings per share. Three utilities, with stock selling at 90%, 100%, and 110% of book value, must increase common equity by 10% to finance expansion. Each company sells stock at the market value at the end of the previous year. Each company earns 10% on equity.

Company A (90% of Book Value)	Year 1	Year 2
Common equity	$1,000.00	$1,100.00
Number of shares	100	111.1
Book value per share	$10.00	$9.90
Price per share (year-end)	9.00	—
Earnings	$100.00	$110.00
Earnings per share	$1.00	$0.99
% change in EPS	—	−1%

Company B (100% of Book Value)	Year 1	Year 2
Common equity	$1,000.00	$1,100.00
Number of shares	100	110
Book value per share	$10.00	$10.00
Price per share (year-end)	10.00	$10.00
Earnings	$100.00	—
Earnings per share	$1.00	$1.00
% change in EPS	—	0%

Company C (110% of Book Value)	Year 1	Year 2
Common equity	$1,000.00	$1,100.00
Number of shares	100	109.1
Book value per share	$10.00	$10.00
Price per share (year-end)	11.00	—
Earnings	$100.00	$110.00
Earnings per share	$1.00	$1.01
% change in EPS	—	+1%

The percentage change in the rate of growth caused by the market/book differential can be formulated as:

$$\frac{o}{e} \times \left[\left(\frac{m}{b} \times 100 \right) - 100 \right]$$

where:

o = dollar value of new stock offering
e = common equity before offering
m = market value of shares
b = book value of shares

Now let us attempt to determine k (expected return on investment in stock), ignoring the problem of circularity, while including and excluding the effect on growth of the market-book differential. Each of three utilities pays a 60-cent dividend. The expert witnesses have determined (based on past experience) that investors expect 4% growth from each utility.

	Company A	Company B	Company C
Dividend	$ 0.60	$ 0.60	$ 0.60
Price	9.00	10.00	11.00
D/P	6.66%	6.00%	5.45%
g	4.00	4.00	4.00
k	10.66	10.00	9.45

Does it make sense to say that investors will pay a higher price for a stock from which they expect a lower return? If the return on book equity to C were reduced to 9.45%, the stock would probably not remain at $11.00. Investors showing that regulators had misjudged their expectations would sell the stock until it fell to a price commensurate with the new, lower return on book equity. Investors base their expectations of return on the price of the stock, not on the underlying book value.

Growth differentials are caused by selling stock at different prices. The differentials are −1% for A, 0% for B, and +1% for C. The g and k of the formula again change, adding to the confusion:

	Company A	Company B	Company C
g	3.00%	4.00%	5.00%
k	9.66	10.00	10.45

Because of the dilutionary effect on current holdings of selling stock below book value, many regulators believe that earnings should be high enough to keep the stock at or above book value. Because a positive correlation exists between return on equity and the market/book ratio, regulators have tried, in the past, to set a return on equity that will keep the stock selling at or above book value. Too high a market/book ratio, though, might indicate to those regulators that the utility is overearning. Therefore, when the market/book ratio is low, selling new shares may be dilutive, but the regulators may have plenty of room to improve earnings if they so desire. When the market/book ratio is high, selling new shares could benefit earnings per share, but regulators could decide that the company is earning too much money. Welch wrote:

> ... The final test that any utility enterprise has to meet, if it is to continue in business, is whether it can sell its securities on the investment market. According to the Federal Power Commission, if the return allowed cannot meet this test—if it has to sell stocks at a discount or bonds at a price giving higher yield than normally prevails in the market—that company is faced with financial difficulties . . .[43]

Bonbright discusses the sale of common stock at a price below book value in terms of "impairing the integrity"[44] of the investment made by previous stockholders. Clearly, sales at prices below book value erode the earnings potential of previously issued shares. If such sales are expected to continue for a long period, purchasers of new shares may intensify their demands for a higher return to offset the expected attrition, and thereby further increase the cost of capital. (The shares of most water utilities have sold above book value in the 1990s, fortunately.)

As with the comparable earnings approach, subjectivity and the capacity for manipulation of data lurk beneath the cloak of financial theory. The formula for k looks objective but is as subjective as the choice of comparable companies in the comparable earnings approach. Should stock price and dividend used in the formula be that of one date, or an average? If the latter, how long a period should be averaged? If the former, at what date? What selection would be representative? The answer of the expert witness is to pick the period that gives the desired result. The next step is to determine g. Should one use a past growth rate and, if so, which period should be chosen? Or should an estimate of future growth be based on investor expectations as divined by Wall Street security analysts?

In a 1978 decision, one commission wrote that the witness "was more pessimistic in his evaluation of investors' expectations of future dividend growth. In light of the company's poor past performance, he was of the opinion that investors anticipated a low rate of growth and were looking to the high dividend yield for the bulk of their return requirement."[45] That statement seems to say that if a company showed bad results in the particular past, investors expect nothing but a repetition of bad results, and deserve nothing better. And let us not forget that the witnesses in the case could pick the particular past period that produces the desired results. In another decision, a commission relied on the projections of "anticipated rate of growth in dividends per share" made by Value Line, a leading investment advisory service. The commission thought that the staff witness should have used a mean estimate for several similar companies, but said that "we believe that the DCF approach . . . provides the best estimate of a utility's cost of equity. We continued to be troubled, however, by the problem of deriving the growth term of the DCF model ... we realize that the projections of a widely circulated investment survey such as Value Line, regardless of their accuracy, may provide a reliable estimate of investor expectations simply because of their influence on investor expectations. We therefore accept the anticipated growth in dividends per share projected by Value Line as the growth term in DCF formula."[46] In effect, the return on equity set by the commission was really determined by the Value Line analyst. The commissioners showed little appreciation of the real problem of the DCF method. Investors' expectations are determined, to a great extent, by what they expect regulators to do. Regulators, in turn, make their decisions based on what investors expect. Perhaps the best way to get a generous rate order is to launch an investor relations campaign to convince stockholders that a great order is on the way. On the other hand, consumer groups could run a campaign to convince investors that a poor order is on the way.

The capital asset pricing model or CAPM[47] approach to determining the proper return on equity is an offshoot of modern portfolio theory (MPT). The return on an investment consists of two parts: a risk-free return (such as that available from Treasury bills) and an additional return for risk. Risk is measured by comparing the volatility of return on a particular security with return in the market as a whole. That risk is measured by use of the familiar beta (B) of MPT. Thus:

$$R = R_f + B (R_m - R_f)$$

where:

R $\quad$ = the return expected from a security
R_f $\quad$ = the return on risk-free securities
R_m = the market rate of return

Note that beta, as used above, does not simply show the price movements of particular stock as a multiple of the price movements of the market as a whole, but, rather, the total return.

Investors have the choice of a risk-free investment, and they will demand a higher return to induce them to invest at a higher risk level. Whether beta is the proper measure of risk, and whether the many assumptions underlying CAPM are realistic, are matters for scholarly debate. Is CAPM workable when applied to solving this problem: what return should be granted in a rate case?

CAPM uses only past data to determine what the investor might expect in the future. Capital markets are unstable. A period in the recent past can be chosen to prove any predetermined hypothesis. Is there any correct past period or is the choice of period subjective? There is nothing wrong with subjectivity, but the use of a supposedly scientific CAPM formula wraps this subjectivity in specious objectivity.

Has the beta for a particular security been stable and will it remain stable in the future? It may be that beta has greater predictive value when applied to a portfolio than to a single security. Industries and companies have life cycles. In the postwar period, utility stocks have oscillated between being dull, income vehicles and growth-oriented ventures, depending as much on the mood of the market as on the underlying situation in the industry.

Does CAPM have predictive value? We are trying to determine investor expectations (investors' predictions of their future returns). We want to know what investors expect to happen, not what already has happened. There is no reason to think that investors know in advance what will happen in a given future period. Furthermore, there is no reason to believe that return to investors is stable from period to period. In fact, the evidence is to the contrary, which provides another reason to be hesitant about applying to the future the return from a particular period in the past.

Another problem exists. How confident one can be about the statistical validity of the risk-return relationship at a given level of risk may affect the results for a particular company or industry more than the results for an entire portfolio. For instance, what if the risk-return relationship in a past period looks like that of Figure 21-6?

The formula for the risk-return relationship is shown in Figure 21-6 by the straight line. But the points are not uniformly distributed about the line for its entire length. The point representing the utility industry (circled in the figure) had a low-risk level, but provided a market return substantially higher than would have been estimated from the risk-return line. In fact, note that all the low-risk stocks yielded returns greater than would have been expected. Vandell and Malernee, years ago, claimed that low beta stocks actually did earn higher returns than they theoretically should.[48] Later academic studies have questioned the connection between beta and return that is such an important part of the use of CAPM in the ratemaking process.[49] If true, a CAPM formula consistently would understate the proper return for those groups.

Stephen A. Ross, a professor at Yale, remarked at a symposium on CAPM that:

> The theoretical relationship between beta and expected return is well known. The theory says the capital market line should rise at a rate equal to the slope of the excess return . . . over and above the risk-free rate. Most empirical studies, however, have not supported this relationship. . . . Beta is not very useful for determining the expected return on a stock. . . . The CAPM is a wonderful theory. . . . It is not useful for telling people about the cost of capital or expected return. . . . I am interested in both the expected return on a stock and the stock's beta. What I have lost is the CAPM's notion that the two are related . . .[50]

The CAPM approach attempts to determine investors' expectations of future return from the past performance of a group of stocks chosen because the stocks

Figure 21-6

Market Risk and Market Return by Industry Group

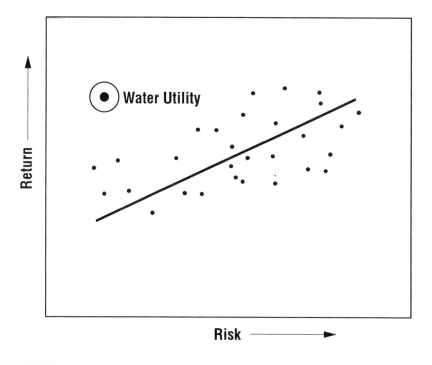

have risk characteristics similar to those of the security in question. The theoretical relationships upon which the approach is based, however, may not provide adequate guidance for the regulator who is trying to set a rate of return.

ALTERNATIVE REGULATORY METHODS

Rate-of-return regulation requires expensive, protracted, periodic rate cases. Government agencies, consumer groups, and water utilities pour enormous resources into their completion. Emphasis on rate base may encourage excessive investment. Fixation on one number, the allowed return, discourages regulated firms from operating more efficiently, because regulators tended to take from the firm any profit earned above that allowed level by reducing prices. For that matter, the system discourages initiative on the part of the regulated firms, too, because the firms could correct income deficiencies through regulated price increases rather than through their own efforts. Rate of return regulation ties up customers, regulators, and utilities in a maze of long delays and arcane procedures. To deal with current problems, regulators have devised new regulatory methods, some homegrown, some taken from British models. The four most common alternative regulatory methods are: range of return, profit sharing, moratorium, and price cap.

Range of return. Rate of regulation is rigid. The regulator sets one number. Anything above that number is too much, anything below it too little. If the regulated firm improves its productivity and thereby increases the return that it earns, the regulator can take away all benefits of better management by forcing the firm to lower prices. If profits fall below the prescribed level, the regulated firm need not work to improve its profitability, because it can achieve a return to the prescribed level through a rate increase.

Regulators, however, can set a range of return around the designated rate of return. As long as the return actually earned stays within that range, the regulated firm cannot raise and the regulator will not lower prices. The company now has the incentive to improve productivity or sales in order to raise probability to the top of the range. On the other side, the company has reason to work hard to keep profitability from falling below the central allowed return because the regulator will do nothing to help the company until the profit falls below the bottom of the range. In effect, the regulator tells the water company: Work hard, and you may keep the benefits of that hard work, up to a point. Do a sloppy job, and you will suffer the consequences, up to a point.

As an example, regulators set 10% as the allowed return, and they establish a tariff that produces a 10% return. They set the range of return, though, at 8% to 12%. As long as the company does not raise prices, it can keep all the profits up to 12% that come from improved productivity or better sales volume. If profits rise above a 12% return, though, the regulators will tell the company to reduce prices enough to bring profits back into the range. Perhaps, though, management becomes sloppy, or business conditions deteriorate enough to depress volume, and return falls below 10%. The company cannot ask the regulators to raise prices enough to bring returns up to the allowed level. In fact, the company has to endure sub-par profitability, without the ability to raise prices, as long as return does not fall below 8%.

Range-of-return agreements might operate for a set period of time, or until conditions change enough to require a new rate case. Range-of-return regulation provides a safety net to the carrier, protection for the consumer, and still furnishes incentives for better management. The method, though, still retains the flaw inherent in all rate-of-return procedures: it makes capital investment the center of the process. That discourages the creation of services that require little or no incremental capital, because those services could not contribute to profitability. The carrier cannot earn a return on a nonexistent investment.

Profit sharing. Range of return regulation operates on a black or white basis, in a way. As long as the company remains in the range (a dead band), the regulator does nothing. As soon as the utility's return moves out of the band, the regulator acts. Yet, what is so sacred about those borders, especially given the ability of companies to manipulate the accounts in order to reach a given level of income?

Regulators can set up a more flexible system that gives carriers even greater incentives. They set up a range of return, as before, with a dead band. When, however, the return rises above the top of the range, the utility does not have to give up all the excess profit. It gives back to consumers part of the excess profit. If the utility management works even harder, and brings returns to a still higher level, then customers get still another refund, but the utility keeps part of the additional excess. At a certain level of return, though, the utility reaches a ceiling, beyond which it must return all excess profits to consumers. The plan, incidentally, need not be symmetrical, with the same sharing formula above and below the dead band. The regulator may be quicker to require price reductions than to allow automatic price increases.

Here is how the plan might work, if it were symmetrical. The regulators set 10% as the allowed return, as before, with a dead band of 8% to 12%. The water supplier can earn any return within the range, without facing action from regulators. If the water utility earns within 12% to 13%, then it must share half of the excess return with customers, by means of a refund. If it earns 13% to 14%, then the utility returns three-quarters of the excess between 13% and 14%. If the return exceeds 14%, then the company returns all the excess over 14%. (Presumably, if the return falls to the 7% to 8% range, consumers pay half of the difference back to the water company, and if returns falls into the 6% to 7% range, then customers pay three-quarters of the difference, and when return hits 6%, customers automatically pay enough to keep the return from staying below 6%. That, however, may not happen.)

Profit sharing, again, encourages the water company to run as efficiently as possible, while assuring that consumers share some of the benefits of the better management. The method, though, requires complicated accounting and repayment procedures, and it is still rooted in capital investment as the basis for decisions.

Moratorium. Regulators and utilities could not devise a simpler procedure. They cut a deal with each other. In return for some concessions for one of the parties to the other, the utility agrees not to raise prices for a designated period of time, unless certain stipulated events take place that would void the agreement. (Sometimes the moratorium continues, but with price changes allowed to cover changes in specific expense items.)

Regulators may sign on to the deal because they want to assure price stability for consumers. The utility might want an extended period of time during which it could try a new strategy and retain the benefits therefrom. (There is little point in taking chances if the regulator immediately appropriates the benefits.)

The negotiations for the deal might be the weak point in the process. Regulators could bargain away valuable benefits to customers in return for price stability, when prices might have declined instead. The utility could lock itself into an unfortunate, multiyear deal, without any way out, when changing markets require flexibility. Is this the regulatory equivalent of trading one's birthright for a mess of porridge?

Price cap. The British pioneered price cap regulation. Stephen C. Littlechild, who commented, "U.S. experience of regulation is not encouraging . . . investment has been distorted and innovation discouraged,"[51] was asked to devise a regulatory system for British Telecom. He got the idea from a strange activity, the Monopolies and Mergers Commission's regulatory scheme for the price of condoms:

> In the UK, the MMC has recently recommended abandoning the attempt to monitor the rate of return on contraceptive sheaths achieved by LRC Products and have instead suggested a requirement that product prices not be increased each year by more than an index of costs less 1.5%; this is to last five years.[52]

Presumably, customers care not about the profitability of the utility but about the price that they pay for service. In price cap regulation, regulators set a price for service at the beginning of a multi-year period. In each subsequent year, they allow price to rise by the percentage increase in the cost of living (the Retail Price Index or "RPI") less a fixed percentage (called the "X factor" in the UK). By keeping the percentage increase in price below the rate of inflation, the regulator forces the carrier to continually seek ways to improve productivity. The British formula is called "RPI−X."

Often, regulators set the price increase for a basket of services, not for each service. The utility can manipulate the prices of the different services, as long as the weighted average price increase does not exceed the percentage increase set by the price cap formula. This flexibility in pricing gives the utility the ability to rebalance the prices of individual services over a period of time.

As an example, regulators set a formula for prices of the increase in the Consumer Price Index (CPI) minus 3% for a five-year period. The utility has two services, A and B, of equal weight. Service A is overpriced and Service B requires price increases. Here is how the system might work, on a simplified basis:

Year	1	2	3	4	5
CPI	3%	5%	4%	1%	2%
X	−3	−3	−3	−3	−3
Price increase allowed	0	2	1	−2	−1
Price increase A	−1	−2	0	−4	−2
Price increase B	+1	+4	+2	0	0

Price-cap regulation encourages greater productivity. It requires simple regulation. But it discourages major capital investments that do not produce almost immediate productivity gains, because the formula does not call for a predetermined and prompt return on the additional investment. Additionally, it might tempt utilities to cut corners. The utility, after all, can keep all the savings generated. Customers of British Telecom and of several Bell Operating Companies experienced service deterioration after the introduction of price cap regulation.

Admittedly, to simply lay the blame after the fact is flawed logic, but some would argue that there was a causal relationship between the regulatory formula and the service problems.[53]

The British, when floating the newly privatized water industry, took note of the capital-intensive nature of the industry, and of the need to make enormous capital expenditures to rehabilitate old plant and meet new environmental standards. Rather than set an RPI − X formula for the water industry, they fixed on a RPI + K formula. The K factor raises prices enough to cover the costs of the projected capital expenditures in the five-year period. Of course, one could argue that the formula could give the utility an incentive not to make the capital expenditures, since it would get paid the K factor, anyway, until the regulator noticed. It also creates a disincentive for the utility to make any capital expenditures (no matter how needed) over the projected number, until the next five-year period. One might argue that the British, in this instance, substituted one set of perverse disincentives for another.

Price-cap regulation, incidentally, is not completely detached from rate-of-return concepts. The regulators have to start the process somewhere. What justifies the initial price? Probably, the initial price provides the company with a reasonable rate of return. How does the regulator decide on the X factor? Probably, the regulator makes a projection of financial results over the duration of the price cap, and then sets an X factor that will keep the returns within reasonable levels as well as challenge the carrier to reduce its costs. How does anyone judge the success of the price cap? Probably, they look at the profitability of the regulated company. British regulated utilities have earned high levels of profits while operating in monopolistic businesses. Company executives argue that high profits result from excellent management. Critics might contend that the high profits derive from inaccurate projections by regulators and from lack of mechanisms to protect consumers.

Hybrids. Regulators and carriers must deal with uncertainty. Conditions change unexpectedly, making what originally looked like a good deal later look like bad public policy. Utilities, conceivably, could have misled regulators about prospects. Regulators could have made unjustified assumptions when setting up multiyear plans. One can mitigate these problems by voiding regulatory pacts, or by building safeguards into the arrangements. The former strategy breeds distrust of participants who cannot or will not uphold their end of a bargain. The latter strategy prevents the problem from getting out of hand.

Regulators can set up a price-cap plan that works within a rate-of-return formula. The regulator might let the price cap operate freely as long as the return remains within the prescribed range. That arrangement corrects for miscalculations that either let a monopolist earn an excessive return or reduces earnings to a level that threatens the financial stability of the utility.

Clearly, the utilities need plans that do away with cumbersome, counterproductive regulation. But, at the same time, consumers need protection from regulatory mistakes.

OTHER ISSUES

Setting the right return and actually earning it are two different matters. In addition, emphasis on strict adherence to rate of return on the historic cost of the assets could produce results that do not benefit the public. Thus, regulators need to deal with practical issues.

Interim rates. Rate cases take time. Conditions change between rate cases, too. The utility may have to request an interim increase, that is, one that takes effect before the regulatory agency has completed its final decision. The utility might have to agree to refund any interim collections in excess of what the final order allows. Among the triggers for interim rates, Janice A. Beecher lists the "need to maintain cash flow and earnings," the unexpected increase in "costs between rate cases," and the need to find offsetting revenues due to "mandatory and water use restrictions."[54]

Acquisition adjustments. Most observers would agree that too many small, under-capitalized water companies attempt to serve the public. Regulators have encouraged larger utilities to take over the smaller ones. The owners of the small companies, presumably, want to make a profit when they sell out, but that profit, the difference between the original cost of the properties less depreciation (the rate base) and the selling price, creates a problem for the regulated buyer. If the regulator sticks to the old definition of rate base, the buyer cannot earn a return on that part of the price that exceeds the original cost less depreciation (called the "acquisition adjustment" in regulatory parlance). Why should any company make an investment on which it cannot earn a profit? Yet customers would be better off if a larger, better-capitalized, more efficient firm ran the local water utility. In fact, the cost of water service might drop, even if the buyer were allowed to earn a return on the seller's profit. As of 1997, 11 states have explicitly ruled that regulators can allow returns on acquisition adjustments and another 15 provide limited approval for such returns. The Pennsylvania legislature, in 1995, actually made "it a *rebuttable presumption* that the price paid for a system in excess of original cost is reasonable and that the excess *shall be included* in the . . . ratebase . . ."[55] Thus, the regulators bend the rules when strict adherence to them hurts the public.

Phase-in. Sometimes the water utility is adding to its rate base, predictably, over several years. Rather than go through several expensive rate hearings, the utility and the regulators work out a procedure whereby the regulator, in advance, permits the utility to raise prices on a predetermined basis, as it completes each stage of the rate base expansion. In a number of utility rate cases in the past, phase-in served a less benign purpose. The utility had requested a huge one-time rate hike, which produced "rate shock." Whether the request was justified or not, the regulator chose not to grant it all at once, but rather raise prices, in a step-wise fashion, over a period of several years. Sometimes, the regulator allowed the utility to recover, over time, a return on the revenues not collected during the early stages of the phase-in.

Ratios. Sometimes the regulator has to deal with a company that has little or no rate base. If it concludes that the utility, as a result, should earn no income, then the utility will not be able to raise capital, or accumulate any financial cushion. The regulator, then, decides to set rates so that the company produces a profit equivalent to a certain percentage of income, picking the appropriate percentage based upon the ratios of more traditional water companies, for instance.

Overall, regulators try to devise less cumbersome procedures for small water utilities. They may set a generic rate of return, for instance, in order to help small companies that cannot afford to launch a full blown rate case. They may set efficiency targets, and provide rewards for companies that meet the targets. They may speed up cases. Whatever the procedure, they cannot deal with thousands of small companies in the same way as they treat the industry's giants.

CONCLUSION

Despite the legalistic and pseudoscientific nature of the process of determining the proper rate of return, the actual determination remains a mysterious process: a mixture of politics, economics, horsetrading, social and financial theory. Few people—other than practitioners of ratemaking—would miss its passing, in its present form. Yet rate of return—the foundation of the existing system—remains the implicit or explicit sanity check for most of the proposed replacements.

Alternative ratemaking mechanisms should produce incentives for more efficient operations, give the consumers some of the benefits of improved productivity, allow the utility to plan for multiyear periods, avoid time-consuming and expensive rate cases, and, in some instances, give the utility greater pricing flexibility.

Still, one retains the suspicion that these methods are not all they appear to be. Range of return and profit sharing add flexibility and incentive to rate-of-return regulation, but they remain rooted in capital investment. Today, though, many successful businesses carry on their functions with few capital assets. Instead, they assemble the services of others in order to produce a product. Is the utility's asset base overemphasized?

The outcome of the moratorium depends on bargaining power and skills, as well as the foresight to discern what constitutes a good deal. Regulators, accustomed to legal, quasi-judicial proceedings that deal largely with past data, may not have the skills needed to extract a good deal on behalf of consumers from a commercially oriented corporation.

Price-cap regulation seems the most beguiling of the alternatives, but in some ways, it is really closet rate of return regulation, in the sense that regulators consider but do not discuss return on investment.

All regulatory methods have flaws. The newer methods, at least, reduce the expenses of the regulatory process. They give the utility some reason to try to do better. At the same time, they need to be designed to assure that the utility does what it should to fulfill its public service function.

CHAPTER 22

The Economic Allocation of Water Resources

A rate system is primarily governed by practical considerations. If added use costs the consumer more than it costs the company, there is probable failure to develop services which would be worth their cost. If added use costs the consumer less than it costs the company, there is a stimulus to wasteful use.[56]

— J. M. Clark

Water is a commodity. Despite all the ardent rhetoric that often surrounds water and water development, water is an economic good. Yes, man needs to drink water to live, but he does not need irrigated golf courses in the desert to survive. To survive, man needs to ingest a quart to a gallon of water a day, depending on activity levels and the environment. After consuming that first gallon, man can choose to consume or not consume water; he will choose his consumption level by comparing the benefit of buying water with the benefits he could receive from spending money on other goods and services.

Economic principles use price to allocate goods in the most efficient way. Those who are critical of using price to allocate water cannot deny that man's desires are unlimited, yet potable water is not. Because the supply of usable water is limited, water that is consumed for one use is not available for other uses. A gallon of water used to wash a car is no longer available to cook food. If water is given away for free, what incentive is there to use it wisely? Equal allocation of the resource does not always yield the best solution. For example, imagine a society which includes a farmer and an urban homeowner. In this society, each member receives 50 gallons of water a day. The apartment dweller only uses 10 gallons a day, and would welcome an opportunity to make some extra money; the farmer uses his full share and would like to buy 40 more gallons, because he can produce $10.00 more of crops with those 40 gallons. The farmer will pay up to $10.00 for that extra water, because he makes more money by paying any amount up to $10.00 and the apartment dweller is willing to depart with his unused 40 gallons. In this case, economic allocation would make both parties better off, even though distribution was considered "equitable" in the initial case. Economics simply seeks to allocate the water in a way that maximizes society's benefit—and increases the availability of the resources to all.

SUPPLY AND DEMAND

Although water is one of the most common substances on earth and covers 80% of the earth's surface, not all of it is available for human consumption. More than

97% of the water on earth is in the oceans, and another 2% is captured in icecaps and glaciers. This leaves less than 1% of the earth's water supply readily available for human consumption.

The United States contains vast water resources, but the water supply is unevenly distributed. This means that some areas spend little on water resources because they are adjacent to water supplies, such as Chicago, which taps Lake Michigan. Other cities must transport their water from hundreds of miles away, such as is the case for Los Angeles.

Although usable water supply is relatively fixed (more water could be manufactured by combining oxygen and hydrogen from the air, but, as with desalinating sea water, it would be prohibitively expensive) the demand for water is a function of human needs and desires. Desires tend to be unconstrained until the individual faces a limiting factor—usually the amount of money he or she has available to purchase consumable goods. In this respect water is really no different from any good; as prices rise, consumption usually falls.

Water is necessary for survival, but several factors, including price and technology, can impact demand for this resource. Low-flow toilets, for example, use only 1.6 gallons per flush, while older, less-efficient models often use 8 or 9 gallons per flush. By changing technology, individuals can maintain their lifestyle, yet use less water. The most common impetus for people to change their behavior, however, is price.

The fact that price affects behavior points out a failing of noneconomic analyses of water allocation. In predicting the future, analysts rely on past events—on past human behavior. Projections of future water use often are based on extrapolations of past trends without seeking to understand the factors that actually drive the demand. Large water projects have been built simply because it was assumed that growth would continue in the future. Electric companies followed this principle of forecasting in the 1960s and found themselves with too much capacity in the 1970s when energy prices rose as a result of world oil markets, and demand for electricity fell. Although the water industry has not suffered the equivalent of oil embargoes, its emphasis on building new supplies to meet demand, rather than attempting to analyze and control demand, has led to the development of very expensive water projects of questionable economic justification. Water use does vary with price. Studies of elasticity of demand reveal that water use decreases as price increases. (The percentage change in quantity demanded divided by the percentage change in price is known as *elasticity*.)

When the demand for water at a given price is greater than the amount of water that can be supplied at that price, water may be in short supply. However, that situation can be rectified by raising the price of water. At the higher price, demand falls. Additionally, suppliers, who see the potential for greater revenues at the higher price level, will seek out new supplies to capture those revenues.

Figure 22-1 illustrates the classic relationship between supply and demand. The horizontal (x) axis represents the quantity of water demanded and supplied. The vertical (y) axis represents the price for each unit of water sold. The intersection of the demand and the supply curves determines the price that will be charged in the marketplace—the market clearing price. Price is the determining factor here. The demand curve slopes downward: as the price of water falls, consumers desire more water. As noted earlier, water is a basic element of human survival and a consumer will pay a high price for water that sustains life. Beyond that, however, water becomes less important. The consumer will pay less for subsequent units of water, perhaps those used for cooking, washing, and sanitation, because while they aid health, they do not determine immediate survival. Only after the price falls further will he consider filling the bird bath in his backyard.

Figure 22-1

Supply and Demand

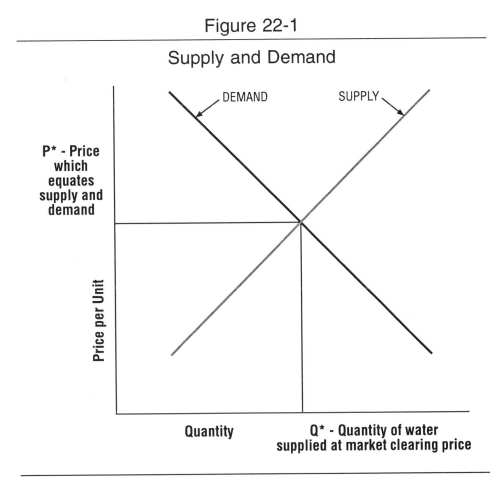

This drop in demand after the satiation of initial needs is known as *diminishing marginal returns*. After the early units of water are consumed, water has less value to the consumer, and he will allocate his next few dollars towards meeting other needs, such as food and clothing. The shape of the demand curve can be understood by way of practical illustration. A very thirsty person walking down the street on a very hot day sees Joe's Water Emporium and walks in for a drink. Joe's Water Emporium charges five cents for a glass of water. The thirsty person desires water so much that he would be willing to pay 15 cents for his first glass of water. Since the value he places on the cup of water is greater than the price that Joe charges him, it makes sense to buy a cup. (When the consumer receives a benefit from consumption that he values more than the price paid, it is a condition known as *consumer surplus*). Drinking the first cup quenches his thirst moderately, but he is still thirsty and wants some more. The second cup will have less value for him and he only would be willing to pay 10 cents for the second cup. After the second cup of water, the consumer is more sated, and values the next cup at only five cents—the price that Joe's Water Emporium charges. Thus, the third cup is the last he consumes. He consumes water up to the point where the satisfaction he gains from drinking the water equals the cost of the water to him—in this case five cents.

The upward sloping supply curve can be explained through further illustration. Imagine a small town that has a well as its only water supply. The well is owned by Joe, who runs Joe's Water Supply, the parent company of Joe's Water Emporium. Since the town has only 100 people, its needs can be met easily by that well. Joe charges consumers one cent per gallon of water. However, as the town grows in population to 500 people, the demand for water increases. Joe begins hauling in water from the pond on the outskirts of town. The cost of providing the water is higher (as he now needs to pay for a horse and cart to haul the water) so Joe needs to charge a higher price—three cents per gallon. This strategy works well for a while, but the town keeps on growing. In the summer the pond level is dropping, and Joe is having trouble meeting demand.

To meet the town's needs, he decides to build a pipeline to tap the river that flows one mile from town. This pipeline will meet the town's demand until the population reaches 10,000 and it will allow people to have running water in their homes—a definite improvement over Joe's equine distribution system. Expanding the supply will cost more than either the well or the pond, but it will be cheaper than building a reservoir. However, Joe will need to borrow money to build his piping and pumping system. In addition to the cost of the new equipment, Joe will also have to pay interest on his loan. Now he will charge five cents per gallon. The cost rises to supply more water, because the cheapest and most easily accessible water supplies are used up first. Only after that are the more costly sources of supply brought into play. Thus as the quantity of water supplied to the town is increased, the cost of supplying that quantity increases, leading to a rising supply curve.

Economic theory underlying pricing allows us to determine the optimal price to allocate water. Based on our discussion it seems that the consumer will get to maximize his satisfaction. He will consume products until the cost to him exceeds the benefit received from consumption. The most economically efficient point of production is where the consumer receives no further net benefit from the consumption of the good, in this case water. The net benefit is the value the consumer receives from consuming the good minus the price of the good. Figure 22-2 illustrates how many units the consumer will demand at a given price. The quantity demanded multiplied by the price per unit represents the revenue a seller could expect, at that given price level.

Figure 22-2

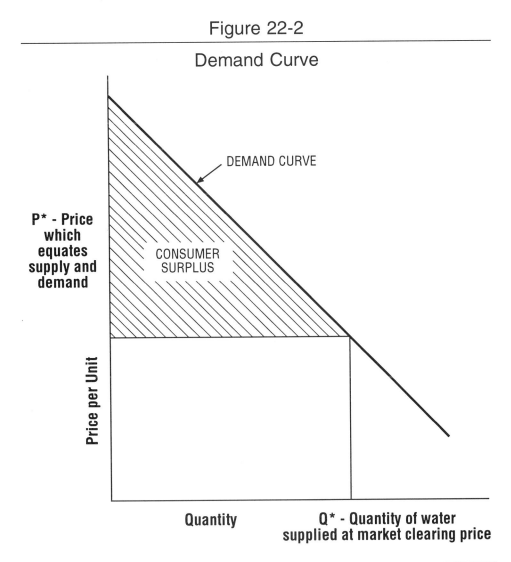

$$\text{Revenue} = \frac{\text{Price}}{\text{Unit}} \times \text{(Units Produced)}$$

A water supplier will project a potential revenue stream from consumers and will seek to produce that supply in such quantity that it will maximize the difference between potential revenues and expenses. This concept is analogous to that of consumer surplus. In this instance, as long as the price that consumers will pay for water is greater than the price the producer is willing to supply it at, it makes sense for the producer to increase his output. This difference is known as *producer surplus*. To maximize his profits, the producer will increase capacity up to the point where the consumer will buy no more. At this point, the price the consumer is willing to pay for an extra unit of water equals the price the producer charges for that extra unit of water. In Figure 22-3, the supply curve shows how much water the supplier will provide at a given price. The supplier demands a higher price for larger quantities because, as mentioned in the discussion of

Figure 22-3

Supply Curve

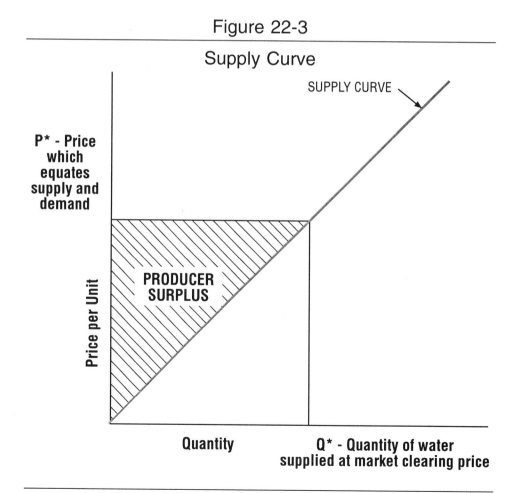

Joe's Water Works, the cheapest water supplies are developed first, to maximize producer surplus.

FIXED VERSUS VARIABLE COSTS

The nature of the total cost curve for supplying water is determined by two types of costs: fixed costs and variable costs, depicted in Figure 22-4. Fixed costs remain level regardless of the output of water.[57] Examples of fixed costs include the land acquired for a reservoir or a water main—those costs remain the same whether 100 or 10,000 gallons of water flow through them. Fixed costs are very high in the water industry, because a large piping distribution system must be built before water can be supplied. Fixed costs are often the largest portion of the total costs of a water distribution system in its early stages of development. Variable costs are a function of the quantity of good produced.

Figure 22-5 looks at the average costs of producing the product. The *Average Cost* is the sum of the *Average Fixed Costs* and the *Average Variable Costs*. In the initial stages of production, average costs tend to fall. Average fixed costs are depicted by the formula:

$$\text{Average Fixed Cost (AFC)} = \frac{\text{Fixed Cost}}{\text{Quantity}}$$

Figure 22-4

Fixed and Variable Costs

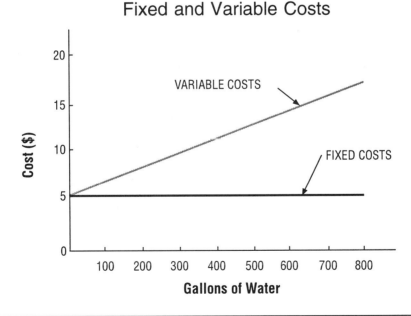

Figure 22-5

Average Costs

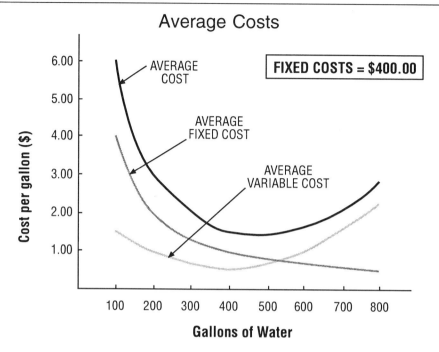

Source:
Ray K. Linsley and Joseph B. Franzini, *Water Resources Engineering*, 2nd ed. (New York: McGraw-Hill Book Company, 1972), p. 166.

Since Fixed Cost is a constant, this is analogous to a mathematical function of the form $y = 1/x$ (if $x > 0$). As fixed costs remain the same, and quantity increases, it is only logical that average fixed costs fall as more of the good is produced.

Average variable costs usually fall for the early units of production, because of economies of scale resulting from increased production. For example, since pumps work most efficiently at a certain speed, it may actually cost less to pump 1,000 gallons per minute than 100 gallons per minute. Or, the water company may be able to cut its treatment costs by purchasing chemicals in bulk. The unit cost for water treatment may then fall as the volume treated increases. Variable costs then fall. However, when an extra pump is required to meet extra demand, or a new treatment plant is required to meet increasing demand, variable costs will rise. Thus, the average variable cost curve tends to have a U–shape. The declining average fixed cost curve always will exert a downward pressure on the average cost curve.

MARGINAL COSTS

Another category of production costs is marginal costs. Marginal cost is the cost of producing one additional unit of production, such as an extra gallon of water. Since fixed costs do not change, marginal costs represent the rate of change of variable costs. Figure 22-6 shows the relation between marginal and average costs. Although marginal and average costs can rise or fall over the range of production, marginal costs will eventually slope upward because of the principle of diminishing marginal returns, as was illustrated in the case of Joe's Water Works. Average cost curves decline when the marginal cost is less than the average cost, because the marginal (additional) unit decreases the average cost. Comparably, average costs increase when marginal costs are greater than average cost, because each additional unit increases the average cost of production. If the average cost does not rise or fall, then marginal cost equals average cost. Table 22-1 provides numeric examples of total costs, average costs, and marginal costs. Figure 22-7 depicts the table graphically.

Table 22-2 provides numeric examples of fixed costs, variable costs, and total costs. Figure 22-8 depicts Table 22-2 graphically.

The most efficient price point, and resulting production level, occurs at the point where the marginal cost curve intersects the demand curve. In Figure 22-9, this occurs at price **P*** and quantity **Q***. Consumers will purchase up to the point where the marginal benefits they receive (as depicted by the demand curve)

Figure 22-6

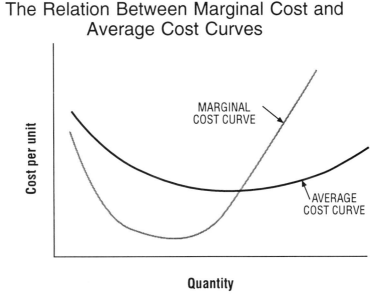

The Relation Between Marginal Cost and Average Cost Curves

Table 22-1

Average and Marginal Costs

Units of Output	Total Costs	Average Costs	Marginal Costs
0	$1.00	—	—
1	1.50	$1.500	$0.50
2	1.90	0.950	0.40
3	2.20	0.733	0.30
4	2.60	0.650	0.40
5	3.10	0.620	0.50
6	3.80	0.633	0.70

Figure 22-7

Average and Marginal Costs

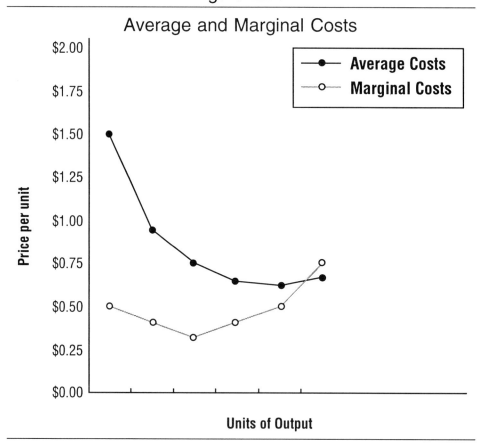

equate the marginal cost curves of the supplier. It does not make sense for the consumer to purchase beyond this point because the cost of consuming each additional unit will exceed the benefit he receives. "Marginal value in use for the products . . . should be set equal to the marginal cost because the costs represent the value consumers and producers place on the resources used up, or the goods

Table 22-2

Types of Cost and Output

Units of Output	Fixed Costs	Variable Costs	Total Costs
0	$5.00	$0.000	$ 5.00
1	5.00	5.000	10.00
2	5.00	2.500	7.50
3	5.00	1.667	6.67
4	5.00	1.250	6.25
5	5.00	1.000	6.00
6	5.00	0.833	5.83

Figure 22-8

Fixed Costs and Variable Costs

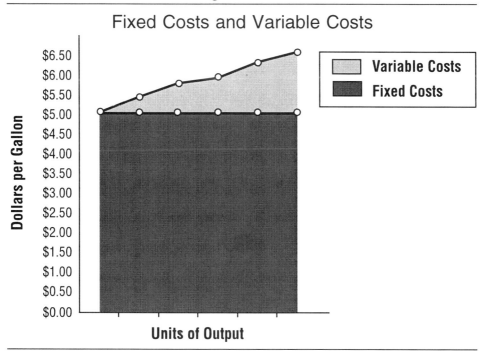

sacrificed elsewhere, in producing one more unit of output in this enterprise."[58] The average cost curve, in Figure 22-9, which plots the average cost of producing each unit of water, is determined by the following formula:

$$\text{Average Cost} = \frac{\text{Cost}}{\text{Quantity}}$$

AVERAGE COST PRICING

Although marginal cost pricing represents the optimal way to distribute water, it is often not priced in that manner. Water companies have often charged water

Figure 22-9

Optimal Production Point

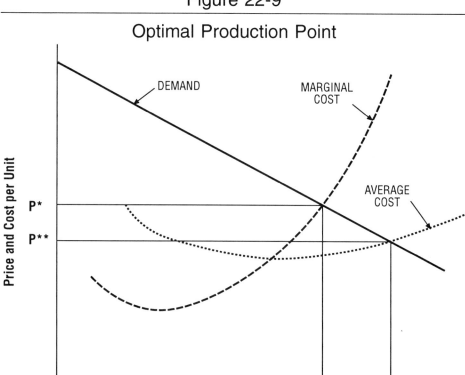

customers the average cost of providing service, including payment of costs of capital. This is not the efficient marginal-cost solution. Consuming at the intersection of the demand and average cost curves **P**** and **Q**** (see Figure 22-9) is not efficient, because each unit supplied beyond the efficient point costs society more to produce than the consumer is willing to pay for the water. Another problem with average cost pricing is that the most expensive customers do not pay their full freight. Their costs are spread among all the users throughout the system and are not borne by those responsible for producing new strains on the water system. Hirshleifer, De Haven, and Milliman in their book *Water Supply: Economics, Technology, and Policy,* present a plan for water utilities to charge marginal costs for water that takes into account the differences in providing services to different customers, something few water systems do.

> The price . . . should be equal to all users (since otherwise employments with higher marginal values in use are being foregone in favor of employments with lower values.) Suppose that at a certain moment of time this price is $30 per unit. Then, if the community as a whole can acquire and transport another unit of water for, say, $20, it would clearly be desirable to do so: in fact, any of the individual customers to whom the unit of water is worth $30 would be

happy to pay the $20 cost, and none of the other members of the community is made worse off thereby. We may say that, on efficiency grounds, additional units should be made available so long as any members of the community are willing to pay the additional or marginal costs incurred. To meet the criterion of equimarginal value in use, however, the price should be made equal for all customers. So the combined rule is to make the price equal to the marginal cost and equal for all customers.

One important practical consideration is that, because of differing locations, use patterns, types of service, etc., the marginal costs of serving different customers will vary. . . . The correct solution is to arrange matters so that for each class of customers (where the classes are so grouped that all customers within any single class can be served under identical cost conditions) the prices should be the same and equal to marginal cost. Between classes, however, prices should differ, and the difference should be precisely the difference in marginal costs involved in serving the two.

Consider . . . two customers, identical in all respects except that one can be served at a marginal cost of $10 per unit and the other at $40—perhaps because the latter has a hilltop location and requires pumped rather than gravity service. If they are both charged $10, the community will be expending $40 in resources to supply a marginal unit which the latter customer values at $10; if they both are charged $40, the former customer would be happy to lay out the $10 it costs to bring him another unit.[59]

Although in this case, the customers are both receiving water, they are not receiving the same commodity. The customer on the hilltop who needs pumped water is demanding a more costly commodity than the customer at the low elevation who is served by gravity flow. Hirshleifer, De Haven and Milliman then conclude with an extremely simple rule for determining how much to charge water customers in order to allocate water efficiently and fairly:

Where water is sold to customers, therefore, the principles we have developed indicate that customers served under identical cost conditions should be charged equal prices and that the commodity should be supplied and priced in such a way that the price for each class of service should equal the marginal cost of serving that class. Where marginal costs differ, therefore, prices should differ similarly.[60]

There is one final consideration relating to average cost pricing. At one time analysts were critical of marginal cost pricing when the marginal cost curve was always less than the average cost curve, a situation known as *declining average costs*. If the utility charged at the marginal cost it could not make any money, and the loss would have to be made up, perhaps by government subsidy, or absorbed by a government-run utility. Although such a situation may have existed in the past, today it is more of a theoretical possibility and does not have much empirical justification in today's market, when sources of new water for urban supply are scarce and very expensive to develop.

PRICING PEAK DEMAND WATER SERVICE

Moving water throughout a system requires energy. In some cases, gravity provides sufficient pressure to deliver supply, but usually pumps are needed within a system to increase pressure. During peak demand periods, more pumping and energy are required. Flattening peaks could lower water supply costs. Water supply systems are built for peak loads, which are often twice the normal level of supply (see Figure 22-10). To meet peak demands, water suppliers have installed pumping capacity and larger pipes, which increase system costs.

Figure 22-10

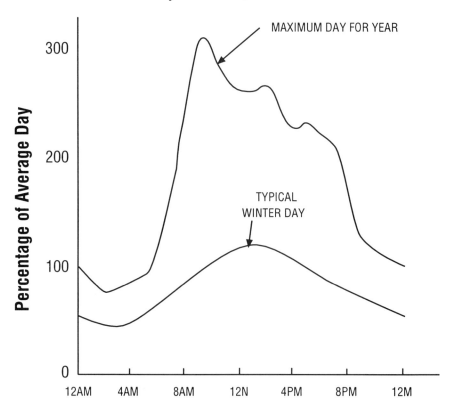

Peak and Average Consumption
Hourly Variation, Palo Alto

Source:
Linsley and Franzini, *Water Resources Engineering*, p. 430.

The quantity of flow through a water system can be described as follows:

Q = AV, where

Q = quantity of water flowing (Volume/time; measured in cubic meters per second (m^3/s)[61]

A = cross-sectional area of pipe (determined by the formula: πr^2, where **r** = the radius of the pipe)

V = velocity of flow (usually measured in meters per second (m/s) or feet per second (ft/s)

The velocity of flow is a function of the energy required from gravity or pumping pressure, to move the water through the system.[62] Inside the water pipe, the friction generated by the movement of the water represents the most important energy loss in a distribution system. This energy loss is proportional to the square of the velocity. Thus, when faced with a requirement to maintain a given flow and pressure, especially for fire fighting, water suppliers tend to prefer to use larger pipes than to increase pumping. Pipe A, with a radius of 12 inches, can carry five cubic feet per second of water with much lower frictional losses than a pipe with a six-inch radius, allowing the water company to provide a given flow and pressure, with less pumping and less energy loss. Overly high pressures are discouraged because these can cause pipes to leak. The larger pipes are necessary to meet peak flows. If peak demand were lower, less capacity would be needed and water would be supplied through narrower, less-expensive pipes with reduced pumping.

Water towers and distribution reservoirs are important parts of the system because water distribution requirements are not evenly distributed throughout the day. Peak demand occurs in the morning and early evening—the same time periods when electric companies experience their peak demand and charge peak prices for that power. Water companies pump water into towers at night when pumping costs are lower in order to take advantage of gravity flow during those times when electric prices are higher. Water towers and distribution reservoirs help smooth out peaks by allowing storage of treated water for peak periods, decreasing the size needed of a treatment plant, or allowing it to be operated for fewer hours during the day.[63]

Fire-fighting requirements also play an important role in design of the water systems. In fact, according to the American Water Works Association, "The determining factor in sizing mains, storage facilities, and pumping facilities for communities with a population less than 50,000 is usually the need for fire protection."[64] Fire insurance rates in a community are based upon the ratings, by the insurance industry, of a community's fire fighting capability through the Insurance Services

Office, that took over the work of the National Bureau of Fire Underwriters. Part of that rating is based on the community's water system, and its capacity to provide a minimum flow of water for a certain period of time. (See Table 22-3.) Although fires are usually infrequent, and do not last long, during a fire the rate of water use can be very high. The need to meet this infrequent demand requires the water company to build a system with far greater capacity than will normally be used. Often 50% of the capacity of the water storage system exists to handle fire fighting needs. When a company builds its system for maximum fire fighting potential, all water consumers pay to benefit those who have fire insurance. A private company would not necessarily have an incentive to overbuild capacity in this way. It really has little interest, monetarily, in the fire-fighting capacity of its system—unless under its franchise agreement it must prepare a water system that meets certain fire fighting standards. Municipal water agencies, which are usually government agencies, may see providing adequate fire fighting potential as a public service.

The yearly peak occurs during the summer, resulting primarily from lawn watering. Lawn watering drives a need for capacity that is often twice that of average

Table 22-3

Fire-flow Capacity Recommended by National Board of Fire Underwriters*

Population	Fire flow (gpm)	Duration (hrs)
1,000	1,000	4
2,000	1,500	6
3,000	1,750	7
4,000	2,000	8
5,000	2,250	9
6,000	2,500	10
10,000	3,000	10
20,000	4,350	10
40,000	6,000	10
60,000	7,000	10
80,000	8,000	10
100,000	9,000	10
150,000	11,000	10
200,000	12,000	10

*"Standard Schedule for Grading Cities and Towns of the United States with Reference to Their Fire Defenses and Physical Conditions," National Board of Fire Underwriters, New York, 1956.
gpm = gallons per minute

Source:
Linsley and Franzini, *Water Resources Engineering*, p. 431.

usage. In fact, "maximum day and peak-hour (plus fire flow) parameters account for some 85% of municipal water system costs."[65] Clearly, smoothing out peak usage could significantly reduce the costs of water systems. Charges based on the potential strain a user could place on the system have been suggested:

> ... the [water] company must provide some excess capacity over the actual average demand it can anticipate. A buyer who has a large connection can then reasonably be expected to pay more in total than a buyer with a small connection, even though both may in a given period actually purchase the same amount. Both have what is in the nature of an option on the water company, but the former has an option for a larger amount than the individual with a small-capacity connection. From the company's point of view the long-run cost of these options is the reserve capacity it holds in readiness to serve. The appropriate charge for this option or for the reservation of this capacity is the cost of providing a fractional marginal unit of capacity, the fraction being based on the system's reserve factor. For example, if the company's practice is to hold in readiness system capacity equal to 50 per cent of the extreme limit of possible maximum demand (all taps wide open), then the appropriate charge for each unit of maximum potential demand (the fixed "demand charge") is the marginal cost of one-half unit of system capacity. The cost is evidently one that is proportional to time and should reasonably be charged as a fixed item in the monthly bill. The additional capacity may, of course, be provided either by better maintenance or new construction.[66]

Some water systems apply variations of these charges by charging a fee, regardless of volume of water used, that is based on the size of the pipe, but there does not seem to be a systematic application of these ideas. Even in the best case, these service fees are crude methods for smoothing peaks, because once a pipe is installed, these fees do not discourage a user from consuming during peak periods. Peaks could be shaved more effectively by using responsive pricing, which is "that pricing schedule that temporally reflects system costs and prices from which the consumer can make his decision to use the commodity at the respective time of usage."[67] The implementation of this solution lies in advanced metering technology and in providing a remote register at the consumer's home or place of business. Such technology would let consumers know how much they are being charged, so they may adjust their water use at times of strain on the water system:

> This remote register would indicate the price level of water in relative or absolute terms at any particular instant. This would allow consumers, with full knowledge of the rates at their prospective time of usage, to sprinkle at incentive prices (e.g., during early morning hours). Also during emergencies such as fires the consumer can be made aware of system requirements and thus comply with high disincentive prices for water use. This system would serve to maintain needed water pressure for fire fighters. At first, reiteration of the pricing schedules using different rate levels could be used to arrive at the load factor that is most efficient from an operating and capital cost viewpoint. Since system peak could be shaved and troughs filled in, average rate levels would be lowered.[68]

OTHER PRICE DETERMINANTS

Spatial factors also influence the economics of water supply, but they are not always accounted for in the pricing system. It costs less to supply customers, especially new customers, in an area with a built-up distribution system. Urban areas have large distribution systems of mains, and it is cheaper to tap into a new supply in a dense area than to build a new line into a low-density housing development. Yet, in many cases hookup fees for new customers do not reflect those cost variations. As a result, customers in urban areas often subsidize the water services of those in less-dense areas. Theoretically, hookup fees should reflect the marginal cost of adding a new user by cost of service class. For example, a new customer in an elevated area that will require pumping should have a higher hookup fee than a customer located in a valley where water flows by gravity. Darr, Feldman, and Kamen further point out that spatial factors not only affect hookup charges, but:

> . . . capital intensity is centered upon the distribution and transmission aspects of the systems' components accounting for 50 to 75% of total costs. Variations in these costs represent the greatest variations between service areas. Empirical evidence verifies this. Using Milwaukee as an example, Hines (1969) has shown that long-run average costs for water supply are lower in the city than for surrounding communities.[69]

On the policy front, these spatial pricing policies may influence planning in areas with regional water systems, illustrating how urban areas may be subsidizing suburban development through water rates.

How are pricing policies designed to promote efficient allocation of water applied by water utilities? Table 22-4 lists the Monthly Rates for Water and Sewer Services for the City of Santa Barbara in California. (Additional tariffs are listed in Appendix I.) This tariff schedule illustrates how Santa Barbara values the water it distributes, and how economic efficiency is sacrificed for other policy goals. Under the city's water service rates, residential dwellings are charged an increasing rate as the residence's consumption increases. This price schedule reflects the fact that the marginal cost of water increases as consumption increases in Santa Barbara. If water supplies for the city diminish, Santa Barbara can turn on its distillation plant, but this is the most expensive source of water the city has. During wet years the plant is not used, because of its cost. The city's commercial and industrial rates are also increasing block rates, although they start at a higher price level than the residential rate. Irrigation users are charged less than residential users for equivalent amounts of water. The price of providing the water is not much different for irrigating a field than the house next door. Yet Santa Barbara, through its pricing, has suggested that irrigators deserve a break on water rates. What this indicates is that without these special rates, irrigation would not be as widespread, and the city considers the water that is used for irrigation as a lower valued commodity. Residential users would be willing to pay a higher price for some of that water, implying that more water is allocated to irrigation than is

Table 22-4

City of Santa Barbara
Monthly Rates for Water and Sewer Service

Customer Class	Water Service Rates (Water is measured in units of one hundred cubic feet (hcf). One hcf equals 748 gallons. Allotments are monthly, except as indicated. See table below for monthly service charges, which are based on meter size and are in addition to metered water charges.)	Sewer Service Rates (Non-residential accounts are subject to a minimum monthly charge by meter size as shown in the table below.)
Single Family Residential	First 4 hcf @ $2.10 Next 16 hcf @ $3.50 All other @ $3.70	$7.16 per month; plus $1.24 per hcf up to 10 hcf
Multi-Family Residential, 1-4 dwelling units	First 4 hcf per dwelling unit @ $2.10 Next 8 hcf per dwellng @ $3.50 All other @ $3.70	$7.16 per month per dwelling unit; plus $1.24 per hcf up to 8 hcf per dwelling unit
Multi-Family Residential, 5+ dwelling units	First 4 hcf per dwelling unit @ $2.10 Next 8 hcf per dwelling @ $3.50 All other @ $3.70	$7.16 per month per dwelling unit; plus $1.24 per hcf up to 7 hcf per dwelling unit
Commercial	100% of base allotment @ $3.50 All other @ $3.70	$1.41 per hcf; subject to minimum charge based on meter size (see below)
Industrial	100% of base allotment @ $3.50 All other @ $3.70	$1.71 per hcf; subject to minimum charge based on meter size (see below)
Irrigation, Residential	Billed as if used through associated residential meter(s); OR Annual allotment of 654 hcf/acre @ $3.50, with all other @ $3.70	Not applicable
Irrigation, Recreation/ Parks/Schools	Annual allotment of 1,404 hcf/acre @ $1.65 Next 240 hcf/acre/year @ $3.50 All other @ $3.70	Not applicable
Irrigation, Commercial	100% of base allotment @ $3.50 All other @ $3.70	Not applicable
Irrigation, Agriculture	Annual allotment of 870 hcf/acre @ $1.32 Next 240 hcf/acre/year @ $3.50 All other @ $3.70	Not applicable
Recycled Water	All usage @ $1.32/hcf	Charges based on type of use. Not applicable for irrigation.
Outside City Limits	130% of corresponding in-City rates	Same as in-City rates, except that residential accounts not receiving City water are charged at maximum rate.

Monthly Service Charges for Water Meters by Size

Meter Size:	5/8″	3/4″	1″	1.5″	2″	3″	4″	6″	8″	10″
Monthly Service Charge	$5.50	$5.50	$13.75	$27.50	$44.00	$88.00	$137.50	$275.00	$440.00	$632.50

Minimum Monthly Sewer Charges by Meter Size for Non-Residential Customers

Meter Size:	5/8″	3/4″	1″	1.5″	2″	3″	4″	6″	8″	10″
Commercial	$13.48	$13.48	$23.52	$40.36	$67.31	$134.56	$168.00	$336.40	$588.71	$925.12
Industrial	$16.80	$16.80	$29.44	$50.37	$84.11	$168.18	$210.28	$420.49	$735.84	$1,156.39

Source: City of Santa Barbara Web site, http://ci.santa-barbara.ca.us/wresourc/bfrate.htm

economically efficient. Santa Barbara also provides recycled water for some uses. That rate is lower than the typical residential rate. This rate may be designed to encourage use of recycled water, or it may indicate that consumers are less willing to pay for recycled water.

Although Santa Barbara has a fairly progressive pricing system that is designed to promote efficient use, the tariff could benefit from two changes. The first would be the addition of a summer peak charge. Summers in Santa Barbara are notoriously dry, which means that the water system faces its highest demands, especially for lawn watering, during the summer months. A peak charge would provide an incentive to reduce summer usage, with less distribution capacity needed. The second change would be to acknowledge Santa Barbara's hilly topography, and the fact that groundwater is a significant portion of its water supply in dry years. It costs more to pump that water up to the higher elevations than to provide it to low-lying coastal areas. Yet, Santa Barbara does not vary its rates based on pumping costs.

The number one use of water in the United States is agricultural irrigation. Roughly 40% of all water withdrawals in the United States are for irrigated agriculture. Excluding the use of water for electric generation (because once used, it flows back to its source), irrigation accounts for 60% of all uses of the United States' water supply. In some areas of the western United States, over 90% of water withdrawals are for irrigated agriculture.

There are several different methods of agricultural irrigation. In the U.S., surface irrigation comprises over 50% of all irrigation volume. Surface irrigation consists of flooding fields and channeling the water into furrows that hold the plants. This is the most water-intensive method of irrigation. Another principle method is sprinkler irrigation, whereby large sprinklers irrigate plots that are usually circular. This method tends to produce more evaporation from the spray and wet foliage surfaces than other irrigation methods. Sprinkler irrigation is less water-intensive than surface irrigation. The most water-efficient method of irrigation is micro-irrigation, which originated in Israel. This method uses tubes with holes that apply water to the roots of plants. It has high capital costs relative to the other methods and is only implemented when water prices rise high enough to make the other irrigation methods uneconomical. However, government subsidies of water projects have kept water prices for agricultural use well below market levels, which has hampered efforts to introduce less-water-intensive methods of irrigation. Water delivered by the Bureau of Reclamation is subsidized by hydroelectric plants and taxes. This subsidy leads to underpricing of water relative to its market value (if it could be sold in a free market) in many regions of the U.S. The way water is used in the Western U.S. best illustrates the impact of these subsidies: Water is transported across the Imperial Valley in the California Desert, one of the hottest, driest parts of the U.S. in open, unlined canals. Water is lost through seepage into the sandy soil and evaporation in a dry, hot atmosphere.

Plant needs for irrigation vary throughout the growing season. This would imply that farmers do not need their water allocations at all times of the year. Under Western water law, irrigators must use their water allocations for beneficial purposes (growing crops) and must return to the supply source water they do not use. Water can only be stored in soil for a limited time. Therefore, outside of the growing season, it does not make sense for farmers to "sit" on their water supplies, when they could easily sell that water to cities that are willing to pay for it. That, however, is not allowed at this time.

Urban interests in the West have traditionally relied upon creation of new water sources for their exclusive use when they are faced with growing demand. Urban water users are willing to pay higher prices than agricultural users, yet agricultural usage commands about 85% of the demand for Western water. Market principles would argue for reallocation of water. (As mentioned in Chapter 13, market principles have not figured prominently in Western water development.) When faced with increasing need for water, urban interests have the options of controlling demand, through pricing increases (since they can predict changes in demand based on estimates of price elasticity of demand for water) or the development of new supplies. One option vis a vis new supplies is to buy up agricultural water and transfer it to urban uses. Other options also exist:

1) Install lining in agricultural canals and purchase what otherwise would have seeped away.

2) Farmers may choose to have less-than-optimal crop development, because their profits are higher by selling water in addition to crops.

3) Farmers may change their methods of applying water, achieving the same level of crop production with less water use. (There is incentive to practice water saving methods if there is potential for a greater profit from both selling water and growing crops with less water.)

ECONOMICS OF WATER TREATMENT

Water treatment plants are built to accommodate peak flows. They need enough capacity to process potable water, especially for those peak summer days of lawn watering. Consequently, treatment plants are overbuilt in comparison to average use. Most are built to handle a peak demand that exists for possibly three months a year (see Figure 22-11). This raises an interesting economic question: could water treatment plants be built more economically if some of the water to meet that peak was not treated, or not so heavily treated? It is not necessary to have 100% potable, fluoridated, chlorinated water to water a golf course. In an era of increasing clean water standards, water suppliers may be able to cut the cost of treating water by treating less water. The costs of protecting a watershed should be compared against the costs of treatment. It may be cheaper to commit more

Figure 22-11

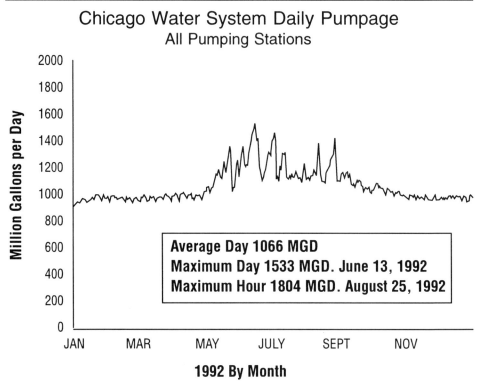

Chicago Water System Daily Pumpage
All Pumping Stations

Average Day 1066 MGD
Maximum Day 1533 MGD. June 13, 1992
Maximum Hour 1804 MGD. August 25, 1992

1992 By Month

Source:
Operating Statistics, Chicago Water System, *1992 Annual Report*.

resources to watershed protection, or to seek out cleaner water sources, than to intensify treatment.

Another option is to supply more water that is not so heavily treated. As mentioned earlier, many outdoor uses do not require potable water, or at least drinkable water, although water used on food crops should be relatively free of harmful organisms. In Israel reclaimed sewage water is used to irrigate agriculture, and is considered pure enough for emergency drinking uses. The distribution of water of varying quality will be more feasible in areas that are installing new pipelines and are able to separate water pipes from the start. In a large city, considerable expense would be incurred to rip up streets to install non-potable water pipes. In areas of high water costs, however, it might make sense to provide large water users with nonpotable water, relieving strain on a treatment plant. (This concept is also discussed in the appendix on conservation.) Nonpotable water would be sold at a lower price because it would cost less to produce. This lower charge might attract large industrial facilities, agricultural customers, and golf course developers as they might find it cheaper to help provide the infrastructure to carry nonpotable water than to pay the marginal costs of expanding a water treatment plant.

HOW DEMAND AFFECTS THE DESIGN OF DISTRIBUTION AND SUPPLY SYSTEMS

When topography allows, water systems are planned to use gravity as the main source of water pressure. Systems are designed to maximize the possibilities to use height differences to promote flow. However, in some areas pumping is necessary. The city of Chicago, for example, draws its water from Lake Michigan, and pumps it to higher altitudes. Water tanks are used to provide gravity flow and ensure sufficient pressure in a system. It is cheaper to pump the water at night than to pay for electric pumping during peak daytime hours. Many water towers were built in earlier days when pumps tended to send pulses of water throughout a distribution system and provided an uneven water flow. Water towers were used to smooth out flows through the system, as the reservoirs within those tanks were large enough to smooth out the pressure variations. Table 22-5 and Figure 22-12 show how storage even reduces pumping needs.

River flows are uneven and cannot always be relied upon to provide adequate water flows for water use (see Table 22-6). River flows vary throughout the year, depending upon climatic region, and there is the possibility that peak river flow may not match the demand for water. River flows also vary from year to year. Storing water during high-flow years, in a reservoir, for use during low-flow years, rather than letting it run downstream, can help assure an adequate supply in dry years. Decisions about reservoir size are made on the basis of estimates of demand. The supply alternatives are evaluated using cost-benefit analysis.

Cost-Benefit Analysis is a method of analyzing the economic efficiency of difference policy options that is often used by the public sector, because the public sector does not seek to maximize profits. Cost-benefit analysis seeks to measure the economic benefits that would arise from building a certain water project and to compare the costs involved in construction of the project. This method is often used by the federal government to justify infrastructure investments. The usual procedure is to discount at a specified interest rate the projected benefits and costs of the project over the lifetime of the project. Those projects for which benefits exceed costs are viewed as an efficient investment. When comparing more than one project it is best to subtract costs from benefits and the most desirable project is the one with the greatest monetary benefits. Some projects compare the ratios of benefits to costs. This is problematic because some projects with larger ratios of benefits to costs may have smaller economic benefits in monetary terms, when costs are subtracted from benefits.

Table 22-5

How a Distribution Reservoir Reduces Pumping Requirements

Hour ending	Demand	Pumping rate	Required from reservoir
0100	0.52	1.00	0
0200	0.46	1.00	0
0300	0.43	1.00	0
0400	0.41	1.00	0
0500	0.43	1.00	0
0600	0.51	1.00	0
0700	0.61	1.00	0
0800	0.91	1.00	0
0900	1.18	1.00	0.18
1000	1.26	1.00	0.26
1100	1.28	1.00	0.28
1200	1.26	1.00	0.26
1300	1.24	1.00	0.24
1400	1.22	1.00	0.22
1500	1.22	1.00	0.22
1600	1.21	1.00	0.21
1700	1.23	1.00	0.23
1800	1.28	1.00	0.28
1900	1.35	1.00	0.35
2000	1.40	1.00	0.40
2100	1.39	1.00	0.39
2200	1.33	1.00	0.33
2300	1.17	1.00	0.17
2400	0.70	1.00	0
Total	24.00	24.00	4.02

Note:

All flow rates in million gallons per hour.

The average pumping rate is determined by dividing the total pumped by 24. The required capacity is the sum of the hourly requirements from storage, or 4.02 million gallons.

Groundwater is not easy to allocate among consumers. The water may be extracted from the ground by users at no charge. The only economic constraint is the cost of pumping operations. As more people draw from an aquifer the water level falls, thereby increasing pumping costs. However, extractors have no incentive to slow well drawdown. Many solutions have been proposed, from government regulation to social benefit taxes to assigning property rights. Brazilians have proposed a solution: since water is a public resource, charge for it. This would allow the government to set a price that could reflect the water's value, increasing the efficiency of distribution. Their idea, however, has not yet been put into practice.

Figure 22-12

Using Distribution Reservoirs and Water Towers to Reduce Pumping and Treatment Plant Capacity

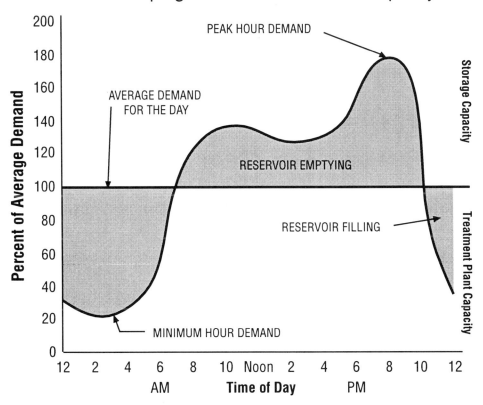

Source:
American Water Works Association, *Introduction to Water Distribution: Principles and Practices of Water Supply Operations*, p. 298.

CONCLUSION

Economic principles offer some guidelines on how to distribute water efficiently. If man values water as a resource or commodity, he can express that value in his willingness to pay for it. Remembering that man needs only a gallon of water a day to survive, it is apparent that although water is necessary to survive, water is an economic good and efficient allocations of supply is not only desirable, but possible.

Table 22-6

Water Storage
(Acre-Feet)

Month	River Volume	Demand	Deficit (−) Surplus (+)	Comulative Reservoir Volume
January	100	20	+80	80
February	100	20	+80	160
March	100	20	+80	240
April	75	75	0	240
May	75	75	0	240
June	50	90	−40	200
July	50	125	−75	125
August	50	125	−75	50
September	75	100	−25	75
October	75	50	+25	125
November	100	25	+75	150
December	100	25	+75	175

This table shows how water can be stored during dry periods for use in wet seasons.

CHAPTER 23

Water Rights and Water Trading

How many economists does it take to change a light bulb? None. The market will do it for them.[70]

— Funny Economist Humor

Marketing and trading have developed quickly in the restructured electric and gas industries. Even in the water supply industry, which generally retains a regulated structure, water marketing and trading have begun to offer market-oriented solutions to what once seemed intractable political disputes. Publicly traded corporations, as well as private investor groups and companies outside the fold of the regulated water distribution utility, have entered the business to exploit and capitalize on market inefficiencies. Huge government-owned utilities and federal bureaucracies are beginning to turn to market-oriented processes to solve the problems of supply and demand. The federal government sees this market as a means of dealing with water shortages in the west. The states and municipalities of the Colorado River Basin are working together to introduce private transactions into the industry.

THE EVOLVING "WATER RIGHTS" INDUSTRY

Generally speaking, the capital markets are a powerful force. The economics behind the laws of supply and demand, although they can be temporarily adjusted or altered, will typically stand the test of time and drive people or entities to behave in a rational fashion. These forces of supply and demand, and the efficient allocation of natural resources, can unleash powerful economic, political, environmental, and emotional reactions. In the western half of the United States, these economic forces are increasingly straining against powerful political bureaucracies over the allocation, transportation, and pricing of one of the most important natural resources available: water.

In the western portion of the United States (west of the 100th meridian), water is represented by real property rights, as opposed to the riparian doctrines practiced in the eastern portions of the United States. These property rights are known as "water rights," and are based on a specific set of pre-Constitutional legal doctrines. Complicating matters, water rights have been classified into many different categories, including senior and junior rights, ditch rights, agricultural rights, and consumptive rights (which may be further broken down between indoor consumptive and outdoor consumptive rights). These categories date back to the late 1800s. Luckily, water volumes can be easily measured and quantified, whether in a flowing river, a lake, reservoir, or an underground aquifer. Otherwise, nobody would be able to sort out the various claims to the water.

For years, the West and Southwest prospered and grew because supplies of water were more abundant than the demands of the population, which first settled areas where the water supplies were adequate and were provided naturally. As the population grew, however, people began to settle in more remote areas, including the desert. By manipulating the flows of water, westerners transformed desert wasteland into thriving cities and plentiful farms. Eventually, however, the demands for water began to exhaust the natural supply. Where an artesian well in Southern California once geysered water like the famous oil wells of Texas, pumps are now required to lift the water to the surface. Indeed, the amazing growth of Southern California and the southwestern portions of the United States depleted, in approximately one generation, the natural underground aquifers that were created over many years.

The issue facing the populations in these regions is that most water supplies have already reached a point of exhaustion, and many municipalities are finding it increasingly difficult to secure long-term supplies to satisfy their populations' need. This is a serious problem. Water is a finite resource, which simply recycles itself naturally through the hydrologic cycle. More importantly, there are no substitutes for water, as there are for electricity, healthcare, and transportation.

BACKGROUND PRIMER

Western water bureaucracies—either state or federal—typically control the supply of the region's allocated water. Numerous dams were built in the 1940s and 1950s for the primary purposes of irrigation and flood control. Farmers were allocated federal water supplies at very attractive rates. The theory was that the cost of agricultural produce would also be minimized. Many of these same agencies, today, continue to artificially subsidize the price of water for agricultural purposes. Consequently, prices are too high for municipalities that want drinking water and too low for farmers and irrigation cooperatives—many of whom are growing low-value crops in the areas that they are farming. The importance of the subsidy to agricultural users cannot be minimized. Farmers have title to the property (the water) and have legal rights providing for their water usage. The fact that water supply is mispriced is not their concern. They can control their methods of irrigation and farming in order to save water. However, if farmers were to embark on this path, they would expect to be compensated for their trouble. That compensation comes in the form of private—and often enormously profitable—water sales.

In an effort to avoid artificial price schemes and realize a "market" value for the water, private companies and investor groups are turning to market-based transactions, in which farmers or other entities sell or lease their water allocation (their water rights) to municipalities or other end users. The math is simple. At present, the government subsidizes the agricultural industry, in part through the allocation of "free" water to grow crops. Inhabitants of municipalities use or eat the crops, which, admittedly, have a low cost. When a farmer changes his farming procedures to minimize water usage and to produce excess water for sale to others, why not sell that excess (at a profit) to municipalities? For that matter, if the farmer is growing low-value crops such as soybeans, why not end the farming altogether, and just sell the water allocation to thirsty city dwellers at big profits? Some are outraged at the extraordinary profit potential these farmers could receive for their surplus water supplies. Others argue that, under the doctrine of "use it or lose it," these surplus water rights of the farmer's must pass on to the next user or get placed back into the water basin. Farmers claim that it is their water to use, and creating a surplus makes it their profit to capture. The real question for city dwellers, though, should be whether city dwellers end up better off by purchasing water from farmers (who make a big profit on the transaction) or by seeking other sources of water, such as desalination.

Hidden water subsidies, however, produce other "hidden" taxes, such as tax dollars needed to pay for extremely expensive water reclamation projects. Many governments are finding that this may not be the most cost-effective use of the natural resource. For example, although higher agricultural prices raise the cost of living for a municipality, a secure, long-term supply of water provides incrementally more benefits in the form of job creation and regional attractiveness for the tax base. Farmers, on the other hand, are not too keen on relinquishing their water rights, which are viewed as valuable assets without proper compensation. Farmers are willing, though, to change their methods of farming in order to conserve the water and subsequently supply it to other end users.

In addition to the imbalance between supply and demand, there is an even more important issue that is associated with the geographic location of the water. Basically, some regions receive more rainfall than others or are natural storage basins due to the geology of the landscape. This obvious fact needs some development, because it has major implications for water marketing and water transfers. Major cities, such as Phoenix, Arizona, cannot exist without a secure supply of water. Consequently, huge aqueducts need to be constructed to transport the water to the city. These water pipelines travel enormous distances across the desert, and much of the water is lost to evaporation. Indeed, Lake Mead, which is a primary water source for Las Vegas, and the other Colorado River reservoirs evaporate approximately two million acre feet (651.7 billion gallons) of water a year, which is almost 15% of the Colorado's average flows.[71] So the question becomes, who creates water supply transactions to meet an increasing municipal need—public or private entities?

WATER MARKETING

The free-market exchange of water rights is called water marketing. Water marketing is the means by which developers will secure a supply of water for a golf resort or residential neighborhood. A secure, long-term supply of water enables a municipality in Southern California, Arizona, Nevada, Colorado, or New Mexico to project its financial and tax planning needs and to plan for future growth and development. Likewise, a free market for water will encourage a farmer to conserve, alter, store or "bank" his water supplies in order to take advantage of price disparities that create profit opportunities in the market. Despite these many advantages, the water transfer procedure remains complex and controversial for many reasons. One of the most difficult problems is to achieve cooperation between many special interest groups that share little, if any, common ground. It is an old fight between the farmers, environmentalists, and city slickers. Another issue is the sheer complexity of western water doctrine. Many of these laws rest on the "use-it or lose-it" concept, and restrictions revolve around the issues of who can claim "saved" or "conserved" water under salvaged water rules. Finally, there are the physical constraints surrounding the ability to transfer water from one delivery point to another.

The flows of electricity, natural gas, and water all require significant capital expenditures for transportation infrastructure, but only water production and usage is so constrained by geographical location. Electricity and gas are easily transported in and out of regions. Delivery hubs are well established. Except for the extraordinary event, supply always matches demand. Energy may take a circuitous route from producer to consumer. The water supplier, on the other hand, requires direct physical conduits from basin to basin, in order to transfer water. Water suppliers cannot deliver water from Lake Mead to Los Angeles via Colorado, Idaho, and Oregon in the same way that an electricity generator can send energy from Hoover Dam via a circuitous route to Los Angeles.

WHAT GETS TRADED?

So, how does water actually get traded? How does a thousand acre-feet of water move from one underground aquifer near a mountain range to a small municipality on the beach a hundred miles away? Technically speaking, westerners do not trade "water" the way a 12-year old trades baseball cards. The process works more like the way investors trade shares of stock, whereby ownership interests are represented by a percentage of the total, and monitored by large computer systems. With water, the *property rights* get traded. Generally speaking, a farmer can buy, sell, or swap certain water rights in exchange for other water rights, or cash, or crops, or feedstock. The water marketing and trading industry, still in its infancy, is not dissimilar to the emerging electric marketing and trading industry. It has a commodity-like product, water, which is easily measurable. It is readily transferable, assuming a transmission network has capacity to transfer the product. It has tremendous price volatility associated with the time of day, or time of year. It is needed and the demand is basically inelastic. Unlike electricity, however, water can be stored or "banked." The point is, there is no reason why water should not be trading freely within our capitalist system.

Water rights are traded in many creative and innovative ways. Farmers have been trading water among themselves for many years, creating active private markets. In California, the Westlands Water District established an electronic bulletin board several years ago, enabling farmers to buy and sell annual entitlements to federal water in an effort to expedite transfers and adjust to volatile weather patterns. In addition, developers have turned to private entities to secure long-term supplies of water for recreational resorts of residential markets. In some sections of the country, for example, a resident cannot secure a building permit for a home unless he can demonstrate that he has a 100-year supply of water. Imagine the incentive these types of rules provide for entrepreneurial farmers, or other private entities, to meet the demand for water around the booming growth areas of southern Nevada or the Colorado Front Range.

Water transactions typically involve complex contractual arrangements of scheduled water deliveries. They are not unlike electric contracts. Contractual arrangements include scheduled price increases, escalation clauses, and credit protection. Water must meet specific quality standards. Contract terms are dependent on time of delivery, seasons, firm or interruptible status, and are subject to the physical constraints of transportation from delivery point to delivery point. In addition, some contractual arrangements may take place years before the water is ever scheduled to be delivered. For example, in 1985, the City of Mesa, Arizona, purchased 11,000 acres of agricultural lands with irrigation rights to pump water from the property, which it does not intend to use until the year 2005. In the meantime, Mesa leases the land to farmers at a rental that covers its carrying costs.

Water banks also are emerging as another important tool for facilitating water transfers between private and municipal users. These water "banks" are generally operated by a government entity and serve as independent intermediaries between buyers and sellers. However, many municipal districts and other private entities with attractive geological formations are providing the ability to "bank" water. In water "banking," water users with excess supplies deposit some or all of their water rights into a "bank" for storage or rental by third parties. The bank sets a price, and establishes the timing and eligibility of rights for withdrawals and injections by recipients. Water banks offer many advantages to market participants. They certainly make trading easier by standardizing the trading and regulatory processes. Historically, water banks have been political entities that had limited-profit or nonprofit status.

Private entities have started to energize a private, third-party water banking market away from big government agencies. For example, the Cadiz Land Company, in addition to owning agricultural land in California, owns land (and the water rights) covering an underground aquifer in the Mojave Desert. This land is very close to a major aqueduct that supplies Southern California. The company is building a pipeline to connect its aquifer to the Colorado River aqueduct and plans to transfer and "bank" water for end users. In essence, during wet, rainy seasons, customers can inject their surplus water into the Cadiz aquifer, which they can withdraw during periods of drought. Cadiz would charge rental fees for the storage and transaction fees for the injection and withdrawal.

Separately, the Catellus Development Corporation, in early 1998, announced that it was in talks with Coachella Valley Water District and the Metropolitan Water District of Southern California to provide dry-year water. The Metropolitan Water District said it would enter into preliminary agreements with Catellus and Coachella, to explore the feasibility of several water-supply projects. The program with Catellus could provide water storage for up to 600,000 acre-feet in groundwater basins underlying Catellus' property in the Mojave Desert. During dry spells and droughts, up to 150,000 acre-feet could be drawn annually from the basin for use throughout urban Southern California. Coachella's water district and the Metropolitan Water District will study desalinating the Whitewater River, which drains agricultural-irrigation water to the Salton Sea, as a new source of water supply. The agencies also will investigate the potential for storing water in groundwater basins underlying the upper and lower Coachella valleys.

In Southern California, many coastal municipalities and cooperatives have found that their aquifers provide an excellent hedge against the activities of the Metropolitan Water District (MWD). The MWD is an independent government agency that is exempt from normal regulation. In addition, and potentially more importantly, these natural formations provide a barrier to the "leaching" of salt water from the Pacific Ocean into a region's fresh water supply. This barrier represents a tremendously valuable barricade for many farmers and water distribution utilities.

The biggest activity in water transfers and marketing is taking place between the farming and urban communities. This is a function of the western adage that "There is no shortage of water, there is only a shortage of water rights" (that is, for use by cities). Basically, the water of the western Colorado River Basin states is misappropriated, or misallocated among its users. Because the agricultural community is allocated a disproportionate share of the region's water rights, at rates massively subsidized by the government, there is less water (fewer water rights) available for municipal uses. The result, not surprisingly, is a price-subsidized water market controlled by government agencies. The crops being grown in California, such as alfalfa, peanuts, and cotton, are all extremely high users of water. It is no wonder that there is not enough water to maintain municipal growth and development at reasonable costs. Unfortunately, these same high-water-volume crops command extremely low cash values. A free-marketer would utilize his valuable water rights through a sale or lease of them to others rather than growing low-value crops. Clearly, the demands of municipal usage are beginning to strain the balance for the supply of water rights.

TRADING OPPORTUNITIES: SOUTHERN CALIFORNIA AND THE SOUTHWEST

Consider the situation in Southern California: California's population is projected to grow to almost 50 million over the next 30 years. The state actually has a huge supply of available water, both from the Colorado River as well as from the northern sections of the state. In Southern California, most of the supply is procured from the Colorado River basin, whose total allocation is controlled by the Department of the Interior. Currently, California is allotted approximately 4.4 million acre-feet of water from the Colorado. However, since the states of Arizona and Nevada have not been using their full allocations, California has enjoyed using up to 5.2 million acre-feet of supply every year. As Arizona and Nevada experience their own increased growth rates, however, they have given California notice that they plan to use (and/or bank) their full allotments of water. Therefore, California needs to start thinking about procuring almost 1.0 million acre-feet of water per year. The issue is not as dramatic as one might think. Almost 3.9 million acre-feet of the Colorado supply (87%) are allocated to agricultural water districts in the Imperial and Riverside counties. In essence, these districts pour the water into the desert in order to grow crops, instead of having the water go to municipal usage within the cities. California can readily solve its future water supply issues by encouraging municipalities to purchase the water from the agricultural districts—basically, transferring the water rights from farms to cities.

So, how does California secure its future water supplies? One answer is to simply take it. In the 1974 movie *Chinatown*, the evil and corrupt city of Los Angeles outwitted poor, unsuspecting farmers from the Owens Valley. Sadly, the basic facts around the story, that is, the taking of water from Owens Valley to supply Los Angeles, are true. In today's day and age, however, that kind of "taking" of property is hard to get through the court system without a long, protracted fight. Interestingly, the MWD still specifically discusses the option of taking water from agricultural districts. Another just-as-controversial option would be to drain Lake Powell. Building a desalinization plant that would convert Pacific Ocean water into fresh water would be another option, albeit an extremely costly one. Or, California's cities can simply purchase the necessary water requirements from the agricultural concerns on the open market.

The City of San Diego, for example, is at the tail end of the Colorado River water allotment in Southern California, and is rightfully nervous about its future supply. San Diego is also the largest captive customer of the MWD, which has preferred to maintain a dominant position in Southern California's water market. San Diego, therefore, began a process to take on greater control of its water supply. Over the past few years, the city began structuring a transaction with the Imperial Valley's Imperial Irrigation District (IID) to secure approximately 200,000 acre-feet of water for approximately $250 per acre-foot. Many municipal users in the city, who cannot wait for the newly secured water supplies, have begun to complain about the windfall profits that the agricultural district would reap (because it is purchasing the water from the federal government for around $13 per acre-foot and will sell it to San Diego for $250).

Enter the famous oil and real estate investors from Texas, the Bass brothers. The Bass brothers, in 1995 and 1996, purchased for $80 million approximately 50,000 acres of land (and the underlying water rights) in the Imperial Valley of California. They hoped for a long-term arbitrage play against the dwindling supplies of water. The Bass brothers intended to pool their resources with the IID and sell surplus water to San Diego for almost 40% less than the MWD was charging. The proposed 75-year contract would provide the IID farmers an extraordinary premium on their water resources. Predictably, the political uproar has been deafening. The MWD is vigorously opposing the transaction. San Diego is the MWD's largest customer. The transaction would represent one of the first cracks in the MWD's monopoly.

In August 1997, US Filter emerged as a purchaser of the Bass brothers' land holdings, for approximately $250 million of its stock (which represents a 10% equity position in the company). US Filter, a California-based environmental technology firm, can utilize its resources to conserve and recycle much of the region's water. The day the transaction closed, US Filter began to manufacture one of the Imperial Valley's first reuse/recycle systems.

If the MWD is successful in blocking the Imperial Valley transaction, San Diego still will need to readdress its supply needs. Options include desalination of Pacific Ocean water, building another adequate pipeline system from Northern California, or reclaiming sewage water, but some of those environmentally friendly solutions will prove to be much more expensive than private water transfers.

California—especially Southern California—is the most widely covered example of what private water markets could accomplish. But what other types of transactions can be structured with water rights? The answer is: as many creative structures as can be dreamed up. As an example, the state of Arizona has notified the state of California that it intends to utilize its full water allotment from the Colorado River. Many farmers and private entities with access to the canal systems can provide storage for Arizona (for a fee) by injecting the water into underground aquifers. Once the state decides upon an appropriate use for the water, the state can withdraw the water (for another fee). Or Arizona can sell its allotment to California, to San Diego, to the Imperial Valley or, assuming the governments agree, to Mexico. Or Arizona can redistribute other water supplies into Nevada's booming Las Vegas region. In fact, late in 1997, Secretary of the Interior Bruce

Babbitt proposed new rules that would "allow states ... to sell water to ... neighbors for a profit."[72]

This leads us to other water marketing examples. Golf course and hotel developers, either in Nevada or Arizona, need to secure long-term water supplies to keep the courses green and the pools filled. These long-term supplies can be met easily by farmers or other private entities looking to utilize their excess marketable water rights. These long-term contracts are typically tied to the prices set by the MWD, which have been increasing roughly 9% per year through 1997. The contracts, incidentally, can be hedged against inflation. The returns to the suppliers can be very attractive indeed.

Many people have begun to capitalize on the complex and little noticed industry of water marketing and water rights transfers. For example, two publicly traded companies are engaged in water marketing. These are the Cadiz Land Company and Western Water Company.

Western Water Company is an example of an independent water provider positioning itself to capitalize on the forthcoming opportunities of water marketing. The company's principal business is the development, packaging, and sales of water, water rights, and water-related services to municipalities and other users. This company had a market value of about $100 million at the end of 1997, but has already established a leadership position in the Colorado River Basin region.

The Cadiz Land Company has a similar but different strategy. Cadiz acquires and develops water-related land as well as agricultural assets. Cadiz has created a complementary portfolio of land, water, and agricultural operations that are integrated within the Southern California region. Much of the Cadiz landholdings are located near major aqueduct systems, which provides the company with an ability to transport water supplies on an "as-needed" basis. Cadiz, like Western Water, only bigger and more diversified, had a small market capitalization, only $275 million at the end of 1997. Combined, the two entities reach almost $400 million in market capitalization, which would make them the fourth largest investor-owned water utility. Neither has any significant Wall Street research coverage. Both are plagued by illiquid trading volumes in their stocks.

CONCLUSION

In water marketing, it is clear that the private market is the only solution. The physical and political circumstances are such that big government can no longer build more dams or canals to help with water shortages. The process of water allocation is not exempt from the economic laws of supply and demand. If government agencies and bureaucracies continue to send incorrect pricing signals to the users of a product, the growth in consumption patterns will lead to social and economic problems. Allowing a "free" market to set the prices for water could set in motion the reform of many government funded projects. Consumers will conserve water, and their usage patterns will alter, and water resources in the West will be utilized far more efficiently than before.

CHAPTER 24

Summary

Private enterprise free from the interference of the sovereign power never existed within the range of recorded history—not in ancient times, not in the medieval ages, nor in Puritan New England, nor in the California vigilante days.[73]

— Arthur Stone Dewing

The American water supply and wastewater industries seem safely mired in the swamp of conventional regulation. Nobody attempts to compete with the utility as a public supplier of services. The large companies prosper. The bill for services takes a small percentage of the average consumer's income. People who want a connection to the system get it. Most consumers drink the water without ill effects. They swim in the water—at designated places—without fear of disease. What is the problem?

Look at it this way. Overall water supply is fixed, but demand is rising. More practically, though, inexpensive local water supply is unchanging in quantity (except where the locals are mining the acquifer). New increments of supply, whether from deeper wells or distant rivers or new reservoirs or even from desalination will cost more, barring dramatic changes in technology. Yet, the pricing process, only to a limited degree sends the signals to consumers that will encourage them to take into account the incremental cost of their consumption.

In some respects, water pricing and regulation is like that of the electric utilities in the 1970s, but even worse in that some water utilities still do not charge customers for usage, but rather by flat rate, or by a proxy measure for usage. All customers, at least, had electric meters. To begin, many water utilities do not charge appropriately for usage at peak, despite their need to build facilities to meet peak demand. Second, the regulators base returns on historic cost of property, despite the far higher cost of meeting new demand. This lag sends the wrong signal about economic costs to consumers. Furthermore, the regulators set low depreciation rates that dampen the incentive to replace old (and leaky) equipment. Utilities do engage in water conservation measures (just as electric utilities engaged in energy conservation), and the regulators do allow for revenue adjustments that offset the lower volumes, but the same regulators send the opposite signal when they adhere to rate base as the key to the regulatory process. Adding to rate base promotes growth of earnings, after all, and companies want to increase their earnings, not stagnate.

The government helps create the belief that water is a free resource by letting people appropriate the water without payment. What would happen if potential water users were required to bid against each other for the right to take water from the environment? (They have to bid to buy frequency allocation to use the airwaves, nowadays, after all.) In much of the country, nothing of consequence might happen due to the plentiful nature of the water supply. But in others, bidding for water rights might dramatically affect the economy of the area. The people who valued water the most would get it. Of course trading in water rights would accomplish much of the same thing, and it would align the interests of stakeholders with public policy goals, in that some of them (that is, the agricultural water rights holders) could make a profit. People tend to favor reforms that line their pockets and oppose reforms that take money away from them in order to enhance the public good.

Any pricing scheme should take note of the likelihood that this is an increasing cost industry that purveys a resource that is absolutely essential to all. Janice Beecher, however, comments that "Rising prices raise concerns about customer affordability."[74] No doubt regulators recoil from the large percentage increases in price requested by water utilities that have installed new facilities, just as embarrassed city council members do when they realize that the water departments need a hefty price hike to meet bond-funding requirements. But one has to distinguish between affordability of service and unwillingness to pay more if one can get away with paying less. The average water bill—at least—is less than what many people lay out for gas or electricity or telephone service.

Perhaps the problem really is that American regulatory procedures have simpler aims, to assure that water supply meets standards, and that water suppliers earn no more money than the amount set by court decisions and debt service requirements. As Beecher commented in her monumental study of water regulation:

> In regulatory environments, formal methods and procedures often are emphasized. Yet some of the most perplexing policy problems, many of which require creative solutions, do not lend themselves to formal consideration.[75]

Meeting our future water needs in an efficient and socially acceptable fashion requires creativity on the part of regulators, more use of market-oriented solutions, and a recognition that decisions made today will have public policy impact generations from now.

NOTES

1. Joe S. Bain, *Industrial Organization* (New York: John Wiley & Sons, Inc. 1959), p. 589.

2. 94 US 113 (1877).

3. Henry Steele Commager, ed., *Documents of American History* (New York: Appleton-Century-Crofts, Inc., 1949), p. 147.

4. Francis X. Welch, *Cases and Text on Public Utility Regulation, Revised Edition* (Washington, D.C.: Public Utilities Reports Inc., 1968), pp. 6–7.

5. Ibid., p. 8.

6. Ibid.

7. Ibid., pp. 10–11.

8. Ibid., p. 11.

9. *Bastard v. Bastard*, Kings Bench, 2 Shower, 82 Cited in Welch, *Public Utility Regulation*, p. 242.

10. 169 US 466.

11. In an 1886 decision, *Stone v. Farmers' Loan and Trust Co.* (116 US 307), the Supreme Court moved away from *Munn*, asserting that the courts could review rates set by a legislature. It was not until *Smyth v. Ames*, though, that the Court laid out standards of reasonableness for fixing rates.

12. Welch, *Public Utility Regulation*, p. 279.

13. Ibid.

14. *Missouri ex rel. Southwestern Bell Telephone Co. v. Missouri Public Service Commission*, 262 US 276.

15. Welch, *Public Utility Regulation*, pp. 285–92.

16. *Bluefield Water Works & Improv. Co. v. West Va. Public Service Commission*, 262 US 679.

17. 272 US 400.

18. Clair Wilcox, *Public Policies Toward Business, Revised Edition* (Homewood, Ill.: Richard D. Irwin, Inc., 1960), p. 570.

19. 262 US 679, 693.

20. *Federal Power Commission v. Hope Natural Gas Co.*, 320 US 591.

21. Welch, *Public Utility Regulation*, 301–02.

22. Arthur Stone Dewing, *The Financial Policy of Corporations* (New York: The Ronald Press Co., 1953), pp. 309–10.

23. Bain, *Industrial Organization*, p. 590.

24. James C. Bonbright, *Principles of Public Utility Rates* (New York: Columbia University Press, 1961), p. 9.

25. Ibid., p. 13.

26. Ibid.

27. Ibid., pp. 14–15.

28. Wilcox, *Public Policies Toward Business*, p. 540.

29. Alfred E. Kahn, *The Economics of Regulation: Principles and Institutions, Vol. 1* (New York: John Wiley & Sons, Inc., 1970), p. 20.

30. Bonbright, *Principles*, p. 18.

31. Welch, *Public Utility Regulation*, p. 478.

32. *New England Telephone and Telegraph Company v. Maine Public Utilities Commission* (390 A 2d 9, June 28, 1978).

33. Arthur Andersen & Co., *Return Allowed in Public Utility Rate Cases* (1960), first page of 1929 cases, no page number.

34. 66 PUR (NS) 212.

35. Welch, *Public Utility Regulation*, p. 301

36. Richard H. Adelaar and Leonard S. Hyman, "The Comparable Earnings Approach as a Useful Tool in Utility Regulation," *Public Utilities Fortnightly*, 4 March 1971.

37. In Adelaar and Hyman, the authors eliminated from the sample regulated industries, industries with high concentration ratios, and two other small industries. The remaining sample consisted of 32 S&P industry groups comprising 191 major firms. The authors found that rate growth in sales was an important determinant of rate of return. Because the company's demand for capital is growing faster than capital markets as a whole, the company must pay more for capital to induce portfolio managers to take the added risk of having a large percentage of their portfolios in a single security. The article also argued that to compete successfully in capital markets, faster-growing utilities must be allowed higher returns than slower-growing utilities. In another article (Leonard S. Hyman, "Utility Stocks in 1967–72: A Tale of Woe," *Public Utilities Fortnightly*, 28

February 1974), the author indicated that the total return on a utility stock investment might have been reduced when the utility's need for new equity capital was high.

38. Adelaar and Hyman, "Comparable Earnings Approach," p. 31.

39. Analysis based on Adelaar and Hyman, "Comparable Earnings Approach." That, in turn, is based on Myron J. Gordon and Eli Shapiro, "Capital Equipment Analysis: The Required Rate of Profit," in Ezra Solomon, ed,. *The Management of Corporate Capital* (New York: The Free Press of Glencoe, 1959), pp. 114–145.

40. Adelaar and Hyman, "Comparable Earnings Approach," p. 33.

41. Leonard S. Hyman, *America's Electric Utilities: Past, Present and Future* (Arlington, Virginia: Public Utilities Reports, 1994), pp. 205–207.

42. Alfred Rappaport, *Creating Shareholder Value* (New York: The Free Press, 1986), p. 149.

43. Welch, *Public Utility Regulation*, p. 486.

44. Bonbright, *Principles*, p. 249.

45. *Re Blackstone Valley Electric Co.* (RI PUC) 24 PUR4th 318, Docket No. 1289, Feb. 17, 1978.

46. Arkansas Public Service Commission, *In the matter of the application of Southwestern Electric Power Company for a general rate increase*, Docket No. U-2793, February 3, 1978.

47. For two easy to read (but unsympathetic) analyses of CAPM, see Robert F. Vandell and James K. Malernee, "The Capital Asset Pricing Model and Utility Equity Returns," *Public Utilities Fortnightly*, 6 July 1978, and Gerald J. Glassman, "Discounted Cash Flow versus the Capital Asset pricing Model (Is g Better Than b?)," *Public Utilities Fortnightly*, 14 September 1978.

48. Vandell and Malernee, "Capital Asset Pricing Model," p. 27.

49. Hyman, *America's Electric Utilities*, p. 207.

50. Stephen A. Ross, "Is Beta Useful?" in ICFA Continuing Education, *The CAPM Controversy: Policy and Strategy Implications for Investment Management* (Charlottesville, Virginia: Association for Investment Management and Research, 1993), pp. 11, 13.

51. Stephen C. Littlechild, *Regulation of British Telecommunications Profitability, A Report to the Secretary of State*, February 1983. Quoted in Alex Henney, *A Study of the Privatization of the Electrical Supply Industry in England & Wales* (London: EEE Ltd., 1994), p. 272.

52. Ibid.

53. "Service Quality: US West Goes Back to Regulation," *PUR Utility Weekly*, 5 April 1996, p. 3.

54. Janice A. Beecher, *Sourcebook of Regulatory Techniques for Water Utilities* (Washington, D.C.: National Association of Water Companies, June 1997), p. 3.4-1.

55. Ibid., p. 1.2-1 (italics in the original).

56. J. Maurice Clark, *Studies in the Economics of Overhead Cost* (Chicago: University of Chicago Press, 1923, 12th impression, 1962), p. 324.

57. Algebraically, let Fixed Costs be denoted by FC and Quantity be denoted by Q. Then if we differentiate the fixed costs with respect to quantity, FC/Q = 0.

58. Jack Hirshleifer, James C. De Haven, and Jerome W. Milliman, *Water Supply: Economics, Technology, and Policy* (Chicago: University of Chicago Press, 1960), p. 56.

59. Ibid., pp. 40–41.

60. Ibid., p. 41.

61. In the English system, common flow rates used in describing water system flows are: a) cubic feet per second (ft^3/s) (b) gallons per minute (c) million gallons per day (MGD). Most engineering calculations describing flows in pipes and distribution systems are made in terms of m^3/s or ft^3/s.

62. The energy continuity equation is:

$$Z_1 + \frac{P_1}{\gamma} + \frac{V_1^2}{2g} = Z_2 + \frac{P_2}{\gamma} + \frac{V_2^2}{2g} + h_L$$

with z = altitude of pt. 1
P_1 = pressure applied at point 1
V_1 = velocity of flow at point 1
Z_2 = Elevation at point 2
P_2 = Pressure at point 2
V_2 = Velocity of flow at point 2
g = acceleration of gravity
h_L = head loss—energy lost in transit, primarily due to friction in piping systems.
γ = specific weight of water in lbs/ft^3 (For fresh water the specific weight is 62.4 lbs/ft^3)

From, Robert L. Daugherty, Joseph B. Franzini, and E. John Finnemore, *Fluid Mechanics with Engineering Applications*, 8th ed. (New York: McGraw-Hill Inc., 1985), p. 93.

63. Water towers and distribution reservoirs serve other purposes that are less related to our economic discussion, such as reducing the pressure surges within a distribution system that result from turning pumps on and off. *Introduction to Water Distribution: Volume 3: Principles and Practices of Water Supply Operations* (Denver, Colorado: American Water Works Association, 1986), p. 300.

64. Ibid., p. 5

65. Peretz Darr, Stephen L. Feldman, and Charles Kamen, *The Demand for Urban Water* (Leiden, The Netherlands: Martinus Nijhoff Social Sciences Division, 1976), p. 25

66. Hirshleifer *et.al., Water Supply*, pp. 101–102.

67. Darr, *et. al., The Demand for Urban Water,* p. 26. Darr, Feldman, and Kamen apply William Vickrey's concept of responsive pricing to develop a more efficient solution, than capacity charges, to the problem of shaving peak loads.

68. Ibid.

69. Ibid., p. 27.

70. Anonymous

71. Jim Carrier, "The Colorado: A River Drained Dry," *National Geographic,* June 1991, p. 4.

72. Todd S. Purdum, "U.S. Acts to Meet Water Needs in the West," *The New York Times,* 19 December 1997, p. A36.

73. Dewing, *Financial Policy of Corporations,* p. 312, footnote e.

74. Beecher, *Sourcebook for Regulatory Techniques,* p. 5.4-1

75. Ibid., p. 9.3-1.

PART V
Financial Structure

CHAPTER 25

The Basics of Corporate Organization and Finance

. . . the world is becoming less capital-intensive . . . we live in a business world that shuns assets. . .[1]

— Robert H. Lessin

The financial structure of the water supply industry is based on certain fundamental tenets:

1. The water supply industry is capital intensive.

2. The industry is a natural monopoly.

3. The business risk to shareholders in the competitive industry should be replaced by financial risk to shareholders in the regulated monopoly.

The type of organization chosen for the water supplier depends on legal, financial, and strategic goals. Each structure determines how the supplier raises money for its expansion, how it charges for services, who owns it, how it determines investment policy, and how it rewards its owners.

First, let us consider the three tenets of water supply finance, and then plunge into issues of business organization and investment decisionmaking.

CAPITAL INTENSITY

Everyone knows that the industry is capital intensive, that it takes three or four dollars of plant to produce one dollar of revenue. Because the customer should not be expected to pay for that much capital equipment in a short time, the cost of the plant is written off over many years. All of that is accepted as natural. The naturalness, however, is not that it may be, in part, a result of the history of the industry and how people made money in it.

The regulatory process affects capital intensity. After all, we are looking at a ratio determined by dividing capital by revenue. Therefore, if revenue can be lowered, the ratio rises. Most regulators see their job as one of keeping down the revenue that the company receives. On the other hand, the utility gets paid a return on capital invested. Therefore, according to some academics,[2] managements expanded the capital invested in the business, because the more capital that was invested, the higher the income of the utility. In other words, managements tried to enlarge the numerator and the regulators to decrease the denominator, thereby raising the capital intensity of the business.

Some of the tendency toward capital intensity may also derive from financing policies of the past, when some holding companies bought operating utilities at inflated prices. Many of the organizers also made money from the engineering fees charged to captive companies and from the sale of the utility's securities. Fees and commissions both escalated with the need to build and raise money.

The low cost of money that prevailed for much of this century also encouraged capital-intensive solutions. If the company could borrow cheaply, why not do so? Furthermore, the pricing and billing for water services often did not encourage consumers to conserve water. Wasteful usage patterns forced water suppliers to put in more assets. Thus, a low cost of capital may have encouraged water suppliers to add more investment than was required.

The point of the discussion is not to deny that the industry requires a great deal of capital to produce a dollar of revenue, but to assert that the industry's capital intensity should not be accepted as completely natural. Capital intensity may have resulted, in part, from regulation, monetary policies, greed of promoters, and other factors. Inertia probably carried the day for years after capital intensity ceased to be a virtue. Nowadays, with price increases hard to extract from regulatory agencies, and so much money required to update old equipment and to meet new environmental standards, it seems less likely that water suppliers would seek the most capital intensive solutions.

FINANCIAL RISK

Standard theory holds that the business of the utility as a natural monopoly is not as risky as the business of a company in a competitive industry. Therefore, the utility can take greater financial risks (i.e., borrow more money) than the average industrial firm.[3] Again one asks whether that statement developed from self-evident characteristics of the industry, or as a rationalization for other practices. In the days of the holding companies, for instance, managements attempted to assure their control by means of ownership of a large percentage of the stock of the parent holding company. To minimize the amount of investment needed to control the holding company empire, the constituent companies financed their capital needs as much as possible by sale of debt. Another possibility is that because the utility industry tended not to be highly profitable, capital was leveraged to bring return on equity up to acceptable levels. Whatever the origins of the practice, the industry raises a large part of its capital by the sale of debt. Those financing practices have not changed for decades.

264

NATURAL MONOPOLY

Water and wastewater suppliers can raise money at low cost for long periods of time because those who furnish the funds believe that the investment is safe, meaning that competitors will not enter the market, take away the customers, and leave the water supplier unable to pay its debts. Basically, that is what people said about electric, gas, and telephone services. They were wrong. Bottled water suppliers, of course have taken a small part of the market, but the basic water and wastewater monopolies seem intact. Water has no substitute, and few other businesses would want to put in the pipes and facilities to transport and treat such a heavy, low-value product for the modest profit earned by the water suppliers. At least not yet.

FORMS OF ORGANIZATION

It is important to know if an entity is a public or a private organization. Many agricultural water suppliers are cooperatives, owned and managed by the farmers that take the water, whose primary purpose is to supply water at a low price. Those organizations are neither fish nor fowl. Most urban water suppliers and wastewater treatment firms are government agencies or are owned directly by local governments. Almost all the remaining firms of any size are private corporations established to produce a profit for their owners.

Public water suppliers differ from private companies in other ways. As governmental entities, they do not pay income taxes to the federal or state governments. Usually, they do not pay state and local taxes, although they may make contributions in lieu of taxes to local governments. When they need to raise money from outside sources they can do so only by borrowing the money. And, as a general rule, the interest payments that they make on their borrowings are not subject to federal income taxation, meaning that the lender pays no income taxes on that source of income.

Be careful of terminology. We have defined public and private in terms of government versus investor ownership. In the world of private sector finance, businesses are classified as "publicly held" versus "privately held." People often refer to "public" and "private" corporations. In financial jargon "public" or "publicly held" means that the business has many owners who can buy and sell their shares in the stock market, and the business is obliged to furnish certain financial information to investors. "Private" or "privately held" means that the business has a small number of shareholders, stock is not traded in the market, and the business does not have any obligation to furnish financial information to the public. Most of the small, investor-owned water and wastewater companies are privately held. Many exist in a twilight zone. They are technically public corporations, but they have a small number of shareholders, and their stock rarely trades, and they furnish only a minimal amount of information to the public. Perhaps a dozen or so water companies in the United States have the characteristics common to most publicly held corporations.

Private business ventures usually organize as sole proprietorships, partnerships or corporations. One person owns a sole proprietorship. If the business makes a profit, that profit goes directly to the owner. If it loses money, and has to pay off business debts, the proprietor is personally responsible, unless the credit agreement absolves him from responsibility. The sole proprietorship has two drawbacks. First, not many people have enough money to start or expand a big business with their own money. Second, most people do not want to run a business in which they could lose their personal as well as their business assets if their business fails.

Often several people pool their money to build up a business as partners. The partnership agreement should specify the duties of the partners as well as how the partnership divides up the profits and losses between partners. As in the case of proprietorships, each partner is individually responsible for all the debts of the partnership. Sometimes the partnership has general and limited partners. The general partner, who manages the business, is responsible for debts of the partnership if it fails. The limited partners simply put in their money and hope for a profit. The partnership agreement will spell out the duties and obligations of the two classes of partners.

Partnerships often restrict the ability of the partners to sell their partnership interests. They may require a sale back to the partnership at a price set by the partnership agreement. They may require approval by other partners of sale of the interest to an outsider. Those restrictions make it difficult to sell partnership interests to investors who want the ability to buy and sell shares at any time, at a price that reflects the market's evaluation of the ownership interest. The master limited partnership (MLP) is an organization with a general partner who runs the partnership, and many limited partners who can buy or sell their ownership positions in the marketplace. Tax laws, however, limit the kinds of businesses that can employ the MLP structure.

General partnerships have the same disadvantage as sole proprietorships: the partner takes on unlimited liability for losses incurred by the partnership. Partnerships and sole proprietorships have one big advantage over corporations. The business does not pay income taxes. Only the proprietor or partner pays taxes on any profits earned, and this difference reduces the overall tax payments.

CORPORATIONS

Corporations (from the Latin word *corporare*, to form into a body) are legal entities that exist independently of their owners. The corporation's charter specifies which activities the organization can undertake. It establishes a board of directors that must choose officers, set corporate policies, and make major decisions. The corporation first raises funds by selling shares of common stock. (The corporation may have the power to raise money by selling preferred stock, which pays a fixed dividend. It may borrow money, too, in its own name.) Each share has an equal ownership position in the corporation, an equal vote in the election of directors, unless otherwise specified, and an equal share in any distribution of profit. If the corporation fails, shareholders' loss is limited to whatever they paid for the share. They have no responsibility for the losses of the corporation. It is a separate legal entity. (In other words, if you paid $10 for a share of stock, and the corporation subsequently collapses after piling up huge debts that it cannot pay, your stock becomes worthless. You have lost $10. You are not responsible for the corporation's debts. If you were a sole proprietor or partner of a business that failed, you would be held responsible for the debts of the failed business.)

Corporations must pay income taxes on their profits. The corporation may distribute part of the after-tax profit in the form of dividends to shareholders. The shareholders pay an income tax on the dividend distributions. This gives rise to the phenomenon of double taxation. Consider two businesses, one a partnership and the other a corporation. The partnership pays out all its earnings to the partners. The corporation pays out all earnings to shareholders in the form of dividends. The corporation income tax rate is 35%. All the individual partners and shareholders are in the 35% bracket, too.

Here is what happens:

Partnership		Corporation	
Revenues	$1,000	Revenues	$1,000
Operating expenses	500	Operating expenses	500
Pretax income	500	Pretax income	500
Income tax paid by partnership	0	Corporate income tax	175
Partnership profit	500	Net income	325
Profit distribution	500	Dividends	325
Partners' income tax on distribution	175	Shareholders' income tax in dividends	114
Partners' profit after income taxes	325	Shareholders' profit after income taxes	211

Note that the partners and the partnership laid out $175 for income taxes while the corporation and the shareholders paid $289 in taxes. The partners paid a tax once, but the shareholders really paid taxes twice on the same flow of income. In order to mitigate this problem, some corporations pay out small or no dividends, but that policy only defers the day of reckoning.

In short, the corporate structure incurs more taxation than partnerships, but it offers limited liability and it can raise large sums of money from many investors. Most large business ventures utilize the corporate form of organization.

THE HOLDING COMPANY

Often for legal and financial reasons, the business enterprise might want to sepa-rate its operating components into different legal entities. For example, the owner of water suppliers in several states would find advantages in forming a separate corporation to own the water facilities in each state. Doing so would make it easier to sort out the expenses and assets associated with serving customers in that state, information needed by regulators when they set prices. Furthermore, putting each operation into a separate corporation insulates the good operations from those with problems. The people who lend money to an operation that gets into trouble can only seize the assets of the business with the problem, not the assets of the other corporations.

At the same time, investors do not want to own shares, separately, in numerous companies. And the various companies could save money if they engaged in certain activities on a joint basis. To solve those problems, corporate financiers invented the holding company. This is a corporation that owns the common stock of several operating companies that perform services for customers. Some businesses even form sub-holding companies under the holding company, in order to segregate the operating companies into groups.

Investors in holding company shares, and those who lend to holding companies or their affiliated operating companies, must understand that the separation between companies within the holding company system, and the organization of companies within the system, affects the safety of investments. The operating company, which collects revenues directly from the customers, usually is the safest component of the organization.

Let's look at an extreme example. Universal Water Holdings Corporation owns five regulated water utilities, and three unregulated businesses that sell chemicals, perform engineering services, and distribute bottled water. Universal creates two sub-holding companies, Regulated Utilities, Inc. to own the water utilities and Unregulated Enterprises, Inc. to own the three unregulated businesses. Universal and its sub-holding companies own all the shares in each of the components of the Universal empire, but each component borrows money on its own. Figure 25-1 shows the structure of Universal's holdings.

First, notice that each corporation in the Universal family raises money from stockholders and from lenders, but at different ratios, depending on the appro-priate debt ratio for the particular business. Second, each company might borrow money on different terms that are determined by the nature of the individual business. Third, Universal raised $500 from shareholders. It borrowed additional money, so that it had $1,000 to invest in the stock of the two sub-holding compa-nies. They, in turn borrowed $300 between the two of them, so that they could buy $1,300 of stock in their subsidiaries. The subsidiaries, in turn, borrowed

Figure 25-1

Holding Company Financial Structure

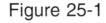

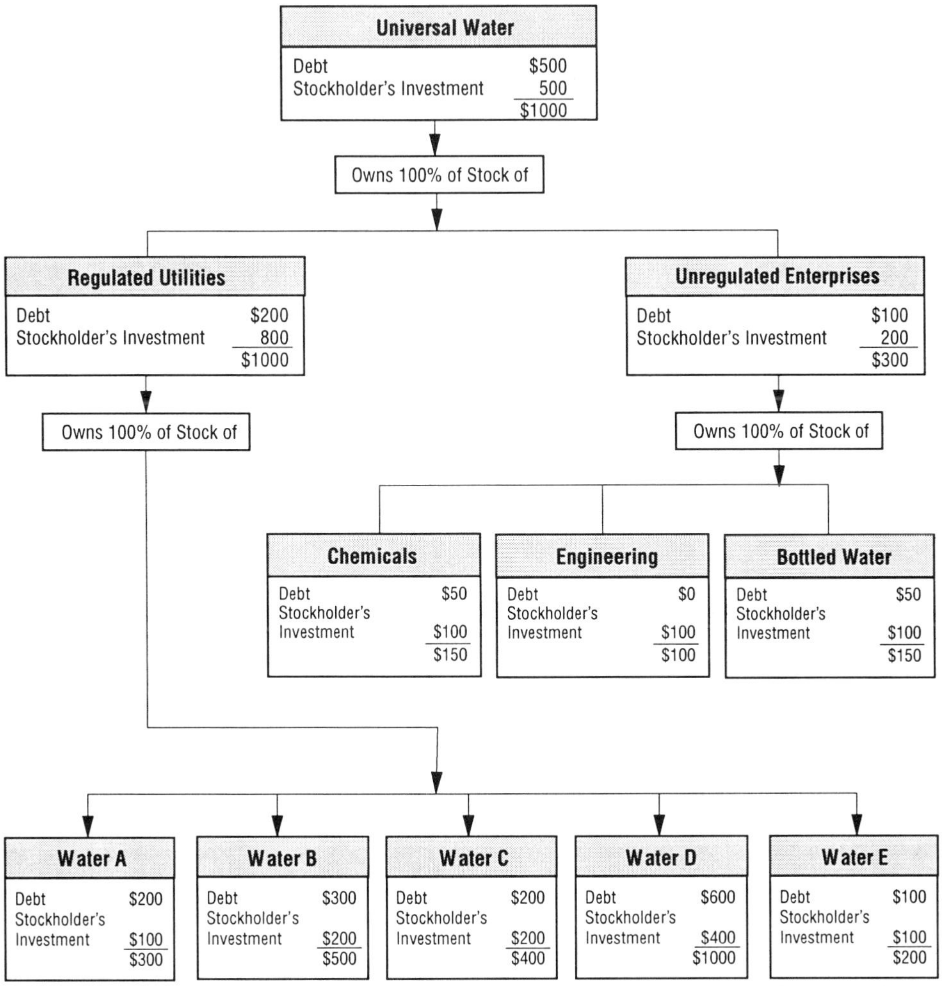

Universal Water	
Debt	$500
Stockholder's Investment	500
	$1000

Owns 100% of Stock of

Regulated Utilities	
Debt	$200
Stockholder's Investment	800
	$1000

Unregulated Enterprises	
Debt	$100
Stockholder's Investment	200
	$300

Owns 100% of Stock of

Owns 100% of Stock of

Chemicals	
Debt	$50
Stockholder's Investment	$100
	$150

Engineering	
Debt	$0
Stockholder's Investment	$100
	$100

Bottled Water	
Debt	$50
Stockholder's Investment	$100
	$150

Water A	
Debt	$200
Stockholder's Investment	$100
	$300

Water B	
Debt	$300
Stockholder's Investment	$200
	$500

Water C	
Debt	$200
Stockholder's Investment	$200
	$400

Water D	
Debt	$600
Stockholder's Investment	$400
	$1000

Water E	
Debt	$100
Stockholder's Investment	$100
	$200

$1,500 altogether, so that they could buy $2,800 worth of assets. Overall, note that Universal and its affiliates borrowed $2,300 while stockholders put up only $500. Yet, for no company within the holding company empire does debt represent more than two-thirds of capitalization.

This financial arrangement creates the potential for wide swings in the earnings of the shareholders of the parent company, and also creates peculiar problems of priority. Usually, lenders get first call on earnings and assets. But in the example, the stockholders of the eight operating companies have priority over the lenders to the sub-holding companies, and the stockholders of the sub-holding companies have priority over the lenders to Universal.

Let's see how it works, ignoring income taxes. (See Figure 25-2 and Figure 25-3.) Consider two situations, when business is good and when it is bad. When it is good, each of the operating companies earns a 20% return on its capital, and pays an interest rate of 10% on all loans. With $2,800 of capital, the operating companies earn $560. With $1,500 of debt, they pay $150 of interest. That leaves a profit of $410 to pay to their shareholders, the two sub-holding companies, in the form of dividends. Those two companies have borrowed $300 altogether, and they pay $30 of interest, leaving them with a profit of $380, which goes up to Universal. That company, in turn, pays $50 in interest on its $500 of debt, leaving $330 for its stockholders as dividends.

In a bad year, though, earnings fall to 8% on the capital of the operating companies, or $224. Interest expense, however, remains at $150, leaving only $74 for the shareowners, the two sub-holding companies. They collect the $74, out of which they must pay $30 interest. That leaves only $44 for Universal, which has to fork out $50 in interest, but it has collected only $44. Universal's stockholders lose money. Universal cannot pay the extra $6 because it put all its money in the subsidiaries. It has to raise more money, or it will go bankrupt, and stockholders will lose their investment. Note what happened. If you were a stockholder or lender to the operating companies, you would have collected your profits or interest. If you were a lender to Universal, you would have collected some of your money. If you were a stockholder of Universal, you would have lost money. Remember that the operating companies at the bottom remained profitable, but not as profitable as before. Universal, on the other hand, showed a swing from extraordinary profitability to loss.

During the years before the stock market crash of 1929, financiers put together complicated utility holding company empires that featured many sub-holding companies and huge amounts of debt (as in our example). Using this type of structure, the financiers could, through investment in a small amount of stock in the top holding company, control vast assets. When the Great Depression came, consumers reduced their purchases from the utilities (many consumers could not pay their bills), profits fell at the operating company levels, and the profits sent up to the sub-holding or holding companies were inadequate to pay the interest on those companies' debt. Many of the holding companies collapsed into bankruptcy. Some of today's large water companies are the remnants of the failed holding companies. As a result of the experience of the Great Depression, modern holding companies avoided convoluted corporate structures and excessive use of debt.

OTHER BUSINESS ORGANIZATIONS

Businesses must tailor their structures to meet many peculiar needs. Two separate businesses might decide to work together, for instance, because neither has all the skills needed for a particular effort, or neither has enough money, alone, to finance the effort. They will pool their resources and management to create a *joint*

Figure 25-2

Flow of Income in Good Times

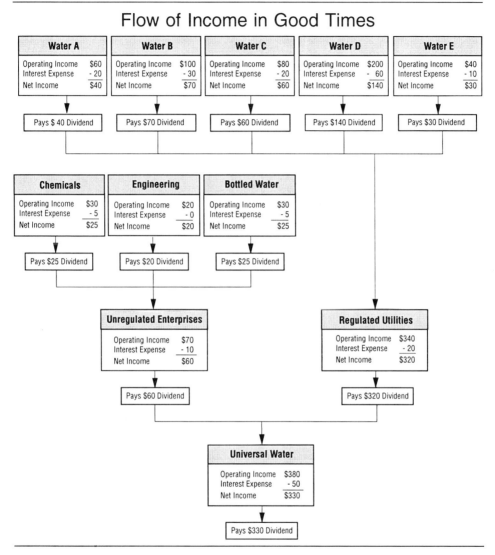

venture, a separate organization staffed with people from both parent companies, with capital investment or assets contributed by both parents. Sometimes several firms agree to work together on a particular goal through an *alliance*, which might involve pooling of resources, or just jointly furnishing a product to a customer. Two firms with complementary talents, for instance, might agree to work together to bid on certain types of contracts.

A company might decide to separate out one project from the rest of the business, because it does not want to put the financial backing of the entire firm behind the project. The company sets up the project as a separate company, and buys

Figure 25-3

Flow of Income in Bad Times

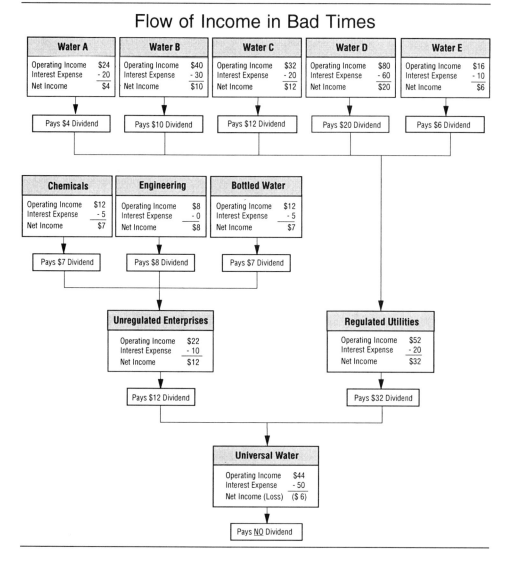

enough stock in the new company to get it going. The new company then borrows money to complete the project (let us say a water treatment facility). The lenders make the loan based on the expected ability of the project to make enough money to pay interest on the loan and then pay off the loan. The lenders cannot go to the parent company for payment if something goes wrong at the project. Often, lenders who engage in *project financing* demand that the project have a long-term contract to sell its output to a strong and reliable customer. In effect, the lenders rely on the contract from the customer in place of the financial backing of the parent company that owns the stock of the project.

Finally, a business might arrange to operate and improve an asset owned by another entity, rather than to actually own the entity, because the owning entity has access to low-cost financing. As an example, a city sewage department might own a sewage treatment plant, which it financed by selling tax-exempt debt that pays a low interest rate. The city, though, cannot run the facility efficiently. A private firm comes along, offering to run the facility and fix up the equipment, for an annual fee based on the volume treated. Why does the private company not buy the facility, and sell the services, in the same way as any other business? The reason is that the private company would have to pay a higher cost for its capital that the city government, and doing so would raise the price it would have to charge for the service. The *contracting* arrangement takes advantage of both low-cost public financing and the higher efficiency of the private operator.

When doing business, firms must maintain organizational flexibility that allows them to meet their goals in the most efficient manner possible. Nowadays no structure is right for every business opportunity.

INVESTMENT DECISIONS

Corporation executives and investors often focus too much attention on financial structure and too little attention on the most important aspect of financing: making the right investment decision, which means investing funds to produce the highest possible return commensurate with risk incurred, or better yet, investing the funds to earn a return in excess of the cost of capital.

As an example of the former criterion, you have the opportunity to invest your money in building a ski resort or in building a water supply company for a new development. You make the following list of investment factors:

Ski Resort	Water Utility
• Highly variable weather conditions in area.	• Predictable source of water supply.
• Only road to area is often impassable during the winter.	• All homes in development have buyers.
• Proposed new road has been held up by a lawsuit.	• Development is near an expanding metropolitan area.
• Manager has beach resort experience.	• Reasonable regulation.
• No other ski resorts in the area.	• Manager has built and run water companies.

Clearly, investment in this ski resort is risky. If there is no snow, you have to spend money to manufacture the white stuff. If it snows too much, your customers cannot get to the resort, and it does not look as if the new road will be built in the near future. Furthermore, the manager's winning record on the beach may not have prepared him for the snow belt. On the other hand, there is no competition nearby. The odds are that there is a 50% chance of making a big profit, and a 50% chance that you lose everything. The water utility, however, looks like a sure thing. The water is there. The customers are there. They cannot live without water. You know, too, that you can invest your money in U.S. Treasury bonds, which

273

are absolutely safe, and pay a 7% return every year ($7 in interest for $100 invested) and you know that an average business investment returns 12% per year. The ski operator says that his projections indicate a 13% return on investment. The water company promoter points out that regulators will let the utility earn an 11% return. The ski operator promises more, but the business is so uncertain that you have little confidence in those projections. You decide to settle for an almost certain 11% return instead of a questionable 13% return, especially considering that an average market investment should produce 12%.

Financial theorists and management consultants have developed a means of determining the appropriate level of profit for a given level of risk, although more and more academics have started to question the usefulness of the numbers derived. Basically, the method equates risk with variability, measured by *beta*, a measure of how variable the business is relative to the market as a whole. (For instance, on a grossly simplified basis, a beta of 2.0 indicates that the stock will go up or down twice as much as the market. A utility company, on the other hand, might have a beta of 0.5, meaning that it moves up or down only half as much as the market.) The more variable are the earnings or the stock price, for instance, the more unpredictable the results of the investment, and the greater the risk.

Notice, in Figure 25-4, that the water company (whose beta is 0.5) looks as if it will provide a return above the required level of return at the low-risk level, but the ski resort (whose beta is 2.0) will provide a predicted level of return well below that required by the risk. The analysis shows what most investors see intuitively: do not take big risks unless you see an opportunity of making a big profit.

Figure 25-4

Market Risk vs. Rate of Return

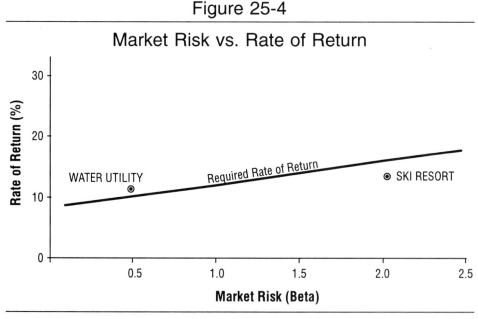

Cost of capital, really, is the return that investors demand for the use of their money, which is the same thing as the required return shown in Figure 25-4. Some corporate managements think that if they do not get the money directly from investors (for instance, they take it out of earnings that they have retained in the business, or they borrow the money from a bank) that they are exempt from this key precept of capital budgeting. They are not. Every corporation has a cost of capital that is determined by the type of business it is in, and the risks of that business. (Modigliani and Miller won a Nobel Prize for developing this concept.) If the management cannot figure out how to invest funds in a way that earns the cost of capital or better, they should give the money back to the owners of the business.

Let's look at two examples. In the case of company A, cost of capital is 10%, meaning that shareholders could earn 10% on the money if it were invested in other businesses, and they won't give any money to A unless it earns at least 10%. Furthermore, the shareholders can earn 6% by putting the same money in the bank. Company A's management does not like to pay dividends to shareholders because it claims that it has so many good ways to invest in expanding the business. It then takes $100 that it has saved up from past profits, invests the money in new machinery, and that investment now earns an extra $6 per year for shareholders. The management gloats because it has increased the profits. The shareholders, on the other hand, are furious. They could earn a 6% return, without any risk, by putting the money in the bank. They want 10% on their investment in A, because that investment is a lot riskier than money in the bank. They would have been better off if A's management had not put the $100 into machinery, but had, instead, given the money to shareholders. (For this discussion we are ignoring the impact of income taxes on decisionmaking.)

In the case of Company B, cost of capital for the entire corporation is also 10%, and the management wants to buy new machinery, but it has no retained earnings to fall back on, and the shareholders have made it clear that they will not buy new shares to give the company money to buy the machinery, because they think that the 6% return is inadequate. So the management goes to a bank, and borrows $100 to buy the machinery, at an interest cost of 5% ($5 per year). Once the transaction is made, management tells the shareholders, "This is a great deal. We're making $6 per year from the machinery and we're only paying $5 per year in interest, so you're ahead of the game by $1 per year, and you didn't have to put up any money to get the extra profit." Are the shareholders happy? No. They point out that the loan increased their risk level, in return for a tiny extra profit. If the machinery doesn't work, or customers decide to buy the product from somewhere else, where does the money come from to pay off the debt? From the shareholders' funds, of course. They might lose $100 from their investment. Is $1 per year enough to compensate for that risk?

One could argue that making investments on the basis of their earning more than the firm's cost of capital is irrelevant to regulated water utilities. After all, they make any investment required to serve customers, and regulators are bound by law to set a return on investment equal to cost of capital. That argument is true in theory. Unfortunately, it is often untrue in practice. Regulators tend to act after the completion of the investment, which means that the investment might earn no return until the regulator acts. Then, if paying for the investment requires too high a price increase, the regulator finds a way to cut that increase, and, in the process, reduce the real return earned. The water utility must not act as if any investment will produce the required return. Instead, it must choose those investments that serve the customer most efficiently, reduce costs, or produce the most income per dollar of investment. Doing so will reduce reliance on regulators, and reduce the temptation on the part of regulators to hand down punitive rate orders in order to save consumers from big rate hikes. That is a long-winded way of saying that even regulated utilities, nowadays, have to apply businesslike decisionmaking to the investment process.

DISCOUNTED CASH FLOW ANALYSIS AND DECISIONMAKING

Many of the small water companies face difficult decisions, as they attempt to remain financially viable while they still attempt to serve customers at a reasonable cost and make all the investments needed to comply with health and environmental rules. As noted by Wirick, Borrows and Goldberg:

> Much as water flows are central to water system engineering, cash flows are central to water system financial management.... If water utilities cannot generate cash flows that, after appropriate discounting, exceed the cost of capital investments, it is unlikely that the water utility will be financially healthy.[4]

In deciding whether or not to make an investment, a prudent manager will attempt to estimate the cash flow that the investment will produce when it goes into service. (That cash flow comes about because consumers will pay for the additional product or service produced by the investment, or because the investment allows the company to produce its output at a lower cost, and therefore generates cost savings. Either way, the investment also produces greater cash flow for the firm.)

The additional cash flow, however, comes only after a cash expenditure that buys the investment. The firm certainly will not make the investment unless the additional cash flow equals or exceeds the investment, but is that good enough?

Consider two possible investments, A and B, both made at the beginning of year 1, both of which wear out and become useless by the end of year 10. Obviously, project A is a loser. Who would invest $100 in order to collect $71 over the 10 following years? On the other hand, project B looks like a winner, because it brings in more cash than was invested initially. But is it really? The firm could take the same $100, put it in the bank to earn 5% per year and, at the end of the

276

Decisionmaking Based on Cash Flow

Year	Project A		Project	
	Cash Flow	Expected Cash Flow	Cash Flow	Expected Cash Inflow
1	$100	$10	$100	$ 11
2		9		11
3		9		12
4		8		12
5		7		11
6		7		12
7		6		12
8		6		13
9		5		12
10		4		13
	$100	$71	$100	$119

10 years get back the original $100 plus $63 in accumulated interest. Obviously if the firm can earn 5% as an alternative use of its funds, it will not invest in project B either. If, however, the available interest rate were only 1%, putting moncy in the bank would produce only $10 of interest, which would make the $119 look better. If interest rates reached 1.8% per year, then the investor would collect $19 in interest, and might be indifferent to locking away the money in the bank for 10 years or investing in project B, if both choices involved the same amount of risk.

The firm, then, will make the investment if the cash flow produced not only exceeds the investment but also produces a return on that investment that equals or exceeds cost of capital. Budget analysts, however, will tackle the question in a different way. They determine the present value of future cash flows, at a given discount rate. In other words, they determine how much they would pay now for a cash payment that they will not receive until some time in the future, if they wanted to earn a certain interest rate on their money. This is exactly what purchasers of U.S. Savings Bonds do. As an example, if you were owed $100, payable in five years, but needed cash right now, you would go to a moneylender who would discount the note. If the moneylender demanded an 8% discount rate, he would pay you $68.10 for the note. (Turning the matter around, $68.10 invested at an 8% interest rate, earns $31.90 of interest, to reach $100 in value in five years.) In this case:

PV = present value
C = cash payment expected
r = required rate of return
n = number of years

$$PV = \frac{C}{(1 + r)^n}$$

To decide whether to make an investment, we need to calculate the net present value (NPV), that is, the present value of the excess of present value of the cash flows received over the value of the initial investment (I). For instance, the water company decides to invest $100 in a new pump part that will save the company $25 per year for five years, until it wears out. The company has to earn 8% on investment in order to cover its cost of capital.

$$\text{NPV} = \quad -I + \frac{C_1}{(1 + r)} + \frac{C_2}{(1 + r)^2} + \frac{C_3}{(1 + r)^3} + \frac{C_4}{(1 + r)^4} + \frac{C_5}{(1 + r)^5}$$

$$= -\$100 + \frac{\$25}{(1.05)} + \frac{\$25}{(1.103)} + \frac{\$25}{(1.158)} + \frac{\$25}{(1.216)} + \frac{\$25}{(1.276)}$$

$$= -\$100 + \$23.81 + \$22.67 + \$21.59 + \$20.56 + \$19.59 = \$8.22$$

Note that the pump passes the hurdle. The investment prodes a positive net present value, indicating that it will earn more than an 8% return.

The real problem, though, is to choose the appropriate discount rate. Regulated utilities might pick their weighted average cost of capital or rate of return, but that cost is based on past history, on what the company paid for capital. Clearly the utility has to look at what capital will cost when it makes the investment, not what it cost when it made a previous investment.

Of course, there is still another problem. The budget analyst has to make accurate projections of future cash flows for this procedure to work. That famous warning, "Garbage in, garbage out" applies to this procedure as well. In order to err on the side of caution, the budget analyst could make conservative (low) projections of cash flow, or could "employ a higher discount rate than might otherwise be expected."[5] If the particular project is riskier than the run-of-the-mill project, then the analyst should apply a higher than normal discount rate.

CONCLUSION

The water supply industry developed its financial policies as a result of natural monopoly, ownership, need for capital, and the accidents of history. Those policies may be understood best by examining the financial statements that report on the policies, the statements of income and retained earnings, the balance sheet, and the statement of cash flows, and then by considering the financial results produced in the marketplace by the companies.

Now for the warnings. Numbers have a misleading exactness. Financial accounts sometimes seem to hide good news and often paper over the bad news, all done legally. When you look at the numbers, always ask how much cash is coming in or going out. A big business is no different than a candy store, in that respect. More cash has to come in the door than go out for the business to succeed. When measuring returns (profitability), take account of the cash returns, not what the bookkeepers claim is profit. Take into account the timing of cash inflows, when making investment decisions. A promised big cash inflow 10 years from now is less certain and less valuable than a smaller cash inflow this year. Remember that you make decisions for the future. You do not make money investing in the past. That means that you have to make good projections of future activities, and properly assess the risks involved in making the investments. Too many executives and investors make the decision first, and then manipulate the projections and assumptions in order to justify the decision. All those computerized scenarios look scientific. They are not.

In short, properly used, the financial statements provide information and guidance. Improperly used, they mislead the unwary. But when all is said and done, you cannot run or understand a capital-intensive, regulated industry without a well-defined accounting system.

CHAPTER 26

Government Water Supply Organization and Finance

Since at least the late 1950s it has been argued that local government need not provide and produce goods and services.[6]

— Stephen P. Morgan and Jeffrey I. Chapman

Governments or government agencies furnish water and wastewater service to the majority of American communities. Those entities operate under different legal, regulatory, taxation, and financial rules than do privately owned suppliers. Yet they have to deal with the same operating issues and environmental restrictions. They, too, have to raise large amounts of capital. Swings of the capital markets affect their cost of capital as well. The investors that lend them money are just as concerned about the safety of their investments as the investors in the securities of private water suppliers. And their customers are just as unhappy about paying more for services as are the customers of investor-owned utilities.

PUBLIC VERSUS PRIVATE

Students of government have produced reams of paper explaining why public or private ownership is better. Basically, the proponents of public ownership note that water and wastewater are natural monopolies, lacking the competitive market disciplines that force private businesses to run efficiently. Furthermore, providing water and waste services constitutes a vital public service that should be made available to all at the lowest possible price, and perhaps at no cost to those who cannot afford it. In addition, the provision of those services creates public benefits, such as water for fire hydrants, better health for inhabitants, parks located around reservoirs, and in-place infrastructure that encourages growth within the community. In other words, society as a whole gains from inexpensive and widespread service. Private suppliers would not price their products or run their services to produce those benefits if doing so would reduce their profits.

Opponents of public ownership point out that government-owned utilities do not pay taxes, so governments lose revenues. The low price of water has a corollary, then: higher taxes. Furthermore, argue the opponents of public ownership, government-owned utilities are inefficient, make decisions for political reasons, and have more employees than they need. The evidence on efficiency, however, is mixed.[7]

Some people have worked out means to meld private initiative and public operation. The public water supply operator can contract out certain tasks to the private party that can accomplish them at the lowest price. The public water supply entity, then, uses the competitive process to find the lowest cost outsourcing firm. Obviously, if the public water operator can do the same job, with its own people, for less, it will not let the contract to the private firm.

Debating the merits of public versus private ownership is not the point here. Huge governmentally owned entities do dominate the industry, and we must understand their organizational and financial policies.

ORGANIZATION

Basically, publicly owned water and wastewater entities come in one of two shapes. They are departments within the local government, or they are separate government agencies that exist to supply certain utility services to the public directly, or to other utilities that, in turn, serve the public directly. As an example, consider the water and sewer department of the Village of Sleepy Hollow. The tiny village in New York's Hudson Valley, installs, owns, operates, and charges residents for water use, and covers sewer costs through village taxes. The Water Department, though, is just one more office in village government. In a snowstorm, water department workers will clear the streets and shovel sidewalks with everyone else. When the village needs to add to the water system, it takes out a loan backed by the village's credit.

The Las Vegas Water District, on the other hand, is a government agency separate from other government agencies, created by the state of Nevada, to provide water in Clark County. The Board of County Commissioners serves as the board of directors of the District. Not only does the District charge customers for water, but it also has taxing power. The district has annual revenues of around $100 million, and it has invested over $500 million in utility plant.

The Metropolitan Water District was created by the State of California back in 1928 to build and operate the aqueduct that transports Colorado River water to Southern California. The MWD's aqueduct is over 240 miles long. The District has another 750 miles of pipe used to deliver the water to the 27 public agencies that participate in its operations. Those agencies collect the taxes that pay those who lent the MWD the money it needed to build the system. Water deliveries are allotted to participants proportionally to the tax payments. (The revenue from sale of water covers only the MWD's operating costs.) The MWD is a huge organization, having invested over $3.7 billion in utility plant. Revenues exceed $700 million per year.

Sometimes, the state might want to establish a special agency that helps out the multitude of small municipalities and water agencies that would have a difficult time getting the best terms from lenders because they are so small. New Jersey, for instance, set up the New Jersey Wastewater Treatment Trust, a government agency that borrows large sums of money in the market, and then lends the money to smaller government entities for investment in local sewage treatment facilities. The Trust has made over $600 million worth of loans, some of which were in amounts of a few hundred thousand dollars.

Government entities can be as diverse as privately owned businesses. The differences between public and private, however, revolve around motivation.

The privately owned concern provides a service to the public in order to make a profit for its owners. It may furnish additional services that do not directly produce a profit, if the owners desire, or because the owners believe that these activities, indirectly, will improve profits. But the directors of a private corporation must exercise care that they do not stray too far from their principal purpose, which is to maintain a viable, profitable business. Regulation of the private water company further complicates matters. State regulatory agencies may question whether ratepayers should cover any costs not directly associated with water services. At the same time, if the corporate charter allows, the private water firm can engage in all sorts of unrelated profit-making activities, as long as the corporation does not attempt to saddle water ratepayers with the costs. The government agency, however, can engage in the public service activities expected of a government agency. It has not been established to earn a profit, although its creditors may require it to earn enough money to cover the costs of borrowing. And the government agency should not (and usually cannot) stray into unrelated profit-making enterprises.

MUNICIPAL FINANCE

Because governments are not supposed to be profit-making entities, and because they have no owners, governments and government agencies cannot sell shares that entitle the owner to a piece of the profits. They can only borrow money, which they must pay back with interest. Financiers refer to all state and local government financing, generally, as "municipal" financing. Something like 37,000 entities raise money in the municipal bond markets. Most municipal debt pays interest that is exempt from federal income taxation.

Municipal agencies can raise money at a lower cost than can private utilities. They do not have to pay income taxes either, which further reduces costs. Consider this example: Water Company A is a private company. It has borrowed $500 by selling taxable debt at an 8% interest rate. It has to earn 12% on its shareholder investment of $500. Utility B is a government utility that can borrow $1,000 at 6%. It pays no taxes. It must collect enough revenue, though, to cover all operating expenses, plus 1.2 times the interest costs, as required by its bond agreement. Both companies sell the same amount of water. Both have invested $1,000 to build the system, and they have the same operating expenses.

	A	B
Revenues	$332	$272
Operating expenses	200	200
Operating income	132	72
Interest cost	40	60
Pretax income	92	12
Income tax (35%)	32	0
Net income	60	12

Cost of capital, income taxes and tax-exempt debt do matter to a capital intensive business like water. The private firm has to charge more to provide the identical service as the municipal entity, unless it can operate at a level of efficiency that offsets the inherent disadvantage that it has due to its higher cost of capital and its need to pay taxes.

Basically, there are two kinds of municipal obligations. *General obligations*, also called full faith and credit obligations, are backed by the taxing power of the government agency. That power does not guarantee payment, because the government can only tax business' property and people that remain within its jurisdiction. Too high a tax rate might drive away businesses and residents, so there is a limit on how much tax revenue that the government can collect.

Revenue bonds represent the second kind of municipal obligation. The issuer of the bond (perhaps the local water and sewer authority) pledges to pay the interest and principal of the bond from the revenues that it generates from sales of water, from hook-up charges and from sewer usage charges. Often, the city government issues revenue bonds that have a *lien* (meaning that the money goes directly to those bondholders) on the revenue of the water department or what is left of that revenue after designated expenses have been paid. Despite the fact that the city is issuing the bond, the city makes it clear that it will not pay the debt if water revenues are insufficient. The *prospectus* (sales document) usually has a disclaimer on the front cover that says something like this:

> The bonds do not constitute an indebtedness or general obligation of the city and are not payable from funds raised or to be raised by taxation.[8]

Buyers of revenue bonds must understand that they, in effect, have invested in a business venture. The government entity will not, and perhaps cannot, tax residents to pay off the debt if the revenues fall short of estimates. The bond agreement may call for the agency to charge enough for its services to cover expenses plus debt service (interest plus the year's payment of bond principal), but the agency can only collect if it has enough customers. Government water utilities try to keep profits at moderate levels above debt service costs in order to keep down the cost of a service vital to public health. They do not salt away a lot of extra cash to pay off debts just in case the proverbial rainy day does come.

Various state government agencies have set up special loan funds that provide subsidized loans to water suppliers. According to Wirick, Borrows and Goldberg, "Many of these state funding programs give preference to public systems."[9] The Safe Drinking Water Act Amendments of 1996 also make loans available to all water suppliers, but the state administrators of the funds may be instituting rules that "initially (or permanently) exclude investor-owned utilities."[10] The government-owned water utilities, therefore, may have additional sources of low-cost financing beyond tax-exempt bond sales.

THE FINANCING PROCESS

A water agency needs to raise enough money to build a new treatment plant. The agency obtains an estimate for the cost of the plant. Its business managers now must determine whether the revenue from current and projected customers will allow it to meet the debt service obligation for the money it will have to borrow. If not, the agency will have to consider adjusting its price of service. After making the calculations, the agency decides to sell revenue bonds of $10 million to pay for the facility. The investment bankers, who will sell the bonds to investors, estimate that the interest cost for the bonds will be around 6% ($60,000 per year). They recommend that the agency pay back $1 million per year over the 10 year life of the bond. The debt service schedule, then, looks like this:

Table 26-1

Debt Service for Financing
($ Millions)

Year	Beginning of Year Principal	Interest	Debt Repayment	Debt Service (Interest & Debt Repayment)
1	$10.0	$0.60	$1.0	$1.60
2	9.0	0.54	1.0	1.54
3	8.0	0.48	1.0	1.48
4	7.0	0.42	1.0	1.42
5	6.0	0.36	1.0	1.36
6	5.0	0.30	1.0	1.30
7	4.0	0.24	1.0	1.24
8	3.0	0.18	1.0	1.18
9	2.0	0.12	1.0	1.12
10	1.0	0.06	1.0	1.06

The agency projects that the expenses of operating the new plant will reach $2.0 million per year. The bond agreement requires the agency to change customers enough to generate revenues that cover existing operating expenses plus 1.2 times debt service. The business manager says that existing revenues just barely cover existing operating expenses plus 1.2 times debt service. The water agency, then, will have to raise prices by $3.92 million in the first year in order to cover the additional expenses plus 1.2 times debt service.

The agency now goes to a law firm that specializes in municipal bonds, to make sure that it has complied with all of its internal rules, and to make sure that the bond qualifies for federal tax exemption. Then it goes to the bond rating agencies, in order to get the quality rating that most investors demand to see before they buy. (Some government agencies buy credit insurance, which commits a large insurance company to pay the interest and principal in case the government agency fails to meet its obligations. Credit insurance makes investors happy, and they will settle for lower interest rates from an insured bond.)

The water agency now sells the bonds to an underwriter (usually an investment banking firm or the municipal bond department of a commercial bank). The underwriter then resells the bonds to investors. (The underwriter's profit, or spread, is the difference between the price it paid the water agency for the bond and the price it charges investors for that same bond.) The underwriter needs that spread because it takes a risk. Investors might not want to pay the price demanded, in which case the underwriter would have to sell the bonds for a lower price, and take a loss. For that matter, conceivably nobody would buy the bonds, leaving the underwriter with them. Note, however, that the water agency got its money from the underwriter, no matter what happens afterwards.

From that point to the time that the water agency pays back the debt, the agency pays interest on the bonds every six months. Investors who need their money back ahead of the bond maturity date have to sell the bonds to other investors, at whatever is the market price of the bonds. (Yes, even municipal bond prices fluctuate.) Only at the date the bond matures does the water agency have to find the money to pay it off. (In our example, the agency pays off some of the debt every year.)

MAKING INVESTMENT DECISIONS

Obviously, government agencies do not have the same motives for investment decisions as private firms. At the same time, taxpayers and customers have a right to expect that the government agency will choose the investment that best serves the consumer and the community at the lowest cost. Yet, the history of the water industry provides numerous instances of government entities making short-sighted decisions designed to keep down taxes or water bills in the short-term, which had to be undone at great expense later. And some purely political decisions ended up costing the customers big money. In one Western state, water authorities pushed for a particular project because it was cheaper than building a desalination plant, an alternative that only an Arabian prince would have considered seriously. In an Eastern city, the local government, impelled to act by a drought, considered three alternatives for the water system: taking water out of a nearby river (would upset neighboring cities), meter water consumption (would upset voting consumers) or take water from a distant watershed (most expensive). They took the third choice.

In deciding whether or not to invest in a particular project, the government agency should employ the same type of discounted cash flow analysis as the private water supplier. Even governments do not have access to unlimited amounts of capital. Putting funds into projects that cannot pay their way puts pressure on the finances of the water supplier, which must find extra funds from its other projects in order to support the money-losing project. Yet, government agencies might argue that they have to support certain money-losing projects because those projects provide important benefits to the community at large.

Governments have created cost/benefit analysis as a means of making decisions that take into account the benefits of the decision to the community. The cost of the project is the money invested in it plus the interest paid to raise that money. The benefits (aside from water to users) might also include the improved health that comes from drinking cleaner water plus the recreational benefits that come from having a bike path and park at the reservoir. The cost/benefit process, however, suffers from flaws. The analysis might use an incorrect estimate for cost of the project or for the interest rate on borrowed money. And it could easily misestimate the value of intangible benefits.

Well, one could argue, at least we know the cost of capital of the government agency: the interest rate that it will pay to borrow money. So, if nothing else, we can determine the price of services needed to cover the costs of the new investment, and see if the local city council will approve those prices before going through with the investment. But even that line of thinking has its problems. A big bond offering might cause investors to think that they have more than enough tax-exempt bonds in their portfolio from a particular state. If that happens, they will not buy the offerings of other governments within the state unless they can extract a higher interest rate to compensate for the portfolio imbalance. That is a complicated way of saying that the water bond offering might raise the costs of other government bond offerings in the state.

Actually, the choice of the correct discount rate is even more complicated. Municipal water agencies do have the equivalent of an equity element, in the contributed capital component, but that component has no explicit capital cost. Debt cost may include subsidized elements, too. However, if the utility makes a gross error in building the project, if the pumps do not function as expected, if the filtration plant has to be rebuilt because it does not work properly, if the pipes leak too much, the customer, in the end, bears the risk, because the utility will unload all of the extra expenses on the customer. In other words, the investment risk is there, and the water supplier should use a discount rate for the decision-making process that takes into account the risk, even if the supplier can saddle the consumer with the costs, after the fact. The government supplier, which expects to raise funds at a set rate whether it invests in project A or project B, should not choose to execute the higher-risk project just because it can force customers to pay the bills if the unfortunate events take place. To quote Wirick, Borrows and

Goldberg again, "The discount rate applied to future streams is intended to adjust for risk; risk is not reduced merely because the interest paid is low."[11]

Probably the best controls over spending decisions reside in the public nature of the entities and in the political process. One local government agency does not want to be cited as providing a service at a higher cost than a similar agency in a neighboring city. Those comparisons make the local politicians look bad. For that matter, the local politicians do not want to explain unnecessary price increases to voters, either.

Managers of government water utilities could claim that private water utilities have no greater incentive than they to choose the most efficient projects for investment. Neither the government nor the investor-owned utilities face the rigorous discipline of the competitive market, which would force them to operate and invest most efficiently in order to survive. That is true, but private utilities do have to put up with second-guessing from regulators who act as proxies for the market.

Probably it is safe to say that neither regulators nor voters provide the continuous discipline that a competitive market would. But, so far, we do not have a competitive market for water.

CONCLUSION

Government-owned water suppliers come in many sizes and shapes. They raise funds in the capital markets, usually by selling tax-exempt municipal bonds. Their low cost of capital reduces the price that they need to charge for their services. They often keep prices down, too, in order to provide a vital public service at the lowest possible price. At the same time, a poor investment decision could have a negative impact on price of service greater than the benefits derived from access to low-cost capital.

Financing procedures, financial analysis, and goals obviously differ between the private and government water suppliers, but both sets of entities require statements of income, balance sheets, and statements of cash flows. Surprisingly, the financial statements of the two types of firms are almost alike. For that reason, the discussions of financial statements that follow will treat the characteristics and concepts behind each type of financial statement, rather than emphasize the government-private sector dichotomy.

CHAPTER 27

The Statement of Income and Retained Earnings

The ability to attract needed capital is dependent upon consistently achieving adequate earnings.[12]

— American Water Works Company

The income statement covers a specific time period. It shows the amount of money that customers paid for services within that period (revenues) and the costs that were incurred by the firm to provide those services (expenses). The difference between revenue and expense is the profit or net income that is left for the owners of the business. Some of the income is paid to owners in the form of dividends or a distribution of earnings. The rest is kept by the firm for use in the business (retained earnings) or distribution of earnings. Although that sounds simple, how to calculate both revenues and expenses is a matter for dispute. Accounting procedures that tend to understate revenues or to overstate expenses are "conservative." Procedures that tend to overstate revenues and to understate expenses are "liberal." In addition to annual statements, many utilities provide income statements on a quarterly basis.

SIMPLIFIED STATEMENTS

The following is an example of a standard income statement for an industrial concern:

Sales (revenues)	$1,000
Costs of sales (expenses directly associated with production of product)	500
Depreciation (wear and tear on machinery)	100
Interest (on borrowed money)	100
Total Expenses	700
Pretax income	300
Income taxes	100
Net income (profit)	$ 200

Income statements for utilities have been recast for regulatory purposes as follows:

Revenues	$1,000
Operation, maintenance, etc.	500
Depreciation	100
Income taxes	100
Total operating expenses	700
Operating income	300
Interest expense	100
Net income	$ 200

289

The difference exists because the utility regulator is concerned with the return on capital—the interest paid to creditors of the firm and the profits available to stockholders. In our simplified statement, operating income (after deduction of taxes but before interest expense) represents the income available to pay the owners of the capital that has been invested in the business.

The municipal or governmentally owned water system produces a similar income statement, although the names of the income and expense categories do vary at times from the nomenclature of the investor-owned utilities. Remember that the biggest difference, though, is that the government-owned utilities do not pay taxes:

Revenues	$1,000
Operation; maintenance, etc.	500
Depreciation	100
Total operating expense	600
Operating income	400
Interest expense	100
Net income	$ 300

A number of utilities own nonutility subsidiaries. The accountants insist that the income statement add together the utility and nonutility businesses. The statement of income that includes all operations is "consolidated," and might be presented in one of several formats. If we take the two statements shown above, we could add them together in several ways, including:

Utility revenues	$1,000		Utility revenues	$1,000
Industrial sales	1,000		Industrial sales	1,000
Total revenues	2,000		Total revenues	2,000
Expenses:			Expenses:	
Costs of sales	500		Costs of sales	500
Production, maintenance, etc.	500		Production, maintenance, etc.	500
Depreciation	200		Depreciation	200
Operating expenses	1,200		Operating expenses	1,200
Income before interest taxes	800		Pretax operating income	800
Interest expense	300		Income taxes	200
Pretax income	500		Operating income	600
Income taxes	200		Interest expense	300
Net income	300		Net income	300

UTILITY INCOME STATEMENT

The actual water utility income statement is more complicated, as can be seen in the following example. Remember that different companies do use different names for the items shown. The term "consolidated" means that the statement includes the accounts of all companies in the corporate family, showing them, essentially, as if they were one big company.

Consolidated Statement of Income
Investor-Owned Utility Format
($ Thousands)

	Year Ended Dec. 31,	
Line	1996	1997
1. Operating Revenue		
2. Water	$90,000	$95,000
3. Wastewater	10,000	11,000
4. Total revenue	100,000	106,000
5. Operating Expenses		
6. Operation and maintenance	44,000	46,000
7. Depreciation and amortization	9,000	9,500
8. Non-income taxes	8,000	8,500
9. Income taxes	8,700	9,500
10. Total operating expenses	69,700	73,500
11. Operating income	30,300	32,500
12. Other income (expense)		
13. Allowance for equity funds used during construction	500	1,000
14. Other-net	(1,000)	500
15. Total other income (expense)	(500)	1,500
16. Income before interest charges	29,800	34,000
17. Interest charges		
18. Interest on long-term debt	13,000	13,500
19. Interest on short-term debt	1,000	1,500
20. Allowance for borrowed funds used during construction	(700)	(1,300)
21. Amortization of debt expense	800	900
22. Total interest charges	14,100	14,600
23. Net income	15,700	19,400
24. Preferred dividends	1,000	1,000
25. Net income available to common stock	14,700	18,400
26. Average shares outstanding during year	15,000	16,000
27. Earnings per share of common stock	$0.98	$1.15
28. Statement of Retained Earnings		
29. Balance of retained earnings at beginning of year	53,000	58,100
30. Net income available to common stock	14,700	18,400
31. Subtract: Dividends on common stock	9,600	11,200
32. Balance of retained earnings at the end of year	58,100	65,300

The water company sells a certain amount of water in the year at particular prices. Receipts from customers produce *Operating Revenue* (line 1). In this case, the utility furnishes *Water* (line 2) and *Wastewater* service (line 3), and it reports the revenue from each separately.

The *Total Revenue* (line 4) constitutes the collection from customers in the year. The costs of paying employees, suppliers, and the taxes involved in gathering, procuring and distributing the water and handling the wastewater are called *Operating Expenses* (line 5). *Operation and maintenance* (line 6) is a catch-all category that includes most of the expenses directly related to pumping water and wastewater, keeping plant in working order, dealing with customers, and normal administrative duties. Employee salaries and benefits could account for close to half of the total. In addition, the company buys electricity to run its pumps, chemicals to purify water and wastewater, computer services, all sorts of supplies, and, in many cases, the water company buys water from other suppliers, to resell to its own customers.

Maintenance expenses (small repairs and regular overhauls of equipment) were already accounted for in line 6. Plant and equipment, though, wears out over time or becomes obsolete despite the small repairs and eventually must be replaced by more modern and efficient equipment. The company estimates how long the equipment is expected to last and spreads the cost of the purchase over the productive life of the asset. For example, if a machine costs $100,000 and will last for 20 years, the company will show an expense of $5,000 (one-twentieth of the purchase price) each year. That expense is called *Depreciation*. *Amortization* is the spreading over time of the cost of some other expenditure or loss that already took place. For instance, if a big storm did enormous damage, the regulator might tell the utility to set up a storm damage account, and then amortize the expense over five years, that is, only show one-fifth of the expense in each year. Unlike other expenses, *Depreciation and Amortization* (line 7) do not entail paying out money when the expense is shown on the income statement. The utility already has laid out the money.

Non-Income Taxes (line 8) include taxes on real estate and on the company's revenues and are generally levied by state and local governments.

Income Taxes (line 9) are paid to federal, state, and local governments by the corporation. The tax figure does not always represent taxes actually paid in the year. The utility actually pays current taxes, but it also sets aside money for taxes that it expects to pay in the future, and it includes those deferred taxes as an expense, as if it actually had paid them. Like depreciation, deferred taxes do not represent a cash outlay.

Total Operating Expenses (line 10) is subtracted from *Operating Revenue*, leaving *Operating Income* (line 11).

Other Income (Expense), which is shown on line 12, includes the income from various affiliated companies, interest earned on investments, income tax credits, and a variety of other items. Figures shown in parentheses are expenses, not income.

The allowance for funds used during construction (AFUDC) is split into two parts: *Allowance for Equity Funds Used During Construction* (line 13) and *Allowance for Borrowed Funds Used During Construction* (line 20). Let us start by understanding the concept behind AFUDC.

A water utility may have a substantial amount of money tied up for several years in a facility under construction. That money had to be raised by means of borrowing or by sale of stock. The utility pays interest on borrowed money, and stockholders also expect a return on their investment even though the plant is not yet operating. How can the utility recover those costs involved in raising money to build the facility? The answer, in many cases, is to add the cost of the money to the cost of the facility. Once the plant is completed, the utility earns a return on the money used to pay suppliers of machinery, bricks, and construction services, plus a return on the money paid to the suppliers of capital. Furthermore, the utility will recover, by means of depreciation, all the costs of the plant, including the cost of capital.

AFUDC is a mechanism whereby the cost of money is added to the plant account on the balance sheet. The cost of money raised to build the plant (AFUDC) is added to company income and thus increases the stockholders' equity shown on the right side of the balance sheet. Because the balance sheet must balance, under the double entry system, a similar sum is added to the plant account on the asset side of the balance sheet. Money is raised either from stockholders or from creditors (lenders). Regulators decided that the two sources should be separated, because each has a different cost. Therefore, the utility calculates the cost of money that has been borrowed to finance the project, the *Allowance for Borrowed Funds Used During Construction* (line 20). Then, if the project is not funded entirely by means of borrowing, the utility assigns a cost to the equity money that has been raised, usually basing the cost on the return on equity that was allowed in the last rate case. The cost of equity funds is the *Allowance for Equity Funds Used During Construction* (line 13). Accordingly, AFUDC serves two purposes. It allows the utility to recover costs of plant (by means of depreciation) and to earn a return on capital costs incurred while a facility is under construction. In addition, AFUDC removes from the income statement the effects of expenses that have nothing to do with operations for the current year.

In order to clearly delineate the two sources of AFUDC, *Allowance for Equity Funds Used During Construction* (also called *Allowance for Other Funds Used During Construction*) is included in *Other Income*, and *Allowance for Borrowed Funds Used During Construction* (also called *Capitalized Interest*) is shown as a deduction from *Interest Charges*.

Other-net (line 14) includes miscellaneous sources of income (profits from sale of properties, interest earned, dividends collected, and other items, less any taxes owed on that income). This item can swing sharply, due to the odd items that go into it, and companies can manipulate earnings by how they time the inclusion of items in *Other Income*. Note that this line indicates a loss when figures are in parentheses (that is, negative income). The sum of *Allowance for Equity Funds Used During Construction* (line 13) and *Other-Net* (line 14) is *Total Other Income (Expense)*, shown on line 15. Again, negative income, that is a loss, is shown in parentheses.

The sum of *Operating Income* and *Other Income (Expense)*, is called *Income Before Interest Charges* (line 16). This is the income available to pay the owners of capital.

Interest Charges (line 17) are divided into *Interest on Long-Term Debt* (line 18) and *Interest on Short-Term Debt* (line 19). The latter is usually interest paid on bank loans and on commercial paper.

Allowance for Borrowed Funds Used During Construction (line 20) represents that part of the interest on investment in plant that is incomplete and not yet in service. In order to show the interest expense allocable to the year's operations, the utility must subtract the interest charges on funds borrowed to finance an ongoing construction project from total interest paid. Therefore, *Allowance for Borrowed Funds Used During Construction* is shown in parenthesis, to indicate a subtraction from interest charges.

Amortization of Debt Expense (line 21) represents the year's share of the cost of raising debt spread over the life of the debt. For instance, if the utility had to pay underwriters $50 to sell a $1,000 bond issue to the public, and that bond issue had a 10 year life, the utility would amortize the expense of the offering at the rate of $5 per year ($50/10 years). The income statement shows this amortization in the same section as interest charges, because it is as much a cost of borrowing as the interest paid.

The total of *Interest on Long-Term Debt*, *Interest on Short-Term Debt*, *Allowance for Borrowed Funds Used During Construction* and *Amortization of Debt Expense* equals *Total Interest Charges* (line 22).

After interest charges have been subtracted, *Net Income* (line 23) remains for the owners of the business. All owners, however, are not equal. The owners of preferred stock must be paid fixed *Preferred Dividends* (line 24) before common stockholders see any money.

The *Net Income Available to Common Stock* (line 25) is a residual. To calculate the income available per share of common stock, we must know how many shares are outstanding. The number of shares outstanding changes during the year as shares are repurchased or new shares are issued. Standard practice is to use *Average Shares Outstanding During the Year* (line 26) to calculate per share data.

When income available for all common stock is divided by the average number of shares of common outstanding during the year, *Earnings Per Average Common Share Outstanding* (line 27) results.

What happens to the income left over for common stockholders? That is shown in the *Statement of Retained Earnings* (line 28). The *Net Income Available to Common Stock* (line 30) is added to the *Balance of Retained Earnings at the Beginning of the Year* (line 29). Then *Dividends on Common Stock* (line 31) must be subtracted, leaving the *Balance of Retained Earnings at the End of the Year* (line 32).

Several of the water holding companies use a modification of the industrial format for their income statements. In its most complete form, the statement might look like this:

Statement of Income
Modified Industrial Format
($ Thousands)

Line	Year Ended Dec. 31, 1996	1997
1. Operating Revenue		
2. Water	$90,000	$95,000
3. Wastewater	10,000	11,000
4. Total	100,000	106,000
5. Operating Expenses		
6. Operation and maintenance	44,000	46,000
7. Depreciation and amortization	9,000	9,500
8. Non-income taxes	8,000	8,500
9. Total operating expenses	61,000	64,000
10. Operating income	39,000	42,000
11. Allowance for equity funds used during construction	500	1,000
12. Other-net	(1,000)	500
13. Earnings before interest and taxes	38,500	43,500
14. Interest charges		
15. Interest on long-term debt	13,000	13,500
16. Interest on short-term debt	1,000	1,500
17. Allowance for borrowed funds used during construction	(700)	(1,300)
18. Amortization of debt expense	800	900
19. Total interest charges	14,100	14,600
20. Net income before income taxes	24,400	28,900
21. Income taxes	8,700	9,500
22. Net income	15,700	19,400
23. Preferred dividends	1,000	1,000
24. Net income available to common stock	14,700	18,400
25. Average shares outstanding during year	15,000	16,000
26. Earnings per share of common stock	$0.98	$1.15
27. Statement of Retained Earnings		
28. Balance of retained earnings at beginning of year	$53,000	$58,100
29. Add: Net income available to common stock	14,700	18,400
30. Subtract: Dividends on common stock	9,600	11,200
31. Balance of Retained Earnings at the End of Year	58,100	65,300

GOVERNMENT-OWNED UTILITY

The municipal or government water supplier has an income statement similar to that of the investor-owned water supplier. But the format has to reflect these differences:

• The government utility usually pays no federal or local taxes. Thus, the income statement shows no tax charges.

• It raises a large part of its funds through the sale of tax-exempt bonds. Thus, interest expenses eat up a large part of the income from operations.

● It capitalizes an allowance for borrowed funds used during construction at a rate that reflects cost of debt only, since it has no equity capital cost.

● It pays no dividends because it has no stock outstanding, although it may pay part of its earnings to the local government. Some may consider this payment a substitute for the taxes that the utility does not pay.

● The government utility may have to set aside funds on a regular basis for the payment of its debt. Those funds earn interest. As a result, some government utilities earn substantial interest income.

The government utilities' income statements vary in format but, basically, follow the pattern shown here:

Statement of Income
Government-Owned Utility Format
($ Thousands)

Line	Year Ended Dec. 41,	
	1996	1997
1. Operating Revenue		
2. Water	$90,000	$95,000
3. Wastewater	10,000	11,000
4. Total Revenue	100,000	106,000
5. Operating Expenses		
6. Operation and maintenance	44,000	46,000
7. Depreciation and amortization	9,000	9,500
8. Total Operating Expenses	53,000	55,500
9. Operating income	47,000	50,500
10. Non-Operating Income (Expenses)		
11. Interest Income	1,000	1,000
12. Other-net	(1,000)	500
13. Interest on long-term debt	(9,000)	(10,000)
14. Interest on short-term debt	(500)	(500)
15. Allowance for funds used during construction	500	1,000
16. Amortization of debt expense	(800)	(900)
17. Total Non-Operating Income (Expense)	(9,800)	(8,900)
18. Net income	37,200	41,000
19. Statement of Retained Earnings		
20. Balance of retained earnings at beginning of year	53,000	73,000
21. Add: Net income	37,200	41,600
22. Subtract: Payment to city	17,200	21,600
23. Balance of Retained Earnings at End of Year	73,000	93,000

The items in lines 1 through 9 are the same as their counterparts for the investor-owned utility. *Non-Operating Income (Expense)* (line 10) is a catch-all grouping that encompasses all the non-operating items. *Interest Income* (line 11) is derived from the large sums temporarily invested either for eventual expenditure on construction projects, or for disbursement as debt comes due for repayment. Items on lines 12 through 16 are essentially the same as those shown by investor-owned utilities. *Total Non-Operating Income (Expense)* (line 17) consists of all non-operating items, but the bulk of it consists of interest income and charges. *Net Income* (line 18) is the residual, the difference between all revenues and expenses.

Lines 19 through 23 follow the same procedure is the case for investor-owned utilities, except that the government utility can pay a distribution of income to the local government rather than a dividend to shareholders.

CONSOLIDATION

Water utilities might own subsidiaries that furnish services to the utility. Sometimes a holding company owns the utility and an affiliated firm that sells services or products to the utility. How does the group of corporations present its accounts? Not by adding up the revenues and expenses of the component companies. That would constitute double counting. One does not make money selling to oneself. The answer is to consolidate the results. Let us say that the holding company owns a water utility that buys its water disinfectants from a chemical manufacturer owned by the holding company. The holding company has to issue its accounts. It could add up the result as follows:

	Chemical Manufacturer	Water Utility	Total
Revenues	$100	$1,000	$1,100
Expenses	50	600	650
Disinfectant Costs	—	100	100
Total Costs	50	700	750
Profit	50	300	350

The fact of the matter is that the group only collected $1,000 in revenue, from the customers of the water utility. That is all the money that came in the door. As for expenses, the total company may show $750 including payment for the disinfectant, but we know that only half the cost of the disinfectant represents expense; the rest is profit. One has to remove the effect of selling from one affiliate to another. The means to do so is by consolidating, rather than adding:

	Chemical Manufacturer	Water Utility	Eliminate Intra-company Transactions	Consolidated Results
Revenues	$100	$1,000	($100)	$1,000
Total Expenses	50	700	(50)	650
Profit	50	300	—	350

To put it simply, if the water utility had owned the chemical manufacturer, there would have been no pretense that a sale had been made, and we could have ended up in the same place as the consolidated results, without the complications.

CHAPTER 28

The Balance Sheet

Creditor, n. One of a tribe of savages dwelling beyond the Financial Straits and dreaded for their desolating incursions.[13]

— Ambrose Bierce

The balance sheet shows the property and cash owned by a firm and the amounts owed to it (assets). The balance sheet also shows the money that a firm owes to others and the sources of the money used to purchase its assets (liabilities and capitalization). Because what the firm owns equals the resources that had to be raised to acquire those assets, the assets and the liabilities and capital equal each other, or balance. Most companies put the *Asset* side of the balance sheet on the left page and the *Liabilities and Capitalization* (often referred to in financial shorthand as "Liabilities") on the right page. Those reports that attempt to save space put the *Assets* on the top of the page and the *Liabilities and Capitalization* on the bottom. Data are given as of the end of business on a stated day, usually the end of the year or the end of an accounting period. The balance sheet of a water utility is similar to that of an industrial company except that industrial companies generally put current assets and current liabilities at the top of the balance sheet.

ASSETS

The *Asset* (line 1) side of the balance sheet shows the cost of what the company owns plus what is owed to it by others plus the value of some money that the company has already paid for future expenses.

The major items on a utility's balance sheet usually represent physical plant (machinery, buildings, pipes, money spent to build a reservoir, and land) that is being or will be used to serve the customer. *Utility Plant* (line 2) is divided into several categories. The first category is *Utility Plant In Service* (line 3), the cost of which includes not only the money paid to the manufacturers of building products, and for machinery, and to construction workers, but also the return that was paid to those who supplied the money. On occasion, when the utility has purchased plant from others, at a price above the original cost, the acquisition price in excess of cost is included.

Physical plant wears out over time or machinery may lose value because it becomes obsolete. Every year the firm reduces the value of physical assets to reflect the aging process by adding to the *Accumulated Depreciation* (line 4), and then subtracting the *Accumulated Depreciation* from the value of the plant.

Consolidated Balance Sheet
Investor-Owned Utility Format
($ Thousands)

Line	ASSETS	Year Ended Dec. 31, 1996	1997
1.	ASSETS		
2.	Utility plant		
3.	Utility plant in service	$380,000	$400,000
4.	Accumulated depreciation and amortization	70,000	79,500
5.	Net utility plant in service	310,000	320,500
6.	Construction work in progress	23,000	40,000
7.	Net utility plant	333,000	360,500
8.	Other property and investments	10,000	10,000
9.	Current assets		
10.	Cash and equivalents	5,000	4,500
11.	Accounts receivable-net	10,000	10,500
12.	Unbilled revenues	5,000	5,500
13.	Materials and supplies	5,000	5,000
14.	Other	5,000	4,000
15.	Total current assets	30,000	29,500
16.	Other assets		
17.	Income taxes recoverable	15,000	17,000
18.	Unamortized debt and preferred stock expense	5,000	4,100
19.	Other	5,000	5,900
20.	Total other assets	25,000	27,000
21.	Total assets	398,000	427,000

Line	LIABILITIES AND CAPITALIZATION	Year Ended Dec. 31, 1996	1997
1.	LIABILITIES AND CAPITALIZATION		
2.	Capitalization		
3.	Common stock at $1 stated value	$15,500	$17,000
4.	Capital in excess of stated value	40,000	61,000
5.	Retained earnings	58,100	65,300
6.	Treasury stock (at cost)	(5,000)	(5,107)
7.	Total common stockholders' equity	108,600	138,200
8.	Preferred stock	15,000	15,000
9.	Long-term debt	160,000	160,000
10.	Total capitalization	283,600	313,200
11.	Current liabilities		
12.	Short-term borrowings	9,500	10,000
13.	Current portion of long-term debt	5,000	4,000
14.	Accounts payable	4,900	2,800
15.	Taxes payable	5,000	5,000
16.	Interest accrued	5,000	5,000
17.	Other	5,000	3,000
18.	Total current liabilities	34,400	29,800
19.	Other liabilities		
20.	Advances for construction	15,000	16,000
21.	Contributions in aid of construction	25,000	25,000
22.	Deferred taxes	35,000	38,000
23.	Other	5,000	5,000
24.	Total other liabilities	80,000	84,000
25.	Total liabilities and capitalization	398,000	42,000

Net Utility Plant in Service (line 5) represents the original cost of the plant less the depreciation reserve.

Most utility companies have plant under construction to meet the growing demands of their customers. Machinery, buildings, and equipment that are part of an incomplete project are called *Construction Work in Progress* or CWIP (line 6). The sum of all the money invested in plant, less depreciation, is *Net Plant* (line 7).

Many utilities have invested in other businesses. Those investments are shown under *Other Property and Investments* (line 8).

The company's plant account often is called fixed assets because the property cannot be easily moved and cannot be converted quickly into cash. *Current Assets* (line 9), on the other hand, includes cash, items that can be converted quickly into cash, and accounts that will be paid to the company within 12 months.

The utility maintains *Cash and Equivalents* (line 10) to pay expenses. It charges the customers for water used and, until the bills have been paid, the money owed to the company represents *Accounts Receivable* (line 11). (Normally, the utility has subtracted out an allowance for receivables that it may not be able to collect.) In addition, the utility has provided water and services for customers who have not yet been billed, but who will be billed shortly, and that amount, *Unbilled Revenues*, is shown (line 12). The utility keeps an inventory of spare parts, chemicals, office supplies, emergency materials, and other items, all of which are included in *Materials and Supplies* (line 13). *Other* (line 14) consists largely of payments for services that the utility has made in advance of receiving those services. The total of those items makes up *Total Current Assets* (line 15).

Other Assets (line 16) contains the balances of expenditures already made but not yet written off, the cost of purchase of intangible assets, and estimates of taxes that the utility will collect from consumers in the future.

Income Taxes Recoverable (line 17) is usually the largest item by far. Under accounting rules promulgated in 1993, utilities record as a liability the deferred taxes that they will have to pay in the future. In a regulated environment, those taxes are a cost of doing business, which utilities can charge to customers. Those deferred taxes constitute money that the utility will have to pay the government in the future (the liability). The customer, though, has an obligation to pay the utility an amount equal to the taxes that the utility has to pay, and that obligation represents an asset. In other words, *Income Taxes Recoverable* is just like an account receivable, except that the utility will collect it over a period of years.

When raising money, whether by selling debt or preferred stock, the utility has to incur costs. The payments to lawyers, printers, and investment bankers add up. Rather than charge off those expenses in the year incurred, the utility places those costs in an account called *Unamortized Debt and Preferred Stock Expense* (line 18). The utility creates an unamortized debt and preferred stock expense for each individual offering of securities, which is then expensed (amortized) over the life of the offering. The figure shown on line 18 is the sum of unamortized expense for all the corporation's offerings, combined.

Other (line 19) is a catchall that could include goodwill (a payment for a business that takes into account the value of its name and the reputation it has with consumers), and various expenses incurred but not yet passed on to customers.

Total Other Assets (line 20) sums *Income Taxes Recoverable, Unamortized Debt and Preferred Stock Expense* and *Other*.

Total Assets (line 21) is the total of all asset items.

LIABILITIES AND CAPITALIZATION

The *Liabilities and Capitalization* portion (line 1) of the balance sheet shows the amounts that owners invested in the business and the amounts the business owes to its creditors. The utility accounts usually begin with a statement of *Capitalization* (line 2), which shows the amount that has been invested in the business for the long term. Money that cannot be taken out of the business before an appointed time (usually more than one year from the date of the balance sheet) is included in this section.

Common Stock at Stated Value (line 3) is a legal value assigned to the shares. Some common stock has a nominal or par value ($1 a share, for example), which is a holdover from the early days of corporate organization. When such shares are sold to the public, the price paid is usually well above par value. The difference between par value and the price for the stock is called *Capital in Excess of Stated Value* (line 4), also known as *paid-in surplus*. For example, if stockholders purchasing 1,000 shares had invested $6,000 for a stock with a $1 a share par value, the common stock account would look like this:

Common stock ($1 par value, 1,000 shares outstanding) $1,000
Capital in excess of par value 5,000

Usually, part of the year's income is paid to stockholders as dividends and part is retained for future use. The portion not distributed is *Retained Earnings* (line 5).

On occasion, the corporation will buy back its stock from shareholders. Repurchased shares, known as *Treasury Stock* (line 6), are shown at the cost that the corporation incurred in buying them back. *Treasury Stock* is a subtraction from shareholders' investment in the corporation.

The sum of *Common at Stated Value, Capital in Excess of Stated Value, Retained Earnings,* less *Treasury Stock* is *Total Common Stockholders Equity* (line 7). In other words, the money that common stockholders have invested in the business plus the income that could have been paid to common shareholders but was retained instead, less money paid out to buy back shares, is their contribution to the capital of the enterprise.

Purchasers of *Preferred Stock* (line 8) receive a fixed dividend that must be paid before common stockholders can receive a dividend. If the company goes out of business, preferred stockholders must be paid in full before holders of the common stock are paid. In those ways, preferred stock is similar to debt. But the rights of preferred shareholders are junior to those of debt holders, and in that way, preferred stock is similar to common stock.

Long-Term Debt (line 9) is money borrowed for more than one year (usually 10 to 30 years). Much long-term debt is sold in the form of first mortgage bonds. Those are debt instruments that are secured by the property of the corporation. The debenture is another form of debt, secured only by the general credit of the corporation. Both types are sold as bonds, which usually pay interest twice a year.

The sum of *Common Equity, Preferred Stock,* and *Long-Term Debt* is the permanent capital or *Total Capitalization* (line 10) of the utility.

The company has obligations that it must pay within 12 months of the date of the balance sheet. Those obligations are *Current Liabilities* (line 11).

Short-Term Borrowings (line 12) consist of bank loans, commercial paper issued, and any other borrowing that the corporation has to pay back within 12 months. *Current Portion of Long-Term Debt* (line 13) represents that portion of long-term debt that comes due for payment within 12 months. Money that the business owes to suppliers and others, debts incurred in the ordinary course of running a business that have not yet been paid, are *Accounts Payable* (line 14). The corporation also calculates the taxes that it owes, and has not paid yet, but will have to pay within 12 months, and shows *Taxes Payable* (line 15). In the same way, the corporation calculates the interest expenses that it has piled up subsequent to its last payment of interest to creditors, and shows *Interest Accrued* (line 16). Finally, *Other* (line 17) includes miscellaneous items, such as preferred dividends declared but not paid and customers' deposits.

The total of the items in *Total Current Liabilities* (line 18) should be compared with total current assets to determine whether current liabilities are covered by current assets. The difference between current assets and current liabilities is called "working capital." When current liabilities exceed current assets, the company has a working capital deficit.

Other Liabilities (line 19) includes taxes deferred for future payment, and various contributions or advances from customers who pay the utility to make plant additions that benefit those customers.

Advances for Construction (line 20) consists of payments that certain customers make to the utility to furnish funds for certain utility plant additions. Once the customer begins to take service, the utility begins a process of paying back all or part of the advance over a period of time. That portion of the advance that will not be refunded is reclassified as *Contributions in Aid of Construction* (line 21), a category that also includes contributions by consumers to help to fund plant additions made without any expectation of repayment. In some regulatory jurisdictions, the company amortizes the contributions over a long period of time. Regulators normally do not let the utility earn a return on contributions, so the contributions, however large, have no real value to shareholders.

Deferred Taxes (line 22) consists of taxes that the utility claimed that it paid (for accounting and regulatory purposes) but that it really will not pay until sometime in the future. The tax savings come largely from two sources. The utility might have used a higher depreciation rate for tax than for book purposes. Or it received an investment tax credit for purchase of machinery, and it chose to spread the tax savings over the life of the plant, rather than show it in the year in which the credit was taken. (The investment tax credit is no longer part off federal tax law, but many utilities are still amortizing credits taken years ago.) *Other* (line 23) includes various items of deferred income and obligations incurred to employees.

Total Other Liabilities (line 24) sums up all those items.

Total Liabilities and Capitalization (line 25) must, of course, equal total assets.

GOVERNMENT-OWNED UTILITY

Obviously, a water supplier is a water supplier, no matter the owner, and every supplier needs the same assets to furnish the service. It does not, however, raise the funds to buy those assets in the same manner. The typical government-owned water supplier that is run as a separate business entity and does its own financing might have a balance sheet like the following:

On the *Asset* side of the balance sheet, items on lines 1 through 8 are the same as those of the investor-owned utility. *Restricted Assets* (line 9) consists of funds set aside for specific purposes. *Funds for Construction* (line 10) have been set aside for specific construction expenditures. *Funds for Debt Service* (line 11) have been set aside to pay the principal or interest on existing debt. *Total Restricted Assets* (line 12) can amount to a significant sum of money. Items on lines 13 through 24 are similar to those shown on the statements of investor-owned utilities.

Balance Sheet
Government-Owned Utility
($ Thousands)

Line		Year Ended Dec. 31, 1996	1997
1.	ASSETS		
2.	Utility plant		
3.	Utility plant in service	$380,000	$400,000
4.	Depreciation and amortization	70,000	79,500
5.	Net utility plant in service	310,000	320,500
6.	Construction work in progress	23,000	40,000
7.	Net utility plant	333,000	360,500
8.	Other property and investments	10,000	10,000
9.	Restricted assets		
10.	Funds held for construction	5,000	7,000
11.	Funds held for debt service	10,000	10,000
12.	Total restricted assets	15,000	17,000
13.	Current assets		
14.	Cash and equivalents	5,000	4,500
15.	Accounts receivable-net	10,000	10,500
16.	Unbilled revenues	5,000	5,500
17.	Materials and supplies	5,000	5,000
18.	Other	5,000	4,000
19.	Total current assets	30,000	29,500
20.	Other assets		
21.	Unamortized debt expense	5,000	4,100
22.	Miscellaneous	5,000	5,900
23.	Total other assets	10,000	10,000
24.	Total assets	398,000	427,000

Line		Year Ended Dec. 31, 1996	1997
1.	LIABILITIES AND CAPITALIZATION		
2.	Capitalization		
3.	Contributed capital	$100,000	$104,000
4.	Retained earnings	73,000	93,000
5.	Total equity	173,000	197,000
6.	Long-term debt	195,500	203,000
7.	Total capitalization	368,500	400,000
8.	Current liabilities		
9.	Short-term borrowings	9,500	10,000
10.	Current portion of long-term debt	5,000	4,000
11.	Accounts payable	5,000	5,000
12.	Interest accrued	5,000	5,000
13.	Other	5,000	3,000
14.	Total current liabilities	29,500	27,000
15.	Total liabilities and capitalization	398,000	427,000

The *Liabilities and Capitalization* (line 1) side of the balance sheet begins with *Capitalization* (line 2). *Contributed Capital* (line 3) consists of the value of funds and assets that the parent municipality or government agency might have contributed to the water utility plus contributions toward construction made by consumers and by the federal government. Items on lines 5 to 14 are similar to those of investor-owned utilities. In some instances, though, the municipal utility will separate those liabilities payable from restricted assets.

CONSOLIDATION

Often, the corporation owns other corporations. In financial parlance, the parent company owns subsidiaries. The subsidiaries have assets and liabilities, and may even have their own debt outstanding. Let us say that the parent company raises $1,000 by selling stock to investors, another $1,000 by selling bonds to investors, and invests $1,000 each in the common stock of two subsidiaries. Each of the subsidiaries then sells $1,000 worth of bonds to investors in order to raise more capital. Each of the subsidiaries then invests $2,000 in plant and equipment.

Working out the asset side of the balance sheet, each of the subsidiaries has $2,000 of plant and equipment for a total of $4,000. The parent company has $2,000 of assets, consisting of stock in the subsidiaries. On the liabilities side, each subsidiary has $1,000 of debt and $1,000 of equity (a total of $2,000 debt and $2,000 equity) and the parent has $1,000 of debt and $1,000 of equity. Should we add up the figure for the subsidiaries and the parent to get a total? The answer is no. We sense that doing so would be wrong by looking at the assets. The combined group really has $4,000 worth of plant and equipment and nothing else. On the liability side, we do know that the three corporate utilities have borrowed $3,000 in total, but they have only raised $1,000 from shareholders, when the parent company sold stock. The accounts have to be consolidated, not added:

	Subsidiary One	Subsidiary Two	Parent	Consolidating Adjustment	Consolidated
Assets:					
Plant and Equipment	$2,000	$2,000	0		$4,000
Common Stock Investments	0	0	$2,000	($2,000)	0
Total	$2,000	$2,000	$2,000	($2,000)	$4,000
Liabilities:					
Debt	$1,000	$1,000	$1,000	0	$3,000
Common equity	1,000	1,000	1,000	($2,000)	1,000
Total	$2,000	$2,000	$2,000	($2,000)	$4,000

Regulators and creditors of the subsidiaries will look at the balance sheet of the subsidiaries, but common stockholders of the parent will be concerned with the consolidated statement.

CHAPTER 29

The Statement of Cash Flows

*Every company that has put its trust in financial manipulation as a substitute
for purposeful management has eventually come to grief.*[14]

— Peter F. Drucker

The balance sheet tells what the company owns and owes at the end of a given day. The income statement helps to determine the profitability of the firm's operations for a given period. The statement of cash flows analyzes the cash received and disbursed in a given period. Accountants have developed several kinds of cash statements: the statement of change in financial position, the statement of source of funds used for construction, and the statement of cash flows.

VARIATIONS ON A THEME

Let us start with simplified examples. Stock worth $3,000 is sold to raise money. Cash in the bank at the beginning of the year, therefore, is $3,000. The company collects $1,000 in cash profits from its business operations during the year. It pays a $500 dividend to stockholders. The company constructs a new machine costing $6,000. No money is owed on a current basis at the beginning of the period. (Current assets consisted of $3,000 cash in the bank. There are no current liabilities. Working capital is $3,000 at the beginning of the year.) Here is how the statements should appear:

Statement of Changes in Financial Position

Sources of Funds	
Profit	$1,000
Sale of stock	3,000
Total sources of funds	$4,000
Uses of Funds	
Purchase of machine	$6,000
Dividend	500
Total	$6,500
Increase (decrease) in working capital	(2,500)
Total uses of funds	$4,000

Statement of Sources of Funds Used for Construction

Sources of Funds	
Profit	$1,000
Less Dividends	500
Earnings retained in the business	$500
Sale of stock	$3,000
Decrease in working capital	2,500
Total sources of funds used for construction	$6,000

Statement of Cash Flows

Cash flows from operating activities	
Profit	$1,000
Change in assets and liabilities	0
Net cash provided by operations	$1,000
Cash flow from investing activities	
Purchase of machinery	(6,000)
Cash flow from financing activities	
Sale of stock	3,000
Dividends	(500)
Net cash from financing activities	$2,500
Net change in cash and cash equivalents	(2,500)
Cash and cash equivalents at beginning	3,000
Cash and cash equivalents at end of year	$ 500

Variations are possible. The above statements should be viewed as skeletal examples. The *Statement of Changes in Financial Position* and the *Statement of Sources of Funds for Construction* have the advantage of simplicity in concept and terminology. Unfortunately, accountants have opted for the third method, the *Statement of Cash Flows*, which mixes cash flows from operations with changes in working capital, calls spending on machinery a negative cash flow, and puts dividends and stock sales into one category. So that is what we have to work with until the accountants have a change of heart.

THE STATEMENT OF CASH FLOWS

We will start with the statement of a normal investor-owned water utility. Keep in mind that terminology and breakdown into number of items will differ from company to company. (For convenience, the table that follows endorses the financial statement. Thus, changes in all *Current Assets* other than *Accounts Receivable* are shown together as *Other Current Assets*. All changes in *Current Liabilities* other than *Accounts Payable* are shown together as *Other Current Liabilities*. All *Deferred Credits*, from whatever source, are lumped together, too.)

The statement begins with a grouping entitled *Cash Flows from Operating Activities* (line 1), basically what is left over from the year's revenues after the expenses that require cash outlay (such as interest on debt, payments for electricity or purchased water, or salaries) are paid. The first item (line 2) is the *Net Income*, which is reported before adjusting for any items that do not result in cash. To that we must add expenses that do not require cash outlays, or subtract reported income that does not bring in any cash. *Items Not Requiring (Providing) Cash* follow (line 3). Usually the largest such item is *Depreciation and Amortization* (line 4). Any number of other expense categories could follow, but the bulk of them involve *Deferred Credits* (line 5), which usually consists of deferred taxes, that is, taxes that are shown as expenses in the income statement but which will not be paid until some time in the future. For most utilities, the biggest addition to income that involves no current cash inflow is the *Allowance for Equity Funds Used During*

Statement of Cash Flows for the Year 1997
Investor-Owned Utility Format
($ Thousands)

Line		
1. Cash flows from operating activities		
2.	Net income	$19,400
3.	Items not requiring (providing) cash	
4.	Depreciation and amortization	9,500
5.	Deferred credits	3,000
6.	Allowance for equity funds used during construction	(1,000)
7.	Other	900
8. Changes in assets and liabilities		
9.	Accounts receivable	(500)
10.	Other current assets	500
11.	Accounts payable	(2,100)
12.	Other current liabilities	(2,000)
13.	Other	(2,000)
14. Net cash provided by operating activities		25,700
15. Cash flows from investing activities		
16.	Construction expenditures	(37,000)
17.	Allowance for equity funds used during construction	1,000
18.	Other	(900)
19. Net cash used in investing activities		(36,900)
20. Cash flows from financing activities		
21.	Dividends on common and preferred stock	12,200
22.	Debt repayments and securities purchases	
23.	Purchase of treasury stock	(100)
24.	Repayment of short-term debt	0
25.	Repayment of long-term debt	(5,000)
26.	Issuance of securities	
27.	Proceeds from issuance of long-term debt	4,000
28.	Increase in short-term borrowings	500
29.	Proceeds from sale of common stock	22,500
30. Advances and contributions for construction		1,000
31. Net cash provided by financing activities		10,700
32. Net change in cash and equivalents		(500)
33. Cash and equivalents at beginning of year		5,000
34. Cash and equivalents at end of year		$ 4,500

Construction (line 6). Note that this is the first line in parentheses, meaning that it has to be subtracted from the cash inflows shown above it, since it had already been included in *Net Income. Other* (line 7) includes all other reported expenses that do not require cash outlays.

The accounting format just marches on, but we need to stop here for a minute. The items through line 7, the cash flows from operating activities, add up to $31,800. The income statement for 1997, shown on page 291 in Chapter 27, reported $106,000 of revenue. Out of those receipts, after paying expenses, the utility has generated $31,800 to buy new equipment, pay debts, or declare dividends. Some of the cash produced has to be used to invest in the business for the future, or to pay off obligations incurred in the past. The utility might have to pay some suppliers that it kept waiting last year, or buy extra chemicals ahead of time because it looks as if there might be a chemical strike next year.

Change in Assets and Liabilities (line 8) is the next grouping. When *Accounts Receivable* (line 9) increases, it means that the customers owe more to the utility (which presumably has to take cash out of its own bank account to pay suppliers until it gets paid by the customers). On the other hand, a decrease in receivables from customers increases the firm's cash, because customers have paid their bills. Utilities have to keep materials and supplies on hand. They have to lay out money to pump the water even before they get to bill the customer, which creates a receivable for unbilled revenue. In this case, the utility did not have to spend more cash on increasing its inventory and supplies, but it did have to lay out $500 to produce water for which it had not yet billed. Fortunately, it also turned $1,000 of various current assets into cash. As a result, the change in *Other Current Assets* added to cash flow by $500. Suppliers have to be paid, and when *Accounts Payable* (line 11) are brought down, that too requires cash, as in this example. (Of course, if the utility lets the accounts payable run up, it would be reducing cash outflow, at least until the company had to pay its bills.) *Other Current Liabilities* (line 12) includes expenses that the utility has not gotten around to paying. When these liabilities increase, the utility has saved cash, at least until time of payment. In our example, the utility reduced the account, paying the expenses. *Other* (line 13) includes any other change in assets and liabilities that produces or reduces cash.

The total of changes in assets and liabilities net out to ($6,100), that is, reduces cash by $6,100. Adding up the cash flows from operating activities and from changes in assets and liabilities, we come to *Net Cash Provided by Operating Activities* (line 14), a total of $25,700.

Companies do more than work with what they have on hand or what comes from the year's operations. They make investments to enlarge their productive capability, as an example, or sell off properties when they decide to get out of a business. *Cash Flows from Investing Activities* (line 15) includes such purchases and sales. For most utilities, *Construction Expenditures* (line 16) is a large figure, given the need to fix up old plant, upgrade for new environmental and health regulations, and to expand facilities to meet the demand of new customers. The construction figure, though, includes all capitalized allowances for funds, which do not represent an outflow of cash. Accountants, however, choose to adjust the cash flow analysis by only part of the AFUDC. *Allowance for Equity Funds Used During Construction* (line 17) is removed from the total construction figure, and the net outflow of cash for construction (not shown in the statement) really is $36,000. If the company has made *Other* investments (line 18), that would show as an outflow of cash, and if it had sold investments, doing so would have added to cash. Altogether, lines 16 to 18 add up to *Net Cash Used in Investing Activities* (line 19), a total of $36,900.

Note that the utility collected $25,700 in cash from operations, but it has expended $36,900 on its construction program. So far, then, the statement shows that the utility has expended $11,200 more than it has taken in. Obviously, no business can run that way. Where did it get the $11,200?

Cash Flows from Financing Activities (line 20) accounts for how the utility raises much of its cash needs. As a start, though, the utility has shareholders that expect *Dividends on Preferred and Common Stock* (line 21), which are paid out during the year and represent a drain on cash. The utility has to pay off debt, and it might want to buy back some of its shares of stock, all of which requires cash. Those transactions are included in *Debt Repayments and Securities Purchases* (line 22). It will expend funds for *Purchase of Treasury Stock* (line 23), for *Repayment of Short-Term Debt* (line 24) and for *Repayment of Long-Term Debt* (line 25). On the other hand, *Issuances of Securities* (line 26) brings in cash. This utility raised cash from *Proceeds from Issuance of Long-Term Debt* (line 27), *Increase in Short-Term Borrowings* (line 28) and from *Proceeds from Sale of Common Stock* (line 29). In addition, however, potential customers and real estate developers that wanted water service plunked down *Advances and Contributions to Construction* (line 30). The *Net Cash Provided by Financing Activities* (line 31) adds up to $10,700, which is $500 less than the shortfall we calculated previously. In other words, the financings raised less than what was spent, and the deficit is the year's *Net Change in Cash and Equivalents* (line 32). If that sum is added to the *Cash and Equivalents at Beginning of Year* (line 33), we end up with *Cash and Equivalents at End of Year* (line 34).

GOVERNMENT-OWNED UTILITY

The statement of cash flows of the government-owned utility follows the same format. In the end, while some of the line labels may differ, there is almost no difference, conceptually, between the cash flow statements of the investor-owned and government-owned water utilities. Cash seems the most basic of metrics. Obviously it defers no taxes because it pays no taxes, and shows no dividend payments because it has no shareholders.

(See page 312 for Statement of Cash Flows)

Statement of Cash Flows
for the Year 1997
Government-Owned Utility Format
($ Thousands)

Line		
1.	Cash flows from operating activities	
2.	Net income	$41,600
3.	Items not requiring (providing) cash	
4.	Depreciation and amortization	9,500
5.	Allowance for funds used during construction	(1,000)
6.	Other	900
7.	Changes in assets and liabilities	
8.	Accounts receivable	(500)
9.	Other current assets	500
10.	Accounts payable	0
11.	Other current liabilities	(2,000)
12.	Other	(2,900)
13.	Net cash provided by operating activities	46,100
14.	Cash flows from investing activities	
15.	Construction expenditures	(37,000)
16.	Allowance for funds used during construction	1,000
17.	Net cash used in investing activities	(36,000)
18.	Cash flows from financing activities	
19.	Payment to city	(21,600)
20.	Debt Payments	
21.	Repayment of short-term debt	0
22.	Repayment of long-term debt	(5,000)
23.	Issuance of securities	
24.	Proceeds from issuance of long-term debt	11,500
25.	Increase in short-term borrowings	500
26.	Advances for construction (contributed capital)	4,000
31.	Net cash provided by financing activities	(10,600)
32.	Net change in cash and equivalents	(500)
33.	Cash and equivalents at beginning of year	5,000
34.	Cash and equivalents at end of year	$ 4,500

CHAPTER 30

Financial Analysis

The objectives of security analysis are twofold. First it seeks to present the important facts in a manner most informing and useful. . . . Second, it seeks to reach dependable conclusions . . . as to the safety and attractiveness of a given security. . . .[15]

— Graham, Dodd, and Cottle

The balance sheet, income statement, and flow of funds statement provide the raw material needed to analyze the finances of the corporation. But what about government-owned utilities? Does financial analysis apply to them? After all, they raise money by selling bonds. The local government or some insurance fund might guarantee the debt, no matter how bad the financial picture of the water utility. The government-owned water utilities, moreover, have developed ways to siphon off revenues into special funds that are safer than the general flow of revenues for the benefit of certain creditors. For that matter, even the private suppliers are regulated utilities. Many think that regulators will bail them out when they get into trouble. All the utility need do is request rate relief, and the regulator will jack up prices to provide the needed revenues. Right? That is the way many people see the picture.

Unfortunately, shaky finances have a cost. The need to support a weak, municipal utility affects the city's overall credit standing, which, in turn, raises the cost of borrowed money, or the cost, or even the availability of credit insurance. Diverting funds to payment of certain issues of debt may enhance the credit standing of those debt issues that benefit, but it degrades the credit-worthiness of those debt issues from which the flow of revenues was diverted. Investor-owned utilities, too, pay the price for financial weakness in terms of higher cost of capital. In theory, the regulators should pass on those higher capital costs to consumers, but in reality, they may not. They have, after all, charged off the costs of bad decisions to shareholders in the past and they have permitted utilities to go bankrupt in extreme cases.

In short, investors will analyze the finances of the utility, and its parent, and the utility's owner should promulgate financial policies that will withstand such scrutiny.

THE BALANCE SHEET

Water companies are notoriously capital intensive, meaning that they require massive assets in order to serve their customers. Thus, financial analysts must focus more on the balance sheet for water utilities than for most organizations.

The plant account is the most important section on the asset side of the balance sheet. How much plant is actually in service and how much is under construction? In some jurisdictions, the regulator will not allow the company to earn a return on plant that has not been put into service, that is, a return on construction work in progress (CWIP). If a large part of the utility's assets are in CWIP, and the construction program is behind schedule, the utility might be put under financial pressure while trying to finance the project.

For that matter, if the CWIP is not included in the rate base (that is, not earning a return), the utility might need a large rate increase, possibly too large for the regulators to grant all at once, upon completion of the plant. Also, we want to compare the proposed spending program with the plant already in place. A huge spending program in relation to present facilities means that the rate base will grow rapidly, probably faster than operating income will grow unaided by rate relief. That means that rate of return on rate base will drop unless the utility gets a substantial amount of rate relief, which is difficult to obtain all at once. For a quick analysis, compare the capital spending program on utility plant (including AFUDC) with the gross plant of the utility (the sum of plant in service and construction work in progress, before depreciation) at the beginning of the period.

That ratio, then, should be compared with those for other utilities. The higher the ratio of spending to plant, the more likely it is that the utility will require substantial amounts of outside financing to complete the capital expenditure effort, and require large rate hikes to offset the costs of the new capital. Keep in mind that the water utility eventually should collect sufficient revenue to pay the return on new capital. The problem comes about because too big an increase in plant triggers the requirement for too big an increase in rates, in too short a period of time. Remember, too, that the utility did not put in much of the new plant because it had new customers ready to pay, or because the new plant raised the productivity of the system, but rather because the old plant had reached a state of senescence, or because the government ordered new environmental safeguards. In other words, the utility did not add on new plant because the customer demanded new services for which he was willing to pay. Rather, the utility had to make the plant additions, which were not associated with demand for service by customers, and the plant addition triggered the utility's demand for additional revenue from the customer to pay for the additional plant. Too much new plant could create financial stress and regulatory problems. Here is an example:

1. Utility plant at original cost (gross plant in service)	$1,000
2. Less depreciation	200
3. Net utility plant in service	800
4. Construction work in progress (CWIP)	300
5. Net utility plant	1,100

Gross plant = line 1 + line 4 = $1,300

$$\text{CWIP as \% of gross plant} = \left(\frac{\$300}{\$1,300}\right) \times 100 = 23\%$$

Construction program for next three years:

6. Capital expenditures	$400
7. AFUDC	100
8. Total	500

Construction program as % of beginning of period gross plant in service =

$$\frac{\text{line 8}}{\text{line 1}} = \frac{\$500}{\$1,000} = 50\%$$

Think about the situation. The water utility will increase plant in service about 23% when the CWIP is completed and another 50% when the three-year construction program ends. This adds up to big increases for a utility that may be increasing sales 2% to 3% a year, in a basically noninflationary economy. If we define rate base as net plant in service, and figure that CWIP and all construction go into the rate base within three years, then the rate base would rise about 23% per year. The utility, conceivably, might have to raise prices 20% per year to pay for the additions, and regulators might gag at increases of that size.

The capitalization also deserves attention, for both financial and regulatory reasons. When a large proportion of the capital is provided by debt, the company is said to be leveraged. The covenants or indentures that govern the company's borrowing put limits on how much debt can be sold. Many companies borrow large amounts of short-term debt. Some have a permanent layer of short-term debt and thus always owe money to banks or to other short-term lenders. Short-term debt has a different call on assets (if something goes wrong) than does long-term debt, but the obligation to pay is still there.

Some companies exclude short-term debt from their calculations of capitalization ratios. Doing so can be misleading. Here is an example of how inclusion or exclusion of a large amount of short-term debt affects capitalization ratios.

	Amount	Capitalization Ratio or % of Total
With short-term debt		
Common equity	$ 500	41.7%
Preferred stock	100	8.3
Long-term debt	400	33.3
Short-term debt	200	16.7
Total	$1,200	100.0%
Without short-term debt		
Common equity	$ 500	50.0%
Preferred stock	100	10.0
Long-term debt	400	40.0
Total	$1,000	100.0%

Sometimes the utility undertakes an obligation that is equivalent to creating long-term debt. On occasion, the company leases equipment from others on terms that are the equivalent of buying the equipment and borrowing money to pay for it. Electric utilities used to sign long-term contracts to buy electricity from others, and in doing so, undertook a long-term obligation that many credit experts insisted was no different than debt. Today, a municipal water supplier might sign a contract to buy water from another government agency for decades, at terms that pay off the interest and principal of the investment that the government agency made in order to serve the water supplier. This long-term purchase obligation is equivalent to taking responsibility for the debt of the government agency. Analysts should take care that the reported debt of the water supplier, whether investor- or government-owned, includes obligations that are the equivalent of debt.

The final question that deserves attention is: are current assets sufficient to pay current liabilities? In an emergency, selling properties or raising money from outside sources could take a long time, but current liabilities still would have to be paid when due. Current assets include cash or items that can be converted quickly into cash. Therefore, the greater the ratio of current assets to current liabilities, the easier it would be for the utility to meet its obligations. Analysts of the utility industry have had a tendency to ignore the relation between current assets and current liabilities on the ground that a utility can easily sell securities to raise the cash necessary to pay current obligations. Having working capital, however, provides financial flexibility, which has value, in itself.

The ratio of current assets to current liabilities is called the *current ratio*. The difference between current assets and current liabilities is *working capital*.

Current assets $5,000
Current liabilities   2,000

Current ratio = $\dfrac{\$5,000}{\$2,000}$ = 2.5, or 2.5 to 1

Working capital = $5,000 − $2,000 = $3,000

A large amount of short-term debt may create additional risk for the utility. Because short-term interest rates are unstable, the firm's income could be affected by the rise and fall of interest costs. A large amount of short-term debt also creates financing inflexibility. To pay its debts, the utility might be forced to offer long-term securities at an unfavorable time, and might not even be able to raise sufficient funds.

Capitalization plays a role in regulation. Regulators want the utility to raise money in the least expensive fashion to keep down the rates charged to customers. Regulators believe that debt financing is cheaper than equity financing, because creditors have a protected position and therefore settle for lower profits than stockholders, who take the risks. Interest charges, moreover, reduce income taxes, so part of the cost of debt can be offset through lower taxes. Here is how some regulators might calculate costs of capital for two capitalizations:

	Amount		% Cost		After Tax Return Calculated by Regulators	Pretax Return (35% Tax Rate) Paid by Consumers
Example A: Low Leverage						
Debt	$ 300	×	10%	=	$ 30.00	$ 30.00
Equity	700	×	15%	—	105.00	161.54
Total	$1,000				$135.00	$191.54
Example B: High Leverage						
Debt	$ 700	×	10%	=	$ 70.00	$ 70.00
Equity	300	×	15%	=	45.00	69.23
Total	$1,000				$115.00	$139.23
Ratio of A to B					117%	138%

The preceding examples reveal a conflict of interest. The regulator wants the utility to finance by means of debt to keep down the cost of capital. On the other hand, the utility may want to keep down the use of debt because too much debt increases the risk and may increase interest costs enough to offset savings derived from the lower equity ratio. For example, assume that two utilities have $1,000 of capitalization, one borrowed $300 and the other $700, a storm wipes out $200 of each company's assets, and the companies must go out of business. Before stockholders receive anything, owners of debt must be paid in full. What would be left for stockholders?

	Low Leverage	High Leverage
Original assets	$1,000	$1,000
less: Storm damage	200	200
Assets available for distribution	800	800
less: Payment of debt	300	700
equals: Assets available for distribution to stockholders	500	100
Original stockholder investment	$ 700	$ 300
Loss of investment	200	200
Loss as % of investment	29%	67%

THE INCOME STATEMENT

Balance sheets change slowly, but income statements change rapidly. Those changes can tell a great deal about the utility and the direction in which it is going. For that matter, value depends on the income stream. Assets have no value unless they can produce income.

Financial analysts often compare the income statements of different companies in the same business, in order to determine which of the firms operates more efficiently. They compare the income statement of one firm in a given accounting period to the statement of the same firm in a previous accounting period, in order to determine whether the firm is becoming more or less efficient. They examine income statements to determine the contribution of one line of business against another (water versus wastewater, for instance). And, they use financial statements to provide a rough idea of how increased or decreased volume affects profitability. At the same time, the analysis of the income statement may have less in importance in the water industry, with its emphasis on assets and rate of return, than in competitive businesses that work to maintain high margins of profit per dollar of sales and to minimize the assets required to maintain the business.

Ideally, the income statement should look like this:

		%
Revenues	$1,000	100
Costs that directly vary with production, volume, distribution and collection (pumping, chemicals, operating employees, purchase of water from others)	200	20
Margin on sales	800	80
Expenses that do not vary directly with volume sold		
Administrative and general expenses	300	30
Property taxes	100	10
Depreciation	100	10
Total non-variable expenses	500	50
Pretax income from operations	300	30
Interest expense	150	15
Pretax income	150	15
Income taxes ($30 current and $20 deferred)	50	5
Net income	100	10

With this statement, we could draw several conclusions. First, we can determine the utility's sensitivity to changes in sales volume. Assume that the utility has in place all the plant it needs to supply existing and new customers for the foreseeable future. Note, then, that of every dollar of revenue, only 20 cents goes to producing and distributing the product. To put it another way, for every $1.00 of additional revenue, 80 cents flows down to pretax income. That analysis shows that the company would gain greatly if it could convince existing customers to take more water (up to the point at which the utility has to incur the added burden of adding on new facilities). It also shows why the income of water companies is so sensitive to changes in weather conditions that encourage more or less usage, or to drought-imposed water curtailments. Most costs remain unchanged, no matter how much sales volume rises or falls. We might want to compare the situation of this water company to others, to determine which one will gain or lose the most from conditions that would change sales volume.

Second, we can determine how much cash that the revenue stream produces. We know that firms can disguise their profitability (or lack thereof) by introducing accounting gimmicks but they cannot hide the cash content of the income statement. In this case, leaving out various non-cash items, the company brings down $220 of cash (net income of $100 plus deferred taxes of $20 plus depreciation of $100) per $1,000 of revenue. If the ratio changes over time, we would want to know why. Analysts certainly would compare the cash component of earnings from utility to utility. Presumably, investors would prefer to put their money in those utilities that produce the most cash per dollar of revenue, all other things being equal.

Third, analysts will examine how the various components of expenses vary between company, or vary over time for the same company. For instance, they might ask why our utility spends 20% of revenue to actually produce and deliver the water when the average water utility spends only 15%. Does this indicate that our company operated inefficiently? Why does it spend 30% of every dollar on administrative expenses? Is the company hopelessly bureaucratic? Or does some peculiarity of the source of water supply, or the need to comply with extraordinary regulatory rules, force up the company's expenses? Analyzing the company's efficiency through the operating statement produces questions more than it produces answers.

Finally, creditors will analyze the income statement to assure themselves that the utility remains creditworthy. In this case, they note that the income available to pay interest on debt (pretax operating income) is $300, or twice the annual interest charge.

The analyst looking at the statement of the government-owned utility might see:

Revenues	$1,000
Costs associated directly with production and distribution	200
Margin on sale	800
Expenses that do not vary with volume sold	
Administrative and general	300
Depreciation	100
Total non-variable expenses	400
Income from operations	400
Interest expense	200
Net income	200

Comments made about sensitivity of income to changes in volume, and about the efficiency of operations, apply here, as well. Income from operations covers interest expense twice over, too, despite the higher interest expenses (the municipal utility borrows more money). Here, however, the analyst will look for the amount of bonds that have to be paid in the year ($100 in this case), and add that item to interest paid to come up with debt service ($300). How much cash does the utility generate to cover debt service? The answer is $500 (income from operations of $400 plus depreciation of $100). Thus the utility covers debt service 1.6 times.

In reality, of course, the analyses are more complicated, and require understanding of the impact of such items as tax deferrals and allowance for funds.

Despite the jokes about businesses with different sets of books (one for me, one for my partners, one for the accountants, one for the IRS, etc.), large regulated businesses often do have one set of books for the regulator, one for investors, and one for the income tax people. The regulators want the figures laid out in a set order, and they accept some items as costs of doing business and disallow others. Investors require a certain format and accounting standards. The Internal Revenue Service lets the company take expenses that accountants view as out of place in a particular year, and might not consider some normal accounting expenses as legitimate deductions for tax purposes.

The treatment of depreciation probably creates the greatest discrepancy between what the IRS and what the rest of the world accepts. Regulation requires that the utility rate structure must cover all costs of providing services, including income taxes. Yet the income tax on the tax books differs from that reported to shareholders and to regulatory agencies. For instance, the utility might use accelerated depreciation for tax purposes and straight line depreciation for book (reported to shareholders) purposes. In the example that follows, accelerated depreciation produces higher depreciation expense in early years than the straight line method, and its use reduces current payments of income taxes. At some time in the future, though, accelerated will be lower than straight line depreciation, thereby increasing tax payments in that future period:

Accelerated Depreciation
(Tax Reporting)

	Year 1	Year 5	Year 10
Revenues	$100	$100	$100
Operating expenses	30	30	30
Depreciation	20	10	0
Pretax income	$ 50	$ 60	$ 70
Income taxes (50% tax rate)	25	30	35
Net Income	$ 25	$ 30	$ 35

Straight Line Depreciation
(Tax Reporting)

	Year 1	Year 5	Year 10
Revenues	$100	$100	$100
Operating expenses	30	30	30
Depreciation	10	10	10
Pretax income	$ 60	$ 60	$ 60
Income taxes (50% tax rate)	30	30	30
Net Income	$ 30	$ 30	$ 30

The utility uses accelerated depreciation for tax purposes, thereby reducing taxes, but uses straight line depreciation for book and regulatory purposes. In Year 1, the utility actually paid $25 in income taxes. In time, however, the company's taxes will rise (so long as plant subject to depreciation does not also increase). Proper accounting procedure calls for the company to report taxes on the books as if straight line depreciation had also been used for tax purposes. The difference between the $25 actually paid and the $30 that would have been paid represents deferred taxes, which will be paid some time in the future when accelerated depreciation drops below straight line depreciation.

Let us consider the example of a growing utility that writes off $40 of original plant during a five-year period, uses accelerated depreciation for tax purposes, and adds $20 a year to its plant account for five years. In the following statement, the depreciation on additional plant is shown separately. The example is simplified, and does not necessarily show the exact pattern of actual tax depreciation, but rather indicates how tax depreciation is higher than book depreciation in early years and lower in later years of the life of the plant.

Accelerated Depreciation
(Tax Reporting)

	Year 1	Year 2	Year 3	Year 4	Year 5
Revenues	$100	$125	$156	$196	$245
Operating expenses	30	38	47	59	74
Depreciation of plant in service in					
Year 1	16	10	6	4	4
Year 2	0	8	5	3	2
Year 3	0	0	8	5	3
Year 4	0	0	0	8	5
Year 5	0	0	0	0	8
Total Depreciation	16	18	19	20	22
Pretax income	54	69	90	117	149
Income taxes (50% rate)	27	34.5	45	58.5	74.5
Net income	27	34.5	45	58.5	74.5

Note that depreciation for tax purposes does not decline, because new plant is being added. The additional depreciation on the new plant offsets the falloff of depreciation on the older plant. Using straight line depreciation, the income statement would appear as follows:

Straight Line Depreciation
(Tax Reporting)

	Year 1	Year 2	Year 3	Year 4	Year 5
Revenues	$100	$125	$156	$196	$245
Operating expenses					
Depreciation of plant	30	38	47	59	74
placed on service in					
Year 1	8	8	8	8	8
Year 2	0	4	4	4	4
Year 3	0	0	4	4	4
Year 4	0	0	0	4	4
Year 5	0	0	0	0	4
Total Depreciation	8	12	16	20	24
Pretax income	62	75	93	117	147
Income taxes (50% rate)	31	37.5	46.5	58.5	73.5
Net income	31	37.5	46.5	58.5	73.5

Some items associated with the construction program are expensed for tax purposes but are capitalized for book purposes. For example, certain state and local taxes have to be paid on plant under construction. Those local taxes are legitimate deductible expenses for income tax purposes and are used by the utility to reduce its federal income tax payments. By lowering income taxes, the reported operating income of the utility has been increased, as has the rate of return. The question remains whether that is a proper way to match expenses with revenues. The deductible state and local taxes are not shown in the income statement because they are associated with construction of plant and therefore are capitalized. Why should the income tax saving be included in income, for the benefit of current ratepayers who are not contributing to the upkeep of the plant under construction? The solution is to put off tax savings by means of a deferred tax expense item in the income statement.

Income tax savings are also derived from interest charges attributable to borrowing made to support construction work in progress. The logic is identical to that used in the preceding example. If ratepayers do not bear any of the burden of supporting construction work, why should they gain from the tax savings generated? The solution is to set up a deferred tax account as an operating expense to offset the tax savings. An offsetting tax credit is included in other income, because operating income had to be reduced by deferred taxes for regulatory purposes, but there was no reason to change net income.

The various tax laws have created formulas for depreciation, such as double-declining-balance or sum-of-the-years-digits for tax purposes. Another method depreciates property for tax purposes over fewer years than for regulatory purposes. For instance, a utility can depreciate a particular type of plant over a 20-year period for tax purposes, while using a 30-year period for regulatory purposes. Because of the capital-intensive nature of the utility business, depreciation is a major item on both the income and the cash flow statements. The *composite book depreciation rate* is the rate of depreciation of plant in service as shown on the books of the corporation, as opposed to the usually higher rate used for tax purposes. The book depreciation rate is a straight line rate for most utility companies. Furthermore, and this is a key point, the rate of depreciation usually must be approved by the regulatory agency that has jurisdiction over the company. Depreciation is a cost of doing business that must be offset by revenues. The higher the depreciation rate, the more the customer must pay in current utility bills. At the same time, a higher depreciation rate increases cash flow, thereby allowing the utility to finance internally more of its expansion and to have less dependence on the capital markets.

Different kinds of utility plants require different depreciation rates. A telephone company might use 7%, an electric or gas company 3% or 4%, and a water company around 2%. Even within an industry, the appropriate rate will vary. Similar utilities may have different book depreciation rates. A higher rate is favorable for investors, because it creates a greater cash flow.

The *allowance for funds used during construction* (AFUDC) is a credit item in the income statement and is intended to be an offset to capital charges incurred before plant is placed in service. Those capitalized charges are added to the cost of the plant when it goes into service. The utility can then earn a return on the cost of the physical plant plus the capital costs incurred in building the plant. Sometimes the AFUDC rate is higher than the rate of return the utility can earn on the property once it is in service. In that situation, reported earnings are higher during construction than during operation. Unlike the sale of a product or service, AFUDC produces no immediate cash flow. Distortion of earnings and cash flow problems are likely to be most severe for utilities that capitalize construction costs at a high rate. Basically, AFUDC is split into two parts: the portion resulting from raising debt money to finance the construction and the portion allocated to equity funding.

AFUDC suffers from two problems: it assumes that income spread over a period of years (the return on the AFUDC capitalized into the rate base) is as good as the return collected on construction work in progress in the current year, and that a bookkeeping credit is as good as cash. Financial analysis should take note of what proportion of earnings is derived from selling a product and what proportion is from an accounting credit.

Financial theorists, investment analysts, corporate financial people, and bankers now put emphasis on a number that does not appear in the financial statement: *earnings before interest, taxes, depreciation, and amortization*, or EBITDA. This is the flow of cash derived from operations, before payments for interest or taxes. EBITDA is unaffected by accounting gimmicks that make income look better by reducing depreciation or other noncash expenses, or by boosting noncash income credits. Use of EBITDA provides a measure of profitability unaffected by capitalization or interest payments. Someone purchasing an entire business buys the EBITDA cash flow, and then decides how to finance the purchase (with or without debt). A bank lending money to the purchaser would want to know the expected EBITDA because that is the flow that will pay the interest and the principal. EBITDA shows what the business produces, in hard cash, without the distortions. The ordinary income statements of two utilities, for example, look like this:

	Utility A	Utility B
Revenues	$500	$500
Operating expenses	300	300
Depreciation	50	70
Income taxes	35	32
	385	402
Operating income	115	98
Interest expense	50	40
Net income	65	58

Just looking at the income statement, and assuming that both companies have made the same $1,000 investment to serve customers, we might conclude that company A is more valuable, and certainly more profitable. Now let us rearrange the numbers to determine EBITDA:

	Utility A	Utility B
Revenues	$500	$500
Operating expenses	(300)	(300)
EBITDA	200	200
Depreciation	(50)	(70)
Interest	(50)	(40)
Pretax Income	100	90
Income taxes	(35)	(32)
Net income	65	58

From the standpoint of the cash produced from selling the product, both companies produce the same EBITDA, and that EBITDA produces a 20% cash return on the $1,000 invested. Furthermore, each company produces $200 of cash income for every $500 received from customers. That is, they are equally efficient in terms of operations. Company A simply has found a way to make its income statement look better. EBITDA plays an important role in the valuation of companies, nowadays.

To simplify the analysis, restate the income accounts to combine all AFUDC into the other income section and all interest into one line. The standard format and the analytical format are shown below:

	Standard	Analytical
Revenue	$1,000	$1,000
Operating expenses except income taxes	500	500
Income taxes	200	200
Operating income	300	300
Other income:		
Allowance for other funds used during construction	10	30*
Income tax credits	4	4
Miscellaneous	1	1
Income before interest charges	315	335
Interest on long-term debt	30	30
Other interest	20	20
Allowance for borrowed funds used during construction	(20)	---
Net interest charges	30	50
Net income	$ 285	$ 285

*All AFUDC.

Owners of debt and preferred stock examine the income statement to determine the safety of their investments. *Pretax interest coverage,* how much money is available from earnings to pay interest charges, is one of the standards used to determine the strength of a debt security. Although many persons think of a corporation's assets as protection for debt holders, what would the assets be worth if they could not generate income? Pretax income is used for the analysis because interest charges must be met before any income taxes can be paid. Unfortunately, the analytical format is better suited to equity analysis than to debt analysis and is inadequate for calculating interest coverages because it does not give figures on a pretax basis. A condensed format for interest coverage analysis would be:

Line	
1. Revenue	$1,000
2. Operating expenses except income taxes	500
3. Pretax operating income	500
4. Other income	35
5. Pretax income before interest charges	535
6. Interest charges	50
7. Pretax net income	485
8. Income taxes	200
9. Net income	285

Interest coverages:

$$\text{Pretax operating income} = \frac{\text{line 3}}{\text{line 6}} = \frac{\$500}{\$50} = 10.0x$$

$$\text{Pretax income before interest charges} = \frac{\text{line 5}}{\text{line 6}} = \frac{\$535}{\$50} = 10.7x$$

The following example restates a detailed income statement. The numbers are then used to calculate some standard coverage ratios for interest charges.

Line	Utility Analytical (Equity)	Line-by-Line Formula
1. Revenues	$1,000	
2. Operating expenses		
3. Operations*	400	
4. Depreciation	100	
5. Income taxes	100	
6. Total Operating expenses	600	3 + 4 + 5
7. Operating income	400	1 − 6
8. Other income		
9. AFUDC**	80	
10. Miscellaneous	20	
11. Total other income	100	9 + 10
12. Income before interest charges	500	7 + 11
13. Interest charges	300	
14. Net income	200	12 − 13
15. Preferred dividends	50	
16. Net available to common stock	$ 150	14 − 15
17. Average shares of common stock	100	
18. Earnings per average share	$1.50	16 ÷ 17

 * Includes rentals, the interest component of which is $10.
 ** Allowance for equity and debt funds.

Line	Utility Analytical (Debt)	Line-by-Line Formula
1. Revenues	$1,000	
2. Operating expenses excluding income taxes		
3. Operations*	400	
4. Depreciation	100	
5. Total operating expenses excluding income taxes	500	3 + 4
6. Pretax operating income	500	1 − 5
7. Other income		
8. AFUDC**	80	
9. Miscellaneous	20	
10. Total other income	100	8 + 9
11. Pretax earnings before interest charges***	600	6 + 10
12. Interest charges	300	
13. Pretax net income	300	11 − 12
14. Income taxes	100	
15. Net income	200	13 − 14
16. Preferred dividends	50	
17. Net available to common stock	$ 150	15 − 16
18. Average shares of common stock	100	
19. Earnings per average share	$1.50	17 ÷ 18

 * Include rentals, the interest component of which is $10.
 ** Allowance for equity and debt funds.
 *** Also known as EBIT (earnings before interest and taxes)

Pretax income before interest charges (income before interest charges plus income taxes) is the same as revenues less operating expenses other than income taxes.

1) The formula for *SEC Coverage* (used in bond prospectuses approved by the Securities and Exchange Commission) produces the following:

$$\frac{\text{Pretax Operating Income} + \text{Other Income} + \text{Interest Component of Rentals}}{\text{Interest Charges} + \text{Interest Component of Rentals}} =$$

$$\frac{\$500 + \$100 + \$10}{\$300 + \$10} = \frac{\$610}{\$310} = 1.97\text{x}$$

2) *Coverage Based on Pretax Income Before Interest Charges* is an easily calculated substitute for the SEC coverage, especially when rentals are unavailable or are insignificant:

$$\frac{\text{Pretax Operating Income} + \text{Other Income}}{\text{Interest Charges}} = \frac{\$500 + \$100}{\$300} = 2.00\text{x}$$

3) *Interest Coverage Based on Pretax Operating Income* provides a measure of the pretax income from operations that is available to meet fixed charges. The calculation excludes AFUDC (a noncash item) and other income (which may be highly variable). For our purposes, income taxes include all current and deferred income taxes shown in operating expenses. The formula for operating income coverage is:

$$\frac{\text{Pretax Operating Income}}{\text{Interest Charges}} = \frac{\$500}{\$300} = 1.67\text{x}$$

Operating income coverage should be viewed as a conservative way of measuring a utility's standing. It requires a simple calculation, too, and does not need any numbers such as interest component of rentals which may not be readily available.

4) *Cash Income Coverage.* Utilities differ in how much of the revenue can be converted into cash (before payment of taxes and interest) due to different depreciation policies and the existence of other components of income that are not cash revenues. Because depreciation is one of the utility's major noncash expense items, we include depreciation in the ratio shown below. AFUDC, which is one of the major noncash credits in the income statement, should be omitted from a conservative coverage ratio, which is what happens when we look at pretax operating income, which does not include AFUDC. This ratio is calculated according to the formula:

$$\frac{\text{Pretax Operating Income} + \text{Depreciation} - \text{Noncash Credits}}{\text{Total Interest Charges}}$$

In our example, there were no other non-cash components to income, so the coverage would be:

$$\frac{\$500 + \$100 - \$0}{\$300} = \frac{\$600}{\$300} = 2.00x$$

Government-owned utilities can calculate coverage in the same manner. The analysis, of course, becomes simpler because the government-owned utilities pay no taxes. Investors in government-owned utilities, however, usually calculate a different coverage that we will discuss in the section on cash flow analysis.

5) *Preferred Dividend Coverage.* Utilities often have preferred stock in their capitalizations. Much of the analysis that we are using here also is suitable for analysis of preferred stocks, except that the coverage ratio must be adjusted. Take our example, which we have recast for an easier calculation:

	Revenue	$1,000
minus	Operating Expenses (excluding income taxes)	500
plus	Other Income	100
equals	Pretax Earnings Before Interest Charges	600
minus	Interest Charges	300
equals	Pretax Net Income	300
minus	Income Taxes (33 1/3% rate)	100
equals	Net Income	200
less	Preferred Dividends	50
equals	Net Income for Common Stock	150

In a previous illustration, we have shown pretax interest coverage to be:

$$\frac{\$600}{\$300} = 2.00x$$

Using our example, many analysts would calculate preferred dividend coverage as:

$$\frac{\text{Net Income}}{\text{Preferred Dividends}} = \frac{\$200}{\$50} = 4.00x$$

But, as Graham and Dodd pointed out long ago,[16] that would be an absurdity. How can the senior security have less coverage than the junior security? Is the preferred stock really safer than the debt? Thus, preferred coverage has to take into account the senior claims ahead of the stock. Unfortunately, that cannot be accomplished easily because the debt has a claim to earnings before taxes, while the preferred claim is junior to taxes. The solution is to put the preferred claim on a pretax basis, too. We can then ask how much income before taxes has to be earned to pay the preferred dividend. Under that formulation, preferred dividend coverage becomes:

$$\frac{\text{(Pretax Earnings Before Interest Charges)}}{\text{Interest Charged} + \left(\dfrac{\text{Preferred Dividend}}{1 - \text{Tax Rate}}\right)}$$

The income tax rate is stated on a decimal basis, i.e. 33.3% = 0.333. The correct preferred dividend coverage for our example is:

$$\frac{\$600}{\$300 + \left(\dfrac{\$50}{1 - .333}\right)} = \frac{\$600}{\$300 + \$75} = 1.60\text{x}$$

Earnings per share (EPS) analysis is based on the average number of shares outstanding during the year. Because utility companies often sell common stock, using year-end shares could be misleading. For example, only a portion of the money received from the sale of shares may have been put to work to produce income during the entire year.

That point is illustrated in the following example, which shows two identical companies, each of which started the year with 800 shares outstanding and ended the year with 1,000 shares. Company A sold new stock at the beginning of the year and had 1,000 shares outstanding for almost the entire period and, therefore, had use of the money from the new shares for almost the full year. Company B sold new shares at the end of the year and had use of the funds for just a few days.

	Company A	Company B
Net income for year	$1,000	$1,000
Year-end shares outstanding	1,000	1,000
EPS based on year-end shares outstanding	$ 1.00	$ 1.00
Average shares outstanding	999	801
EPS based on average shares outstanding	$ 1.00	$ 1.25

If we had calculated EPS on the basis of shares outstanding at the end of the year, both A and B would have reported $1.00, which would have misled investors into believing that both companies had equal earning power. That clearly is not the case, because B earned $1,000 without having had time to invest the additional funds, as compared to A, which earned only $1,000 despite having had use of the new funds for almost the entire year. On an annualized basis, it looks as if a share of A can earn $1.00 and a share of B can earn $1.25.

What happens to earnings? A portion of earnings is retained and the rest is distributed as dividends to stockholders. The dividend payout ratio is the standard measure of how much of the earnings available to common stockholders is paid out in the form of dividends. On occasion, though, a large part of earnings comes from the non-cash AFUDC. A one-time charge or a one-time credit to income, from an unusual item, also may distort the reported earnings. Here are examples:

Characteristic	Company A No AFUDC No unusual items	Company B High AFUDC No unusual items	Company C No AFUDC One-time loss on sale of property	Company D High AFUDC One-time gain on sale of property
EPS from:				
Selling water	$2.00	$1.50	$2.20	$1.00
AFUDC	—	0.50	—	0.50
Property loss	—	—	(0.20)	—
Property gain	—	—	—	0.50
Reported EPS	$2.00	$2.00	$2.00	$2.00
Dividend	1.20	1.20	1.20	1.20
Reported payout ratio	60%	60%	60%	60%
Dividend payout after excluding from EPS:				
AFUDC	60%	80%	60%	80%
Property loss or gain	60	80	55	80
AFUDC and property loss or gain	60	80	55	120

All other things being equal, we would be more comfortable investing in Company C, if we want a safe dividend. The company's earnings from *continuing operations* (that is, from selling water to customers that the company now services and intends to serve in the future) are the highest relative to the dividend paid, and the only one-time or *non-recurring* item is a loss on sale of some property. Investors who look at reported earnings alone might be fooled into believing that the company's earning power is $2.00 per share, and miss the company's real strength. On the other hand, careless investors might believe that Company D's earning power really is $2.00 per share.

For most purposes, the easiest calculation for dividend payout ratio is:

$$\text{Dividend payout ratio} = \frac{\text{Common stock dividends}}{\text{Earnings available to common stock}}$$

(The analyst also can calculate dividend payout by dividing total common dividends paid by net income available to common stock.)

The payout ratio is one indication of how well the dividend is covered by earnings. Unfortunately the tendency exists to look at the ratio for a single year and to forget that utility earnings can bounce up or down because of the timing of rate relief and the sensitivity of earnings to weather conditions. Investors in water utilities expect stable or growing dividends.

Companies do not raise or lower dividends to maintain a stable payout ratio. A company maintains a stable dividend and lets the payout ratio fluctuate. Most companies have a target payout ratio, which represents an average goal. Remember, too, that the higher the payout ratio, the less able the company will be to raise the dividend, and the smaller the funds the company will retain to finance future growth.

THE CASH FLOW STATEMENT

In a period of high-cost money, the need to borrow money or to sell stock at inconvenient times in the market cycle could have a serious effect on profitability. On the other hand, if a business can generate cash from operations, that money could be invested in profitable ways. Even in the best of times, water and wastewater utilities may require new cash because operations for the year do not generate sufficient funds to finance the purchase of expensive equipment that can serve customers for 40 or 50 years. Customers cannot be expected to pay so much for water and wastewater in a single year that the utility can meet its needs for the next four or five decades.

The cash flows can be analyzed conveniently by rearranging them into a simplified format:

Uses of funds

Capital expenditures	$1,000
Allowance for funds used during construction (AFUDC)	100
Total expenditures for plant account	1,100
Refunding of debt	50
Working capital and misc.	50
Total uses of funds	1,200

Sources of Funds

Retained earnings*	$100
Unbilled revenues**	(5)
Depreciation and amortization	205
Deferred taxes	150
Total internal sources of funds	450
Debt	200
Advances and contributions for construction	100
Common stock	300
Preferred stock	150
Total sources of funds	$1,200

* $150 net income for common stock minus $50 dividend.
** Revenue not yet collected but already shown as income.

Internal sources of funds as a percentage of expenditures for plant account =

$$\frac{\$450}{\$1,100} = 40.9\%$$

Internal sources of funds (less AFUDC) as a percentage of expenditures for plant account (less AFUDC) =

$$\frac{\$450 - \$100}{\$1,100 - \$100} = \frac{\$350}{\$1,000} = 35.0\%$$

We want to know how much of the money spent for construction came from internal sources. In the above example, the answer seems to be 40.9%. Part of the earnings, however, came from a noncash source, the AFUDC. Again, part of the expenditures for plant may not represent cash outlay, but are for AFUDC. There-fore, we could develop a second ratio that excludes AFUDC and shows that 35.0% of cash expenditures for construction (i.e., what was actually paid to the suppliers and builders) came from internal sources.

Sometimes we may want to look at the cash flow from operations before it is dispersed. A strong cash flow is a valuable asset to any business if properly deployed. To do so, add up:

Net income for common stock	$150
Depreciation and amortization	205
Deferred revenues	(5)
Deferred taxes	150
Cash flow from operations	$500

This number tells us how much cash comes in from the day-to-day business of the company. We would also exclude nonrecurring items, such as profit on sale of property, or writedowns of asset value that involve no cash loss at time of the writedown. Many analysts even calculate cash flow per average share outstanding in the same way as they calculate net income per share. They then compare earnings per share to cash flow per share, and might prefer to invest in the company that has more cash flow behind each dollar of earnings per share, or behind every dollar of dividends paid. Unfortunately, that analysis is faulty, because others often have a prior claim to that cash.

The above ratios show how much cash is generated from the sale of utility services. Sometimes utilities finance plant expenditures from sources other than their inter-nal savings or from the sale of securities in the current year or from contributions by customers who want service. For example, funds raised from the sale of securities last year could be used for financing plant construction in the current year.

The utility also can sell assets to raise cash. Occasionally those sources are treated as if they were internal. Nevertheless, growing concerns cannot stay in business by living off assets. That leads us to an interesting conclusion. So long as the utility is growing rapidly (needs new plant), the company is not likely to raise sufficient money from internal sources to pay for its new equipment. The company will only be able to generate cash in excess of current needs (cash that can be used to pay debts contracted in the past) when the company's growth slows or stops. At that time, however, the company may need cash for other items. For example, when growth stops, deferred taxes will have to be paid. For that matter, the plant will cease to expand when demand weakens at a time when revenues could decline badly enough to make it difficult for the company to pay debts incurred in the past. Technological changes do obsolete many products and services, although it is difficult to see what would replace water. However, a prudent management should try to meet its cash needs to the extent possible when that can be done easily.

That brings up the question of how money should be raised. If an industrial firm builds a factory that will last for 10 years, the company might borrow money for the construction and pay the loan over a 10-year period. Because the firm is unlikely to build a plant each year, the loan will probably be paid from the proceeds of the operation. The loan, in short, will be self-liquidating. Water utilities, on the other hand, may borrow annually, plow all cash back into plant, and raise funds to repay the loan from sale of additional securities. Government-owned utilities might claim that they pay down a portion of their debts every year out of operating income. Yet they also take out new loans to pay for expansion.

Inflation adds to the problem. A utility's cash flow from internal sources is derived from a return on and depreciation of the original cost of assets. Original cost is not adjusted for increases in price levels. Accordingly, the utility can only recover by means of depreciation the actual cost of the asset, not the cost of replacement at current price levels. The utility has to sell additional securities to raise cash with which to replace the asset.

How is that problem different from that of other businesses? Most other businesses do not have so much of their money invested in long-lived fixed assets. Other businesses can raise prices on inventory so that the firms can replace the inventory with a like quantity of more expensive goods. They can also raise prices, if the competition allows, to make sure that they have enough cash to replace fixed assets that now cost more. The utility, of course, cannot raise prices at will. So long as regulation and depreciation are based on original cost of property, the utility has a hard time meeting its needs from internal sources in an inflationary economy.

Finally, we have to deal with the question of how investors judge the creditworthiness of government-owned utilities, which is more a matter of cash flow than income statement analysis. The typical municipal has many bond series outstanding. Part of each bond offering usually matures every few years, until all the bonds are paid off. (Private corporations usually issue bonds for a fixed life, perhaps 30 years. The corporation, however, may set aside some funds every year with which it buys back some of the bonds.) The terms of the bond agreement (the "covenant") specify that the municipal utility will maintain revenues high enough to cover operating expenses (operations and maintenance, administration, legal, etc.) plus leave a large enough surplus after those expenses are deducted to cover debt service, plus some. *Debt service* consists of interest expenses plus money required to pay down debt in a particular year. The utility may offer a projection of debt service needs and coverage of debt service when it issues new securities. The utility essentially calculates a modified cash flow forecast. Here is how it works, starting with the income statement.

Operating revenue	$1,000
Interest income	20
Total revenues	$1,020
Operating expenses	
Operations and maintenance	200
Administrative and general	100
Depreciation	100
Total operating expenses	400
Operating income	620
Interest charges	300
Net income	$320

Then look at the statement of cash flows:

Cash flows from operating activities	
Net income	$320
Depreciation	100
Net cash provided by operating activities	$420
Cash flows from investing activities	
Construction	(300)
Net cash used in investing activities	(300)
Cash flows from financing activities	
Redemption of debt	(200)
Issuance of debt	300
Net cash provided by financing activities	100
Net change in cash and equivalents	220
Cash and equivalents at beginning of year	100
Cash and equivalents at end of year	$320

From the above we can construct a calculation of debt service coverage:

Total revenues	$1,020
Operating expenses that require cash outlay	
Operations and maintenance	200
Administrative and general	100
Total expenses that require cash outlay	$300
Cash flows available to meet debt service (net revenues)	720
Debt service	
Interest	300
Redemption of debt	200
Total debt service	$500

We then calculate debt service coverage as:

$$\frac{\text{Cash flow available to meet debt service}}{\text{Debt service}} = \frac{\$720}{500} = 1.44\text{x}$$

Terminology and formula may vary from water agency to water agency, but not the general concept.

SEGMENTATION

Most water utilities sell more than one product to one set of customers. The distribution of customers tells the analyst something about risk and the direction of the business. Geographic diversification reduces the risk that one regulatory agency has too much control over the fortunes of the company. It reduces the risk that economic or weather conditions in one region will unduly affect profitability. On the other hand, too much geographic diversification may dilute management's ability to control the organization efficiently, and diminish the organization's ability to benefit from good conditions in a particular locale. Most utilities specify the area served. Many of them also provide information about the size of the geographic components of the organization.

Breakdown of revenue by customer group provides information, too. Residential customers, for instance, pay more per gallon, usage is steady over time, but weather conditions can cause big short-term fluctuations in revenue. Industrial users pay less per gallon, may bargain hard to get the right price, usage may be related to economic conditions, and loss (or gain) of one big industrial customer could seriously affect profitability. Some water utilities have big wholesale volumes, that is, they sell water to other utilities. Analysts should consider the length and profitability of those contracts. What happens if the buyer decides to go elsewhere for supplies?

Finally, analysts need breakdowns by business segment. The utility may offer water and wastewater services. It may have subsidiary companies that offer other products and services, such as electricity, environmental chemicals, real estate development, or management of the utility facilities of others. Each of those businesses may have different prospects for growth and different levels of risk. Some companies prefer to tell as little as possible about the different segments of the business, possibly because certain segments do poorly, and the management would rather not have to explain the failures. Other companies tell all. Most compromise as follows:

Total Corporate Income

Revenues	$1,000
Operating expenses	
Operations and maintenance, etc.	400
Depreciation	100
Total operating expenses	500
Pretax operating income	500
Interest expense	200
Pretax net income	300
Income taxes	100
Net income	$200

Segmented Income Information

Revenues	
Water	$400
Wastewater	500
Real estate	30
Facilities Management	70
Total revenue	1,000
Pretax operating income:	
Water	325
Wastewater	225
Real estate	10
Facilities management	(60)
Industry segment pretax operating income	$500

The corporation then provides additional information, allocating its assets, capital expenditures, and depreciation expense:

Identifiable assets:	
Water	$1,300
Wastewater	1,500
Real estate	150
Facilities management	50
Total identifiable assets	$3,000

	Capital expenditures:
Water	100
Wastewater	200
Real estate	20
Facilities management	30
Total capital expenditures	350

Depreciation expense:	
Water	50
Wastewater	40
Real estate	5
Facilities management	5
Total depreciation expense	$100

Analysis by segment, in this case, shows that the water business is more profitable than wastewater, whether measured in profit per dollar of revenue, or profit per dollar of assets. That is despite the fact that the utility uses a more conservative depreciation rate for water assets. Furthermore, the utility is laying out a lot of money on new wastewater assets. As for the two non-utility ventures, real estate produces an unexceptional profit and facilities management produces a loss far out of proportion to its size.

OTHER RATIOS

In our previous examples, we have examined ratios derived entirely from a single financial statement. Yet, several key ratios use items from several financial statements.

Investors and regulators want to know rates of return, that is, how much profit is made for every dollar invested. When creditors lend the business $100 in return for $6 a year of interest plus repayment of the $100 principal at the end of a given period, they accept a 6% return ($6 a year for every $100 borrowed). When a stockholder puts money into a new business expecting the business to earn $20 for each $100 invested by stockholders, the investor expects a 20% return ($20 a year for every $100 invested). Shareholders also expect to sell their shares for at least $100, so that the $20 a year does not have to be offset against a capital loss. If the business is set up with $100 from creditors, who expect a return of $6 a year, and with $100 from stockholders, who expect a return of $20 a year, the expected return on the total investment of $200 is:

Debt	$100	×	6%	=	$6
Equity	100	×	20%	=	20
	$200				$26

and: $\dfrac{\$26}{\$200} = 13\%$

The 13% expected return is often called the *weighted average cost of capital*. Using that concept, and others, we will discuss several ratios that can be calculated either to present a picture of the utility's profitability or to approximate the return as calculated by the regulatory agency.

Net Operating Income as a Percentage of Net Plant is one of the easiest returns to calculate. Utilities are allowed to earn a given return on the rate base. Commissions differ in their calculations of both income and rate base. The ratio that we are discussing is rarely used by a regulatory agency but it is helpful to investors. It is a calculation of ability to earn a return on net plant from operations alone (and excludes AFUDC, and other nonoperational income). Consider the following example:

Sample Utility
Income Statement*
($ Millions)

Revenues	$100
Operating expenses	
Operations, maintenance	55
Depreciation	10
Income taxes	8
Total operating expenses	73
Operating income	27
Other income	
Allowance for funds used during construction	1
Other income and deductions (net)	1
Total other income	2
Income before interest charges	29
Interest charges	15
Net income	14
Preferred dividends	2
Earnings on common stock	12
Dividend on common stock	$10

* Restated to include both allowances for funds used during construction in one section as part of Other Income.

Sample Utility Balance Sheet

Assets	
Plant ($400 in service and $100 construction work in progress)	$500
Depreciation	100
Net plant	400
Current assets (all materials and supplies)	50
Deferred charges	5
Total assets	$455
Liabilities and capitalization	
Capitalization	
Common stock and retained earnings	100
Preferred stock	50
Long-term debt	235
Total capitalization	385
Current liabilities	60
Advances and contributions for construction	10
Total liabilities and capitalization	$455

Rate of return on net plant =

$$\frac{\text{Operating income}}{\text{Net plant}} = \frac{\$27}{\$400} = 6.75\%$$

We can also calculate *Income Before Interest Charges as a Percentage of Net Plant*. Many utilities argue that the AFUDC is good income and should be included in calculating returns. Some regulators include CWIP in the rate base and derive the rate of return by using income before interest charges, rather than by using operating income. For the investor who is interested in determining a rough rate of return on the basis of an approximation of the rate base, the ratio under discussion serves the purpose.

$$\frac{\text{Income before interest charges}}{\text{Net plant}} = \frac{\$29}{\$400} = 7.25\%$$

Return on Rate Base, as used in regulatory proceedings, often is calculated differently from the two previous ratios. Here is one method that can be used, with working capital approximated as materials and supplies plus one-eighth of operating and maintenance expenses. Note that advances and contributions are subtracted from rate base because they do not represent capital derived from investors, so investors do not deserve a return on those funds.

Rate base calculation (no CWIP in rate base)

	Net plant in service =	
	Plant in service − Depreciation	$300.00
+	Materials and supplies	50.00
+	One-eighth of operations and maintenance expense	6.87
−	Advances and contributions	10.00
=	Rate base	$346.87

Rate of return on rate base:

$$\frac{\text{Operating income}}{\text{Rate base}} = \frac{\$27}{\$346.87} = 7.78\%$$

Return on Common Equity measures the return on the common stockholder's investment. Return on common equity is a vital component of overall rate of return. A low return on equity usually means that the utility needs (and has a good chance of obtaining) rate relief. On the other hand, a high return on equity might mean difficulty when the company seeks to justify relief. An extraordinarily high return could indicate that the return has no place to go but down and that relief is unlikely before the return has reached a sub-par level.

Return on common equity:

$$\frac{\text{Income available to common stock}}{\text{Common stockholders' equity}} = \frac{\$12}{\$100} = 12.0\%$$

We have based our calculations on the balance sheet at the end of a period. Actually, all the assets may not have been in service for the full year, and therefore may not have contributed to profits. Accordingly, a more meaningful return might be calculated on average plant or on average equity. When regulators calculate earnings, they make adjustments for unusual items. As a result, we should know the formula used or we can simply make approximations for purposes of comparison.

Dividend to Common Equity Ratio, also called dividend-to-book ratio, is another way of looking at the generosity (and perhaps the safety) of the dividend. The utility tries to maintain a stable or growing dividend. Earnings from which dividends are paid tend to fluctuate, due to swings in weather and economic conditions, timing of rate relief, and operating problems. Thus, in some years, the dividend payout ratio is high (when earnings are down) or low (when earnings have risen). We know that regulators set an allowed return on the book value of the common equity. Let us say that 10% is the return set by regulators. The utility, we noted above, is earning 12% on common equity. That should make us nervous about whether those earnings can be sustained. The company seems to be overearning and could be forced to lower prices. What is it paying out?

Dividend to common equity:

$$\frac{\text{Dividend paid on common stock}}{\text{Common stockholders' equity}} = \frac{\$10}{\$100} = 10.0\%$$

The utility is paying out a dividend return on its equity equivalent to the return regulators say it should earn. If the regulators lowered the profit to 10.0% on equity, the company would be paying out its entire income. That would not be prudent policy. If we had just looked at the dividend payout ratio, we would have calculated:

$$\frac{\text{Dividend on common stock}}{\text{Income available to common stock}} = \frac{\$10}{\$12} = 83.3\%$$

and we would have concluded that the utility was paying out only part of its earnings and that the dividend was perfectly safe. That sort of conclusion would be altered by looking at the dividend as a percentage of common equity. A low dividend to equity ratio might be safer, at times, than a low payout ratio. (As noted, the dividend to common equity ratio is referred to as the dividend to book ratio, and calculations are made on a per share basis. That calculation will be discussed in the next chapter.)

Although government-owned utilities do not set prices on the basis of rate of return or set dividend policies either, their managers and owners should apply these analyses to determine whether their policies are prudent, their returns are competitive, and whether the various segments of the enterprise pay their way.

CHAPTER 31

The Market and per Share Ratios and Ratings

. . . a stock is worth the present value of its future dividends, with future dividends dependent on future earnings . . .[17]

— John Burr Williams

The financial statements tell us how much the firm earns, where the money comes from and where it goes, and how much has been invested in the business. Statements do not tell us the present worth nor do they indicate how much investors are willing to pay for the flow of cash coming to them from the business. Statements cannot tell us what the firm would have to pay for additional funds, nor do they show the amount that could be realized from sale of the business. Managements need that information to make investment decisions, and regulators need the information to determine the utility's cost of capital.

COMMON STOCK

The common stockholder is concerned with stock price, dividend, earnings per share, and book value per share.

Price of stock in market	$40.00
Earnings per share (EPS)	4.00
Dividends per share	2.40
Book value per share	30.00

The *price-to-earnings ratio*, P/E, or multiple for the stock, is the price divided by earnings per share. In the above case:

$$\frac{\text{Price}}{\text{Earnings per share}} = \frac{\$40}{\$4} = 10\text{x}$$

Generally speaking, the market is willing to pay a higher multiple for each dollar of earnings when the company is extremely solid (risk is lower) or when earnings are growing rapidly. In the case of a rapid-growth company, investors may be willing to pay 20 times earnings on the theory that earnings are increasing so fast that by next year earnings will have doubled. Accordingly, the multiple is actually just 10 times earnings for next year. In some instances the investor will pay a higher multiple because net for the current year is unduly depressed and will spring back quickly. Conversely, the investor may pay a low multiple if this year's earnings are unduly high and are expected to fall.

The reciprocal of the P/E ratio is the E/P ratio or *Earnings Yield*:

$$\frac{\text{Earnings per share}}{\text{Price}} = \frac{\$4}{\$40} = 0.10 = 10.0\%$$

If investors paid $40 for the stock and all earnings were distributed to shareholders, the return on the investment would be 10.0%. Some regulators in the past have confused the earnings yield with the return that the investor expects. The investor buys not only current but also future earnings. Most investors expect earnings to rise in time. Accordingly, current earnings may not provide a return on current price that fully reflects the return expected by investors.

Since most utility stocks are purchased because they provide the shareholder a current income, the *Dividend Yield* is an important element in the investment decision. Although the price-earnings ratio is meaningful, there can be temporary distortions in earnings per share (caused by weather, delays in rate relief, plant breakdowns, etc.). Investors might view the dividend as an indication of normalized earning power. If so, then it might be better to examine the dividend yield in relation to that of other similar stocks. The dividend yield is:

$$\frac{\text{Dividends per share}}{\text{Price}} = \frac{\$2.40}{\$40.00} = 0.06 = 6.0\%$$

Other things being equal, the investor will accept a lower current dividend yield from an investment in a strong company with good prospects for growth than from an investment in a weaker company with poorer prospects. A lower risk produces a lower return. The prospect of more income in the future will induce investors to accept less income in the present.

The *Total Return* for a stock is the current dividend yield plus growth in value of the shares. Thus, assuming that earnings, dividends, and stock price move together over time, a stock with a 6.0% dividend yield and a 5.0% anticipated growth rate would have an expected total return of 11.0% per year.

Investors often look at the *Book Value* of a utility stock. (Book value is the total amount of stockholders' equity, as shown on the books of the corporation, divided by the number of outstanding shares of common stock.) In many businesses, book value is only of academic interest, because changes in the value and earning power of assets make it likely that a purchaser of the corporation would pay far more or far less than book value for outstanding shares. In the water utility business, rates of return are allowed on book value, and, therefore, book value is a key to the potential earning power of the company. Investors then calculate the *Market/Book Ratio*:

$$\frac{\text{Price of stock}}{\text{Book value of stock}} = \frac{\$40}{\$30} = 1.333 = 133.3\%$$

The Market/Book Ratio indicates to existing shareholders whether new common stock financing will increase or will dilute book value and earning power of their shares. The ratio also indicates to regulators whether return being earned is satisfactory (i.e., high enough to bring the stock at least to book value). In the following example, new stock offerings are made at 50%, 100%, and 150% of book value. The regulator allows the company to earn a 15% return on equity.

	Before Stock Offering	Situation After $1,000 Is Raised by Sale of Stock at		
		50% of Book Value	100% of Book Value	150% of Book Value
Common equity	$1,000	$2,000	$2,000	$2,000
Number of shares	100	300	200	166.7
Book value per share	$10.00	$6.67	$10.00	$12.00
Net income	$150.00	$300.00	$300.00	$300.00
Earnings per share	$1.50	$1.00	$1.50	$1.80

A low market price/book value ratio means that new financing will be dilutionary. On the other hand, if the ratio is low, the company probably is under-earning and potential for improvement exists. The investor must judge whether financing plans will lead to considerable dilution and whether potential for improvement can be realized within a reasonable time.

Sometimes it is easier to calculate ratios from information per share than to go to the statements of the company. The *Return on Book Value* is roughly equivalent to return on equity:

$$\frac{\text{Earnings per share}}{\text{Book value per share}} = \frac{\$4}{\$30} = 0.133 = 13.3\%$$

That calculation is not necessarily identical to return on equity, because the numerator is based on average shares outstanding and the denominator on year-end shares, but it is close enough for most purposes.

The *Dividend Payout Ratio* approximates the percentage of earnings available to common stock that is paid out in dividends:

$$\frac{\text{Dividends per share}}{\text{Earnings per share}} = \frac{\$2.40}{\$4.00} = 0.60 = 60\%$$

Again, the calculation may not produce exactly the same results as using the total dividends paid as a percentage of reported net income, but it is good enough to use.

The *Dividend/Book Ratio* calculates a dividend yield on the book value of the common stock:

$$\frac{\text{Dividend}}{\text{Book Value}} = \frac{\$2.40}{\$30.00} = 0.08 = 8\%$$

Regulators determine return on the book equity of the utility. If the regulator grants a 12% return on equity, and if book value per share is $30, then the utility should earn $3.60 per share (12% of $30), at least in this simplification. Here the dividend is only 8% of book value, which is well below the profit level set by the regulator (and even farther below the $4 or 13.3% return on equity being earned). A high dividend/book ratio may seem to be a good thing for shareholders, but it makes the dividend vulnerable to reduction if business becomes bad or if regulators decide to lower the allowed return.

The various market ratios are affected by the prospects of the individual companies and by alternative investments that are available. A change in prospects for a company or for an entire industry will cause investors to pay higher or lower P/E ratios or to accept lower or higher dividend yields. A change in the returns offered by alternative investments would have the same effect.

The following table illustrates the effect on stock price and ratios of a shift in bond yields from 10% to 13% to 8%, in cases where the alternative is to invest in bonds and investors demand a dividend yield on stocks one percentage point below the interest rate on bonds.

	10% bond yield	13% bond yield	8% bond yield
Dividend per share	$2.40	$2.40	$2.40
Earnings per share	4.00	4.00	4.00
Book value	30.00	30.00	30.00
Stock price	26.67	20.00	34.29
Dividend yield required	9.00%	12.00%	7.00%
P/E ratio	6.67x	5.00x	8.57x
E/P ratio	15.00%	20.00%	11.70%
Market/book ratio	88.90%	66.70%	114.30%

The same logic would apply if a utility has steady earnings, and the returns from other investments rise sharply. Assume that investors were accustomed to buying stock in manufacturing firms that could only earn 10% on stockholders' equity and that investors pay a 10% earnings yield (a P/E of 10x) for that level of earnings. Because utility shares supposedly involve lower risk, investors are satisfied when the utility earns 9% on equity, and the stock sells at a 9% earnings yield (a P/E of 11.1x). If the earnings of the manufacturing firm surge upward to 15% on equity, and higher yields are available from alternatives such as bonds, the investor would now expect a 15% earnings yield (a P/E of 6.67x) on the manufacturer's shares. Because of regulation, however, the utility cannot raise its return above 9%. Yet, the investor demands a higher return (14%) on the market value of the utility investment. Consequently, new investors lower the price they are willing to pay for the utility stock, and thus obtain a competitive earnings yield from the shares. In fact, that is what happened to utility stocks in the period from the late 1960s to the early 1980s.

	Pricing of Utility Stock When	
Utility Stock	Manufacturers earn 10% and their shares sell at 10% E/P	Manufacturers earn 15% and their shares sell at 15% E/P
Earnings per share	$0.90	$0.90
Book value	$10.00	$10.00
Stock price	$10.00	$6.43
Market/book ratio	100.00%	64.30%
E/P ratio	9.00%	14.00%

EBITDA AND DCF EQUITY ANALYSES

In an effort to replicate the procedures followed when corporations value assets, and to mitigate distortions caused by the varying degrees of leverage employed by different corporations, and to value companies that do not show net income, analysts sometimes value the enterprise based on EBITDA (earnings before interest, taxes, depreciation, and amortization).

Consider the case of two companies with similar lines of business and potential for growth. Company A is highly leveraged and employs an unduly low depreciation rate in order to make its earnings look better. Company B runs a normal operation.

	Company A	Company B
Revenues	$1,000	$1,000
Operating expenses	500	500
EBITDA	500	500
Depreciation	50	100
Interest expense	80	40
Pretax income	370	360
Income tax (35%)	130	126
Net Income	240	234
Shares of stock	20	60
Earnings per share	$12.00	$3.90
Assets	$1,000	$1,000
Debt (10% interest cost)	800	400
Common equity	200	600
Total capital	1,000	1,000
Shares outstanding	20	60

If the average stock in the industry sells at 20 times earnings, then the total market value of all the stock of each company and the prices per share would be:

Formula	Company A	Company B
Stock price = P/E × EPS	20 × $12 = $240	20 × $3.90 = $78
Market value = Stock price × shares outstanding	$240 × 20 = $4,800	$78 × 60 = $4,680

Something, however, looks peculiar. We know that A's stock is riskier, because of all the borrowing, and we know that A's management has doctored the earnings to make them look better than they really are by understating depreciation expense. Should we really pay more for A's common stock than for B's? If another firm came along to buy out both A and B, the acquiring firm would have to buy out the common shareholders and take on the obligation to pay the outstanding debt. Would they pay more, in total, for A than for B? After all, the companies have the same revenues and the same cash flows.

	Price for A	Price for B
Payment for debt	$ 800	$ 400
Payment for equity at market	4,800	4,680
Total price for company	$5,600	$5,080

The acquiring firm, in each case, gets $1,000 of annual revenue, $1,000 of assets, and $500 per year of EBITDA (from which it pays interest on debt and from which it collects cash to pay off its debt and to provide a return to investors). The acquiring firm would not pay more for A than for B. In reality, neither would the capital markets. Stock market investors know that A is not as safe (or as honest) as B, and they would pay a lower price. Let us argue that $5,080 is the right price to pay for the entire enterprise (meaning the market value of all stocks and bonds), which is an EBITDA multiple of 10.16x. From that enterprise value (EV) figure, we can calculate the proper market value of the common stock as follows:

	Company A	Company B
Enterprise value	$5,080	$5,080
Outstanding debt	800	400
Market value of common stock	4,280	4,680
Shares outstanding	20	60
Price per share	$ 216	$ 78
Earnings per share	12.00	3.90
Price/earnings ratio	18x	20x

As a practical matter, will many investors compare the P/E ratios, declare that the stock of A is underpriced, and is a bargain that will move up to a more normal 20x earnings? No. The market, as a whole, has figured out the scam. The enterprise value to EBITDA ratio is:

$$\frac{EV}{EBITDA} = \frac{\text{Market value of common stock} + \text{preferred stock} + \text{debt}}{EBITDA}$$

The ratio has been stated ambiguously, because the reader should understand that everyone does not calculate it the same way, and analysts are likely to calculate it differently from company to company. Theoretically, one should use the market values of common, preferred, and debt, but most analysts would calculate using the face value of the senior securities. Anyone buying the business would have to pay off short-term as well as long-term debt, and we already know how omitting short-term debt from analysis can lead to misleading conclusions, but we cannot be sure that those doing the calculations have looked at short-term debt. A consistent and all-inclusive formulation, though, should provide a useful method for investors to compare market valuations.

The EBITDA analysis is the outgrowth of cost of capital analyses by Modigliani and Miller that asserted that a business firm had an overall cost of capital that could not be affected by leverage, other than some benefit for income tax savings.[18] Investors buy a flow of cash (best represented by EBITDA) rather than reported earnings or dividends, say the new breed of business theorists. Investors want a certain return on investment, and if the corporation provides more than that return, it creates value for shareholders and the stock goes up to reflect that phenomenon. If the corporation produces less than the desired return, that depresses the share price. Corporations that simply aim at higher earnings per share every year may not be doing anything to improve shareholder value. As Alfred Rappaport noted, "Ranking at the top . . . in earnings-per-share growth . . . provides little satisfaction to shareholders if such growth is accomplished with investments yielding less than the cost of capital."[19] In a world in which so many people focus on earnings per share growth, that approach may seem peculiar, but it makes sense. Take this example. Corporation X's shareholders want a 15% return from X. They can earn 8% by depositing money in a bank account. Corporation X, however, has a management that fixates on producing earnings per share increases. Here are the results:

		Year 1	Year 2	Year 3
Investment per share (book value) at beginning of year		$100.00	$110.00	$120.00
Earnings per share	+	15.00	15.50	15.75
Dividend per share	−	5.00	5.50	5.75
Investment per share (book value) at end of year	=	110.00	120.00	130.00

In year 1, X actually did earn 15% on the beginning of year equity. (For this discussion, we will assume that the stock sells for book value, in order to emphasize the concept. In reality, shareholders calculate their returns on the basis of the stock's price, not its book value.) In year 2, the company invested another $10 (the retained earnings of the year) to produce only a $0.50 increase in earnings per share, or a 5% return on incremental investment. Shareholders would have made a bigger profit if the corporation had paid them the additional $10 in dividends, and they had put the money in a savings account. In year 3, the management invested $10 more to produce only $0.25 of additional income, for a 2.5% return on incremental investment. In other words, management managed to retain X's record for earnings and dividend growth, but did a disservice to shareholders by investing below the cost of capital. Shareholders in this case, seeing their money dribbled away by management, will sell the stock, and the people who buy will pay a lower price. On the other hand, if the company had reinvested earnings in a way to produce $2 of incremental earnings for every $10 invested (a 20% return), shareholders would have pushed the stock up. This is, of course, a gross oversimplification of a substantial body of financial work, but the point is that earnings growth, alone, does not necessarily help shareholders.

Finally, understand that those buying businesses or making new capital investments buy a flow of cash, and investors might want to consider the concept, too. This is the way it works, again on a simplified basis. Figure that a company will produce $200 per year of cash flow from operations for five years, but will require $100 of investment in the third year to repair a machine. At the end of the five years, the business winds up, and the machinery is worn out and worthless. What should an investor pay now for that flow of cash?

Year	1	2	3	4	5	Total
Cash inflow from operations	$200	$200	$200	$200	$200	$1,000
Cash outflow	0	0	100	0	0	100
Net cash inflow	200	200	100	200	200	900

Certainly the investor will not pay $900, because money received five years from now is worth less than cash in hand. The investor can invest cash in hand and earn interest on it while waiting. If the investor puts $900 in the bank to earn 5% a year, at the end of five years it would be worth $1149. Why give someone $900 now to get back $900 spread over five years? In this case, the investor is making a risky investment, and wants a 20% annual return. In order to earn 20% on each of those net annual cash flows, the investor must pay a price now that will produce a 20% annual return upon receiving the cash payment. The investor figures that the flow of cash (at a 20% discount rate) is worth, at the beginning of the first year:

Year	1	2	3	4	5	Total
Net cash flow*	200	200	100	200	200	900
Net cash flow discounted at 20% per year	167	139	58	96	80	540

*Received at end of year

In other words, the investor who pays $540 right now, at the beginning of the first year, will get all money back plus earn a 20% annual profit from the investment. To say it another way, at a 20% discount rate, the flow of cash we have described has a present value of $540. (Present value can be calculated easily on most calculators, or derived from tables.) The concept of discounting shows why it is incorrect to look just at growth rates over a period of time, rather than considering when the growth takes place. For instance, A and B both double their cash flows over a five-year period:

Year	1	2	3	4	5	Total	Present Value*
A	$100	$110	$120	$150	$200	$680	$498
B	100	160	180	190	200	830	602

*Present value at the beginning of year 1, assuming that payments are made at end of year, at a 10% discount rate.

Now, over the period, both A and B exhibit the same point-to-point rate of growth from base year to terminal year. (More sophisticated methods of calculation would take into account the different distributions of growth, but most Wall Streeters use the beginning and end of period numbers and do not worry about what happens in between.) Would an investor pay the same price for both cash flows? Obviously not, because B brings in the cash sooner, which produces more cash on an absolute basis, as indicated by the totals, but also creates greater present value. The same logic should apply to valuation of earnings and dividend growth rates. A high rate of growth estimate for a five- or 10-year period may sound exciting, but it means less if most of the growth is at the end of the period.

FIXED INCOME

Bonds provide a fixed return (interest) if held to maturity. The *Coupon Yield* is based on the face value of the bond. For example, the 8% series first mortgage bond, due January 1, 2005, pays 8% a year on every $100 of face value. On January 1, 2005, the investor will get back $100 for every $100 face value of bonds issued. Some investors do not choose to hold the bond to maturity and, therefore, sell it at whatever market price is offered. The price offered rises and falls with interest rates. Suppose the market for a bond is as follows:

Years to maturity	=	20
Coupon	=	8%
Price of bond per $100 of face value	=	$90

If we ignore the payment of a bond at maturity, we calculate *Current Interest Yield* as:

$$\frac{\text{Coupon rate}}{\text{Price of bond}} = \frac{8}{90} = 0.0889 = 8.89\%$$

349

If the acceptable interest rate on the above quality of bond rises to 10%, the price for the bond would have to decline to $80 to give new investors a 10% current return.

$$\frac{\text{Coupon}}{\text{Price}} = \frac{8}{80} = 0.10 = 10\%$$

The current yield, however, does not really indicate the total return picture. If investors hold the bond to maturity, they receive not only the coupon every year, but also an extra $10 (in the first case) or $20 (in the second) because they paid less than $100 for the bond. That capital gain is really part of the return expected by investors. The return that includes both coupon and capital gain (or loss) is *yield to maturity*. Tables provide accurate yields to maturity. The investor, however, can calculate an approximate yield to maturity.

Where:

$100 = Face value of bond
C = Coupon rate (for each $100 of face value)
P = Price of bond
Y = Years to maturity

The approximate yield to maturity (A) equals

$$\frac{C + \left(\frac{100 - P}{Y}\right)}{\left(\frac{100 + P}{2}\right)}$$

In the above example where P = 80:

$$A = \frac{8 + \left(\frac{100 - 80}{20}\right)}{\left(\frac{100 + 80}{2}\right)} = \frac{9}{90} = 0.10 = 10.0\%$$

and in the example where P = 90:

$$A = \frac{8 + \left(\frac{100 - 90}{20}\right)}{\left(\frac{100 + 90}{2}\right)} = \frac{8.5}{95} = 0.0895 = 8.95\%$$

Yields calculated by the above formula are rough and used only when bond tables are not available.

Investors planning to put money into tax-exempt municipal bonds, such as those of government-owned water utilities, need to compare the return available in those bonds with returns available from taxable corporate bonds. One can do so using complicated formulas, but the *equivalent taxable yield* provides reasonably good results. The formula must answer this question: how high must the yield be on a taxable bond to produce the same return, after paying income taxes, that the investor could earn from a municipal bond whose interest payments are not subject to income taxes? Consider this example: the investor can buy a water department bond that yields 5%, the investor is in a 40% marginal tax bracket (he pays a 40% tax on additional income), and a similar quality bond issued by an investor-owned water utility yields 9%. Which bond offers the best after-tax return? With all data stated in decimals:

$$\text{Equivalent taxable yield} = \frac{\text{Yield on tax-exempt debt}}{(1 - \text{Marginal tax rate})}$$

In this case:

$$\frac{0.05}{1 - 0.40} = \frac{0.05}{0.60} = 0.083 = 8.3\%$$

In other words, the municipal bond provides the equivalent of an 8.3% return on a taxable corporate bond. The investor can earn 9% on a corporate bond. The investor should buy the corporate bond instead of the municipal bond. To test the proposition, look at it this way. The investor puts up $100 for the corporate bond, and collects $9 per year before paying taxes. His marginal tax rate of 40% requires him to pay $3.60 (40% of $9), leaving $5.40 after tax. The municipal bond provided a $5.00 return on the same $100 investment, without the need for the investor to pay any taxes. The investor, however, is better off paying the taxes on the interest from the higher yielding bond.

Bonds have quality *Ratings* determined by rating agencies. The largest agencies—Moody's and Standard & Poor's—use letter guides, in declining order of quality:

Moody's	S&P	Comment
Aaa	AAA	Best quality, extremely strong.
Aa	AA	High quality, very strong ability to pay.
A	A	Upper medium grade, strong capacity to pay.
Baa	BBB	Medium grade, adequate strength.
Ba	BB	Speculative, future not assured.
B	B	Speculative, undesirable as an investment

A plus or minus or a number (the lower the better) after the letter rating is often added to indicate further gradations in quality. Ratings below Baa and BBB are not considered to be of investment quality. Bonds with ratings that begin with the letter C (not shown here) are of issuers in or near bankruptcy or are extremely speculative in nature. Many investors are prohibited by law from buying bonds with ratings below certain limits.

An investor-owned utility may have several kinds of debt with varying degrees of seniority. First mortgage bonds have the greatest seniority and, in theory, must be paid before securities junior to them. Other kinds of debt have lower credit standings and lower credit ratings. Thus, the investor should not be surprised to see the senior debt with a Aa rating and the junior debt of the same utility rated A. For that matter, the ratings for particular issues may differ from rating agency to rating agency. As a rule, ratings do not differ sharply, but it is not unusual for a bond to be rated Aa by one agency and A by another. That is called a *split rating*.

The government-owned utility offers a far more complicated set of choices for the investor. To begin with the basics, the bond is usually one of two types. The *general revenue bond* (also called full faith and credit obligation) is backed by the unlimited taxing power of the particular government entity. The *revenue bond*, on the other hand, is paid out of a specified stream of revenue, such as collections from water and wastewater customers. If the government agency has misjudged demand for its services, or was unable to complete the project, it could fail. Presumably, the bond ratings of the two main credit agencies would warn investors against potential default, but Feldstein and Fabozzi, in 1991, asserted that, "In fact, since 1975 all of the major municipal bond defaults . . . initially had been given investment-grade ratings by these two commercial rating companies."[20]

Basically, that means that investors who buy revenue bonds must keep track of the fortunes of the issuer, because those fortunes can change. In order to provide comfort to investors beyond the backing of the revenue stream, the issuers can add the backing of others. In the case of a *moral obligation bond*, another government entity, such as the state, has the legal ability to appropriate money to pay. As a solid alternative, the issuer of the bond can buy *municipal bond insurance*. The issuer of the bond pays the interest and principal on the bond. Ability to pay, however, is a far cry from obligation to pay a one-time premium to the insurance company at the time it issues the bond. The insurance company then, guarantees payment of interest and principal for the entire life of the bond. The insurance company cannot cancel the policy.

Feldstein and Fabozzi cite the following criteria for judging water and sewer revenue bonds:

1. Do local residents have to take services from the issuer, or can they set up private facilities?

2. Does the issuer depend heavily on federal funds for completion of projects?

3. Is plant in good condition?

4. Are facilities in excess of peak needs and projected demand?

5. Does the issuer have a good operating record?

6. If the issuer sells its services to other government agencies, how are charges allocated?

7. If the agency sells to agricultural producers, what crops do they grow?

8. Has the utility been able to maintain its required coverage ratios even when expanding its system?

9. Does the utility have reserves to meet emergencies?

10. Can the issuer place liens against the property of those who do not pay their water bills?[21]

Large investors, no doubt, will maintain a careful watch on the water utility. Most others will depend on the bond rating agencies, and figure that people need water and sewage services, so they will pay their bills.

Remember, though, that the market demands a higher yield from riskier bonds. Therefore, bonds with lower ratings generally provide higher yields to maturity than bonds with higher ratings. A drop in rating (the ratings are reexamined and revised periodically) can lead to a drop in bond price (to produce the higher interest rate). Accordingly, investors watch the trend in financial ratios for the companies in which they invest.

Utilities also seek to keep financial ratios at levels that will retain or improve ratings. A lower bond rating might make the bond difficult to sell to certain investors and might force those investors to sell the bonds if the rating fell below desired levels. When investors expect a bond rating to change, they adjust the price that they will pay for the bond (thus requiring a different yield). Accordingly, some bonds provide yields that seem out of line with their present ratings.

Preferred stocks are like bonds in that they pay fixed dividends, but most preferred stocks have no set life. A preferred stock may remain outstanding for the life of the corporation, or it may have some sort of redemption feature that calls for the redemption of the stocks by a certain year. For the standard, nonredeemable preferred stock, investors simply calculate income as:

$$\text{Dividend Yield} = \frac{\text{Dividend}}{\text{Market Price}}$$

When the preferred has redemption features, investors will have to make calculations similar to those for bonds. Preferred stocks have ratings, too, and investors will want to compare ratings and yields, to make sure that they are getting a higher yield if they are buying a lower quality preferred.

As a final point, the difference in yield between rating groups varies over time. When the market is worried about the state of the economy and the ability of weaker companies to weather the storm, a greater yield differential often exists between low- and high-quality fixed income securities. At such a time investors see greater risk in low-quality securities and demand to be compensated accordingly.

CHAPTER 32

Financial Results on the Books and in the Marketplace

A public utility company is not permitted to enjoy the full fruits of its business successes inasmuch as regulation prohibits a return higher than that which is required to attract capital and provide service at reasonable rates. As a result, it does not have the resources available to absorb the major adversities which it encounters.[22]

— Corporation Commission of Oklahoma

Investors, creditors, consumers, managers, and regulators can measure the financial progress of the water and wastewater supplier in several ways. They can judge results from the numbers shown on the financial statements. Although seemingly precise, those numbers actually result from financial conventions that often tell us more about history than the present or the future. They can judge from how the marketplace evaluates the firm, whether from the returns earned on the stock or from the yield on the bonds. Or they can accept the view of the experts, as evidenced in the bond ratings.

INVESTOR-OWNED UTILITIES: WHAT THE ACCOUNTS SHOW

The investor-owned water utility industry consists of thousands of companies, but a few large utilities dominate the industry. A sample of five—American Water Works Company, Inc., United Water Resources, Inc., California Water Service Company, Elizabethtown Water Company, and Philadelphia Suburban Water Company—provides a proxy for the investor-owned industry.

Table 32-1 shows snapshots for industry finances from 1965 to 1996, using those companies as a proxy for the industry as a whole. Revenues for those companies grew as a result of adding customers (some by acquisition of other water utilities) and raising prices. Usage per customer has declined. Investment per customer and per gallon sold both have risen at a pace faster than inflation, as have charges for service. Clearly, new technology has not offset inflation.

As seen in Table 32-2, the business has remained capital intensive, requiring gross plant that is three to six times greater than annual revenue. That ratio fell from the mid-1960s to the mid-1980s, but then rose again, probably reflecting investment in environmental improvements and replacement of old plant. For most of the time period covered, the utilities managed to bring 30% to 40% of revenues down to pretax income before interest charges. Significantly, the companies have been

Table 32-1

Financial Highlights
Five Largest Investor-Owned Water Utilities
1965–1996

	($ Millions)							
	1965	1970	1975	1980	1985	1990	1995	1996
Water Revenues	$140	$208	$307	$465	$753	$1,019	$1,521	$1,642
Income before interest charges	44	61	89	119	190	254	373	434
Net income for common stock	19	23	31	46	83	107	156	191
Total capitalization	747	1,002	1,221	1,424	1,840	2,813	4,642	5,437
Gross plant	889	1,207	1,517	1,879	2,597	4,013	6,796	7,649
Capital expenditures	54	60	52	107	195	312	535	471
Metered customers (thousands)	1,716	---	2,110	---	2,384	---	3,095	3,331
Sales (billions of gallons)	312	---	387	---	402	---	505	511
Sales per customer (thousands of gallons)	183	---	183	---	169	---	163	153
Revenue per thousands gallons	$0.45	---	$0.79	---	$1.87	---	$3.01	$3.21
Gross plant per customer	$518	---	$719	---	$1,089	---	$2,196	$2,296
Gross plant per 1,000 gallons sold	$2.85	---	$3.92	---	$6.46	---	$13.46	$14.97
Consumer price index (all)	31.5	37.5	53.8	79.6	107.6	126.6	152.5	157.0
CPI (water and sewer)	---	---	---	74.0	113.4	150.2	196.5	204.5

Sources:
Company annual reports, *Moody's Industrial* and *Utility Manuals*, and the *Statistical Abstract*.

Note:
Excludes non-recurring items.

able to raise their depreciation rate from 1.2% in the mid-1960s (meaning that utility needs 88 years to recover its investment) to 2.1% in the mid-1990s (which reduces recovery time to 47 years). Note, though, that depreciation recovers the original cost of investment. It does not provide the funds needed to replace old facilities with more expensive new plant.

The water companies, in fact, display the financing characteristics of the classic public utility (Table 32-3). They pay out a large percentage of earnings as dividends, and cannot accumulate enough funds from internal sources to pay for the capital expenditure program. The capital expenditure program, itself, expands

Table 32-2

Income Statement Analysis
Five Largest Investor-Owned Water Utilities
1965–1996

Year	Gross Plant as a Multiple of Revenues (x)	Pretax Income before Interest Charges as a % of Revenues	Depreciation as % of Year-End Gross Plant
1965	6.3	38.6	1.2
1966	6.4	38.6	1.3
1967	6.3	37.4	1.3
1968	6.3	36.6	1.3
1969	6.2	36.0	1.3
1970	5.8	35.8	1.3
1971	5.7	34.8	1.3
1972	5.6	34.4	1.3
1973	5.4	34.1	1.3
1974	5.3	32.6	1.3
1975	4.9	33.1	1.3
1976	4.6	33.4	1.4
1977	4.4	31.0	1.4
1978	4.4	30.3	1.4
1979	4.3	30.7	1.4
1980	4.0	30.7	1.4
1981	4.0	29.4	1.4
1982	3.6	32.2	1.5
1983	3.4	33.3	1.5
1984	3.3	34.3	1.5
1985	3.4	34.0	1.6
1986	3.4	36.2	1.7
1987	3.6	33.5	1.7
1988	3.8	32.1	1.8
1989	4.0	30.6	1.8
1990	3.9	30.7	2.0
1991	3.9	32.6	2.1
1992	4.0	31.0	2.1
1993	4.1	31.4	2.1
1994	4.4	30.4	2.0
1995	4.5	31.3	2.1
1996	4.7	34.0	2.1

Sources:
Company annual reports, *Moody's Industrial* and *Utility Manuals*, and the *Statistical Abstract*.

the plant account at a faster rate than growth in sales volume or customers. This phenomenon could come about for several reasons. First, new plant may be far more expensive than old plant (some of which has been in the ground for decades). Second, environmental protection rules require the utility to add assets regardless of volume of output. Third, this remains the last rate base utility, which may mean that the companies lack incentive to ration capital effectively.

Table 32-3

Analysis of Financing
Five Largest Investor-Owned Water Utilities
1965–1996

Year	Dividend Payout Ratio (%)	Capital Expenditures as % of Year-End Gross Plant	Internal Funds as % of Capital Expenditures
1965	52.1	6.0	39.8
1966	49.5	6.2	41.4
1967	57.4	5.2	44.7
1968	57.4	5.4	39.9
1969	57.0	4.8	45.2
1970	58.3	5.0	43.3
1971	55.0	5.0	44.7
1972	51.1	5.8	40.9
1973	51.8	5.8	41.2
1974	57.3	4.2	51.7
1975	49.0	3.4	76.4
1976	47.3	3.1	89.8
1977	52.8	4.3	66.5
1978	52.8	5.3	51.3
1979	54.2	5.4	51.7
1980	51.3	5.7	54.6
1981	60.2	5.8	47.8
1982	50.6	5.7	66.4
1983	47.4	6.1	69.0
1984	45.2	6.8	69.2
1985	51.7	7.5	60.4
1986	46.5	8.7	54.1
1987	48.5	8.4	49.8
1988	53.1	8.1	45.2
1989	65.2	9.2	32.7
1990	59.3	10.8	46.6
1991	56.8	6.6	55.4
1992	64.9	6.8	52.9
1993	62.5	5.8	62.1
1994	69.9	7.1	45.6
1995	72.2	7.9	39.1
1996	65.9	6.2	57.9

Sources:
Company annual reports, *Moody's Industrial* and *Utility Manuals*, and the *Statistical Abstract*.

For decades, these water utilities have adhered to a policy of financing roughly 60% of capitalization with debt (Table 32-4). They use far more debt than other regulated companies, presumably because of the safety of the water business. However, they have reduced the use of preferred stock in favor of common equity.

Table 32-4

Analysis of Capitalization
Five Largest Investor-Owned Water Utilities
1965–1996

	% of Capitalization		
Year	All Debt	Preferred Stock	Common Equity
1965	62.6	14.8	22.6
1966	65.2	13.8	21.0
1967	63.4	12.9	23.4
1968	64.1	12.5	23.4
1969	63.6	10.9	25.5
1970	64.0	10.6	25.4
1971	64.5	10.3	25.2
1972	63.7	10.1	26.2
1973	65.1	9.2	25.7
1974	65.2	8.9	25.9
1975	64.6	8.6	26.8
1976	62.6	9.6	27.8
1977	62.0	9.2	28.8
1978	61.7	9.1	29.2
1979	61.8	8.8	29.4
1980	61.2	8.4	30.4
1981	60.8	8.8	30.4
1982	60.6	7.5	31.9
1983	59.3	6.9	33.8
1984	58.0	6.4	35.6
1985	57.9	5.7	36.4
1986	57.0	5.3	37.7
1987	57.6	4.6	37.8
1988	58.5	4.2	37.3
1989	60.7	3.5	35.8
1990	63.1	3.0	33.9
1991	61.2	5.0	33.8
1992	60.2	5.2	34.6
1993	60.4	4.6	35.0
1994	59.0	5.4	35.6
1995	59.3	4.9	35.8
1996	59.8	4.1	36.1

Sources:
Company annual reports, *Moody's Industrial* and *Utility Manuals*, and the *Statistical Abstract*.

How have the companies fared as a result of these policies? As shown in Table 32-5, the companies have maintained interest coverages in the 2x to 3x range for most of the period, except during the early 1970s, which was a period of regulatory difficulty and inflation. Returns have moved upward and downward largely as a result of regulatory decisions. The dramatic fall from the early 1980s to the mid-1990s, for instance, reflects the lowering of allowed returns as interest rates have fallen.

Table 32-5

Analysis of Profitability and Coverage
Five Largest Investor-Owned Water Utilities
1965–1996

Year	Pretax Income Before Interest Charges as a Multiple of Total Interest Charges (x)	Income Before Interest Charges as % of Net Plant	Income Before Interest Charges as % of Total Capitalization	Net Income for Common Stock as % of Common Equity
1965	2.82	5.59	5.82	11.53
1966	2.60	5.59	5.76	11.63
1967	2.25	5.75	5.92	9.56
1968	2.35	5.55	5.69	9.49
1969	2.18	5.58	5.73	9.03
1970	2.19	5.88	6.06	8.97
1971	2.09	6.12	6.31	9.06
1972	1.96	6.27	6.66	9.26
1973	1.96	6.51	6.74	9.08
1974	1.76	6.70	6.94	8.38
1975	1.97	6.96	7.25	9.53
1976	2.16	7.33	7.67	10.35
1977	2.11	7.18	7.52	9.69
1978	2.10	7.05	7.56	9.37
1979	2.13	7.21	7.81	9.86
1980	2.17	7.39	8.37	10.70
1981	1.99	7.58	8.41	9.63
1982	2.40	8.63	9.61	11.77
1983	2.62	8.73	9.97	13.06
1984	2.78	9.16	10.66	13.87
1985	2.68	8.83	10.34	12.39
1986	2.88	8.96	10.90	13.72
1987	2.76	8.12	9.84	13.40
1988	2.46	8.20	10.00	12.36
1989	2.11	7.46	9.19	10.12
1990	2.06	7.46	9.01	10.21
1991	2.24	7.93	9.58	11.79
1992	2.20	7.78	8.91	10.20
1993	2.46	7.22	8.70	10.84
1994	2.33	6.45	7.86	9.49
1995	2.34	6.65	8.03	9.42
1996	2.45	6.87	7.98	9.72

Sources:
Company annual reports, *Moody's Industrial* and *Utility Manuals*, and the *Statistical Abstract*.

Basically, the financial statements indicate that the large water utilities have shown steady profitability, reasonably good interest coverages, and a continuous need for outside sources of funds.

INVESTOR-OWNED UTILITIES: MARKET PERFORMANCE

Investors look on numbers in annual reports as indicators of financial progress, but they want those results translated into the right kind of stock price. Of course, what is right? Water companies incur less risk than industrial firms that have to compete for customers. So investors would want industrial outfits not only to report higher returns on their books, but also would expect industrial stocks to provide their owners with higher returns than water stocks. Bondholders, who take the least risk, would expect to earn a lower profit than stockholders.

Table 32-6 presents the five-company water stock index, which has been weighted by the market value of common stock at year-end 1964. The stock price followed the pattern of other utility groups, falling steadily from the mid-1960s to the mid-1970s, a period of inflation and rising interest rates, circumstances that depress utilities because rate increases lag behind inflationary cost increases, and because investors will sell off utility stocks until their dividend yields are in line with the yield on bonds. Although interest rates hit record levels in the early 1980s, earnings and dividends surged, as well, so the stocks held up well. From that point forward, a combination of falling interest rates and rising earnings and dividends propelled the water group to even higher stock price levels.

Table 32-7 shows the total return (change in stock price plus dividend collected), market/book ratio (stock price as a percentage of the book value of the share), return on common equity, price/earnings ratio and dividend yield for Standard & Poor's 400 Industrial stocks and for the five-company water index. In addition, the table presents the total returns earned by investors in a bond index, and the interest yield on Moody's average utility bonds. The numbers show the dramatic change in valuation of industrial stocks, which one might expect, considering the equally dramatic improvement in industrial profitability.

As seen in Table 32-8, the market set a lower P/E valuation on water stocks, and the water companies consistently produced a higher dividend return than industrials. The water companies also earned a lower return on stockholders' equity. No regulatory authority would let a safe water company earn the returns of a typical unregulated firm. Investors in water utilities, however, fared well, with total returns that not only easily beat those of bonds, but also exceeded the total returns of industrial stocks for much of the period shown. The seemingly dull water companies seem to have exceeded expectations. That conclusion, however, is only true on average. In truth, the stock of the industry giant, American Water Works, moved up almost twice as much as the group as a whole. The other

Table 32-6

Water Stock Index
Five Largest Investor-Owned Utilities[1]
1964–1997

Year	Year-End Stock Price	Book Value	Earnings per Share	Dividend
1964	100.0	57.71	6.40	3.04
1965	95.1	60.68	6.49	3.44
1966	77.6	64.43	6.90	3.48
1967	74.4	71.44	6.37	3.58
1968	89.5	74.61	6.62	3.68
1969	66.5	77.66	7.06	3.91
1970	73.9	82.77	7.44	3.93
1971	78.9	86.02	7.98	4.07
1972	75.4	92.72	8.58	4.10
1973	59.7	96.62	9.65	4.31
1974	54.1	101.49	9.27	4.56
1975	77.3	107.20	11.41	4.68
1976	86.3	116.41	13.24	5.21
1977	96.4	131.75	13.41	5.69
1978	93.7	133.16	14.97	6.11
1979	122.9	141.55	16.08	6.81
1980	151.1	151.34	19.07	7.49
1981	77.5[2]	147.44[2]	14.11	7.91[3]
1982	115.3	154.96	17.59	8.77
1983	148.5	166.01	21.03	9.71
1984	173.0	179.48	24.14	10.33
1985	270.4	195.30	23.54	11.01
1986	329.2	208.41	23.96	12.45
1987	292.5	223.01	28.57	13.46
1988	293.1	236.43	28.16	14.18
1989	305.6	245.41	24.07	14.96
1990	266.1	254.29	27.96	15.74
1991	386.2	268.34	31.85	16.91
1992	398.9	281.26	29.03	17.17
1993	442.3	299.86	32.86	18.10
1994	393.5	323.93	32.41	19.00
1995	507.2	336.04	34.26	20.94
1996	577.4	366.50	36.76	22.19
1997	779.0	385.30E	40.34E	24.28

Notes:

[1] Weighted by 1994 market value: 33.4% American, 15.3% United, 14.6% California, 9.1% Elizabethtown, 27.6% Philadelphia.

[2] Reduced by spin-off of Enterra from Philadelphia Suburban.

[3] Excludes 97.07 year end value of Enterra.

E = estimated

Sources:
Company annual reports, *Moody's Industrial* and *Utility Manuals*, and the *Statistical Abstract*.

Table 32-7
Stock and Bond Yields and Performance
1964–1997

Year	S&P 400 Industrials					Five Investor-Owned Water Utilities					Bonds	
	Total Return (%)	Year-End Market/Book Ratio (%)	Return on Year-End Common Equity (%)	Year-End P/E Ratio (x)	Year-End Dividend Yield (%)	Total Return (%)	Year-End Market/Book Ratio (%)	Return on Year-End Common Equity (%)	Year-End P/E Ratio (x)	Year-End Dividend (Yield) (%)	Total Return Long-Term Corporate Bonds (%)	Year-End Yield on Moody's Average Utility Bond (%)
1964	—	223	12.1	18.5	2.97	—	173	11.1	15.6	3.04	—	4.54
1965	13.0	226	12.6	17.9	3.34	-1.5	157	10.7	14.7	3.62	-0.5	4.82
1966	-10.4	187	12.9	14.5	3.05	-14.7	120	10.1	11.2	4.48	0.2	5.65
1967	26.8	220	11.8	18.7	2.97	0.5	104	9.7	11.7	4.81	-5.0	6.57
1968	10.5	225	12.3	18.3	2.84	25.2	120	8.9	13.5	4.11	2.6	6.85
1969	-7.3	196	11.9	16.6	3.26	-21.3	86	9.1	9.4	5.88	-8.1	8.39
1970	2.6	192	10.3	18.7	3.17	17.0	89	9.0	9.9	5.32	18.4	8.45
1971	15.0	204	10.8	18.9	2.77	12.3	92	9.3	9.9	5.16	11.0	7.92
1972	19.9	226	11.7	19.3	2.48	0.8	81	9.3	8.8	5.44	7.3	7.48
1973	-14.7	174	14.2	12.3	3.35	-15.1	62	10.0	6.2	7.22	1.1	8.17
1974	-26.5	113	14.2	8.0	4.97	-1.7	53	9.1	5.8	8.43	-3.1	10.02
1975	36.8	142	12.1	11.8	3.73	51.5	72	10.6	6.8	6.05	14.6	9.87
1976	22.6	157	14.0	11.2	3.65	18.4	74	11.4	6.5	6.04	18.7	8.61
1977	-8.2	127	14.0	9.1	4.90	18.3	73	10.2	7.2	5.90	3.8	8.65
1978	7.5	120	14.6	8.2	5.16	3.5	70	11.2	6.3	6.52	0.3	9.67
1979	18.5	123	16.5	7.5	5.27	38.4	87	11.4	7.6	5.54	-2.2	11.68
1980	33.0	143	14.9	9.6	4.24	29.0	100	12.6	7.9	4.96	0.5	14.48
1981	-6.7	118	14.4	8.2	5.11	20.8*	53	9.6	5.5	10.21	2.3	15.77
1982	20.2	133	11.1	11.9	4.56	60.1	74	11.4	6.6	7.61	35.5	13.55
1983	22.9	153	12.1	12.6	3.96	37.2	89	12.7	7.1	6.54	9.3	13.48
1984	3.6	150	14.6	10.4	3.99	23.5	96	13.4	7.2	5.97	16.2	12.96
1985	30.1	186	12.1	15.4	3.36	62.7	138	12.1	11.5	4.07	25.4	10.82
1986	18.6	216	11.6	18.6	3.02	26.3	158	11.5	13.7	3.78	16.3	8.96
1987	9.2	213	15.1	14.1	3.05	-7.1	131	11.3	10.2	4.60	1.9	10.99

Table 32-7 continued

	S&P 400 Industrials					Five Investor-Owned Water Utilities (1964–1997)					Bonds	
Year	Total Return (%)	Year-End Market/Book Ratio (%)	Return on Year-End Common Equity (%)	Year-End P/E Ratio (x)	Year-End Dividend Yield (%)	Total Return (%)	Year-End Market/Book Ratio (%)	Return on Year-End Common Equity (%)	Year-End P/E Ratio (x)	Year-End Dividend (Yield) (%)	Total Return Long-Term Corporate Bonds (%)	Year-End Yield on Moody's Average Utility Bond (%)
1988	15.6	230	19.1	12.1	3.03	5.1	124	11.9	10.4	4.84	9.8	10.02
1989	28.9	278	18.5	15.3	2.78	9.0	125	9.8	12.7	4.90	13.3	9.31
1990	−0.9	254	16.2	15.9	3.20	−7.8	125	11.0	9.5	5.92	7.4	9.57
1991	30.5	313	10.8	29.4	2.56	35.5	144	11.9	12.1	4.38	18.2	8.76
1992	5.7	356	13.4	26.1	2.52	7.5	142	10.3	13.7	4.30	9.1	8.36
1993	8.8	395	16.0	24.6	2.32	15.4	147	11.0	13.5	4.09	12.4	7.33
1994	3.8	363	21.8	17.2	2.38	−6.7	121	10.0	12.1	4.83	−3.3	8.79
1995	34.3	440	21.6	20.6	1.94	34.2	151	10.2	14.8	4.13	21.6	7.21
1996	22.8	518	24.5	21.1	1.79	18.2	158	10.0	17.6	3.84	3.6	7.65
1997	30.8	623 E	25.3 E	25.6 E	1.49	39.1	202 E	10.5 E	19.3 E	3.12	9.7	7.11

* Includes proceeds of sale of Enterra at year end.
E = estimated
Sources:
Company annual reports, *Moody's Industrial and Utility Manuals*, and the *Statistical Abstract*.

Table 32-8

Stock and Bond Yields and Performance by Periods
1965–1997

	1965–1969	1970–1974	1975–1979	1980–1984	1985–1989	1990–1994	1995–1997
Total Return (%)							
Industrials	5.6	-2.5	14.4	13.5	20.2	9.1	29.3
Water utilities	-1.3	2.0	24.9	33.4	16.9	8.6	30.1
Bonds	-2.4	6.7	6.8	12.1	13.1	8.5	11.4
Market/Book Ratio (%)							
Industrials	211	182	134	139	225	336	527E
Water utilities	117	75	75	82	135	136	170E
Return on Equity (%)							
Industrials	12.3	12.2	14.2	13.4	15.3	15.6	23.8E
Water utilities	9.7	9.3	11.0	11.9	11.3	10.8	10.2E
P/E Ratio (x)							
Industrials	17.2	15.4	9.6	10.5	15.1	26.8	22.4E
Water utilities	12.1	8.1	6.9	6.9	11.7	12.2	17.2E
Yields (%)							
Industrials dividend	3.1	3.3	4.5	4.4	3.0	2.6	1.7
Water utilities dividend	4.6	6.3	6.0	7.1	4.4	4.7	3.7
Utility bonds	6.5	8.4	9.7	14.1	10.0	8.6	7.3
ROE—Bond Yield (%)							
Industrials	5.8	3.8	4.5	-0.7	5.3	7.0	16.5E
Water utilities	3.2	0.9	1.3	-2.2	1.3	2.2	2.9E
Dividend Yield—Bond Yield (%)							
Industrials	-3.4	-5.1	-5.2	-9.7	-7.0	-6.0	-5.6
Water utilities	-1.9	-2.1	-3.7	-7.0	-5.6	-3.9	-3.6

E = estimated
Sources:
Company annual reports, *Moody's Industrial* and *Utility Manuals,* and the *Statistical Abstract.*

companies acted more like small regulated utilities. Perhaps American's size gives it a financial and managerial edge.

INVESTOR-OWNED WATER UTILITIES: BOND RATINGS

Generally, only large corporations sell bonds in public offerings and therefore require credit ratings from the rating agencies. Most water utilities are relatively small, and do not have rated debt outstanding. Thus, credit ratings do not provide as reliable or all-inclusive a gauge of financial health for water companies as for other industries.

Table 32-9 demonstrates that from 1984 through 1997, single A was the modal bond rating in 12 of the 14 years. Over this same time period, though, ratings did trend downward, but the lack of ratings below A- indicates how well water companies have maintained their financial equilibrium. A sample of Moody's bond ratings every five years from 1965 to 1995 also shows single A as the most prevalent rating in each of the years sampled.

Basically, the single A rating is average over all industries, and the water companies have managed to retain that rating despite their reliance on debt, and their

Table 32-9

Standard & Poor's Bond Ratings for Investor-Owned Water Utilities
1984–1997

Year	Bond Rating						% of Ratings	
	AA+	AA	AA−	A+	A	A−	A+ or Higher	A or Lower
1984	0	1	1	2	5	1	40	60
1985	0	2	0	2	5	1	40	60
1986	1	2	0	1	5	1	40	60
1987	1	2	1	2	4	1	55	45
1988	1	1	0	4	3	1	60	40
1989	1	0	0	5	3	1	60	40
1990	0	1	0	3	5	0	44	56
1991	0	1	0	3	7	1	33	67
1992	0	0	2	4	7	1	47	53
1993	0	0	2	5	8	1	44	56
1994	0	0	2	4	10	3	32	68
1995	0	0	2	3	9	3	29	71
1996	0	0	2	3	9	3	29	71
1997	0	0	1	3	8	3	27	73

Source:
Standard & Poor's

need to raise large sums of money for capital expenditures that basically add to the cost of doing business, rather than accommodate new customers or improve efficiency.

MUNICIPAL WATER UTILITIES: WHAT THE ACCOUNTS SHOW

Of the thousands of government-owned water and wastewater utilities, some operate as government departments and some operate as independent agencies, and their organization structure can change over time. Analyzing the accounts of such a multitudinous and disparate group of entities would create numerous problems. Examining the accounts of eight major utilities might present a consistent, representative picture. The sample includes the utilities in Chicago, Los Angeles, Miami/Dade County, Boston, Phoenix, Seattle, Dallas, and Philadelphia. Table 32-10 presents aggregates for the eight utilities. Table 32-11 analyzes the data. As in the case of the investor-owned utilities, the municipally owned utilities are capital intensive, and they write off plant over an almost 50-year time frame. Debt leverage remains steady at over half of net plant, but coverage ratios wobble as a result of weather conditions and the uneven application of price increases. What falls to the bottom line as net profit provides a paltry return on equity, but

Table 32-10

Summary Financial Statements[1]
Eight Municipal Water Utilities[2]
1980–1995 ($ Millions)

	1980	1985	1990	1995
Revenues	$580	$1,020	$1,360	$2,050
Operating expenses	390	640	965	1,325
Depreciation	75	125	185	285
Operating income	115	255	210	440
Other income	35	70	75	80
Income before interest charges	150	325	285	520
Interest	65	190	225	290
Net income	85	135	60	230
Gross plant	$4,225	$6,445	$8,920	$13,410
Depreciation	1,250	1,765	2,310	3,690
Net plant	2,975	4,680	6,610	9,720
All debt	1,560	2,350	3,515	5,065
Equity	1,745	2,675	3,975	5,770
Capitalization	$3,305	$5,025	$7,490	$10,835

Notes:
[1]Partially estimated.
[2]Utilities of Chicago, Los Angeles, Miami/Dade, Boston, Phoenix, Seattle, Dallas, and Philadelphia.

Source:
Moody's *Municipal Manual.*

Table 32-11

Financial Analysis of Eight Municipal Water
Utilities
1980–1995

	1980	1985	1990	1995
Gross plant/revenue	7.3x	6.3x	6.6x	6.5x
Operating income % of revenue	19.8%	25.0%	15.4%	21.5%
Depreciation % of gross plant	1.7	2.0	2.1	2.1
Income before interest charges as multiple of interest charges	2.3x	1.7x	1.3x	1.8x
Income before interest charges as % of net plant	5.0%	6.9%	4.3%	5.4%
Income before interest charges as % of capitalization	4.5	6.5	3.8	4.8
All debt as % of net plant	52.4	50.2	53.2	52.1
All debt as % of capitalization	42.2	46.8	46.9	46.7
Net income as % of equity	4.9	5.0	1.5	4.0

Source:
Moody's *Municipal Manual*

considering that much of the equity has been contributed by others, the return on money contributed by the municipality or retained from earnings might actually achieve a respectable level in the 5% to 10% range. As for ability to finance from internal sources, assume that capital expenditures equate with increase in gross plant, and that an average of beginning and end of period net income and depreciation approximates the annual average figure in the period. Then, as shown in Table 32-12, municipal water utilities would be as incapable of financing capital needs internally as investor-owned utilities, unless they raised prices.

MUNICIPAL WATER UTILITIES: BOND RATING

The municipal bond ratings have undergone a major transformation. In the 1960s and 1970s, rating of double A or single A dominated the count. Then, the near collapse of New York City and the perilous finances of other cities forced changes in municipal finance. The cities established special funds into which water revenues flowed, and the owners of certain series of bonds received a first call on those revenues, thereby establishing a seniority that improved their bond ratings. The municipal borrowers then added to the safety of their offerings by obtaining insurance against default, which raised the ratings on new bond offerings to triple A. In fact, by 1985, eight out of 11 large municipal water agencies had triple-A insured debt outstanding. To a great extent, the credit rating had meaning only for the remaining uninsured offerings. As shown in Tables 32-13 and 32-14, the ratings have shown little trend over time.

Table 32-12

Municipal Water Utility Financing
($ Millions and %)

	1980–1985	1986–1990	1990–1995
1. Average annual capital expenditures	$444	$495	$898
2. Average annual depreciation	100	155	235
3. Average annual net income	110	97	145
4. Average annual internal funds (line 2 + 3)	210	252	380
5. Internal funds as % of capital expenditures (line 4/line 1)	47.2%	50.9%	42.3%
6. Compound annual increase in gross plant	8.8%	6.7%	8.5%

Source:
Moody's *Municipal Manual*

Table 32-13

Credit Ratings of Uninsured Debt of Municipal Water Utilities
1965–1996

Moody's	1965	1970	1975	1980	1985	1990	1995	1996
Aa	4	4	5	5	4	4	3	3
A	4	3	4	4	4	4	3	5
Baa or lower	2	2	1	2	2	1	1	1
S&P								
AA	4	4	6	—	6	4	4	5
A	6	2	3	—	3	4	4	2
BBB or lower	0	3	0	—	1	1	1	2

Source:
Moody's *Municipal Manual*

Table 32-14

Standard & Poor's Credit Ratings of Selected Municipal Retail Water Systems
1984–1994

Year	AA+	AA	AA−	A+	A	A−	BBB+
1984		1	1		1		
1985		2			1		1
1986		2			1		1
1987		2		2	1		1
1988	1	1		2	1	1	
1989	1	2		1		2	
1990	1	2		1		2	
1991	1	2		1		2	
1992	1	2		1		2	
1993	1	2		1	1	1	
1994	1	2	1		1	1	

Source:
Standard & Poor's

CONCLUSION

Despite the fickleness of weather, the tardiness of regulators and city councils in raising prices, and the heavy demands placed on water utilities by environmental requirements and the need to rehabilitate old plant, so far the water utilities have managed to raise debt at low costs due to high credit ratings, and earn a competitive return for shareholders. The performance is all the more remarkable given the minimal growth in demand for water and lack of technological breakthroughs that would improve the workings of the industry.

CHAPTER 33

Summary

Inside the flat fruity voice was reading out a list of figures that had something to do with the production of pig iron.[23]

— George Orwell

The financial structure and policies of the water and wastewater industry are based on the monopolistic nature of the business and the steadiness of demand over time. The industry relies heavily on sale of debt to finance its expansion. It writes off assets over many decades, and the fact that plant remains in service for long after it has been depreciated testifies to the long life of the assets. Internal sources of funds do not cover capital expenditure needs, due to the low depreciation rate plus the high payout of earnings to those who furnish the capital. The extremely long life of assets, however, creates a problem because depreciation only recovers the original cost of assets, the cost determined decades ago, which is far below the cost of replacement today. As regulators will assert, correctly, the purpose of depreciation is to recover the original investment, and no more. That is true, but the extremely long lives of water plant and equipment exaggerates the differential between original and replacement cost and may create a situation in which the utilities avoid needed new investment for lack of funds.

Taking into account the other obvious discrepancy, namely the gap between growth in demand and growth in plant investment, and the capital intensity of the business, as well, water and wastewater firms need to find ways to economize on the amount of capital invested and the cost of the capital, possibly through cooperative efforts, private/public partnerships and outright mergers. Otherwise, consumers will have to pay for the excess plant that comes from needless duplication, and from the high cost of capital that small or uneconomic suppliers must pay.

For private water companies, the price of the stock makes a difference, whether in financing or in making acquisitions. As long as the price is high, the company can sell new shares without diluting the earnings of existing shareholders. Helped by lower interest rates, water stocks have reached levels in the late 1990s that allow nondilutionary financing. If interest rates rose or the allowed rates of return fell, independent of each other (which is unlikely perhaps but possible), then the water utilities would find themselves in the same unfortunate position as other utilities during periods when returns allowed did not take into account the prevailing cost of capital. Basically, this means that the investor-owned water industry's means of raising capital is vulnerable to changes of economic circumstances, more than it would be if more of its capital needs were funded internally.

Overall, though, financial policies seem appropriate for existing conditions. The government-owned utilities appear to put the risk on bondholders, but few people seem to believe there is much risk involved. Shareholders and creditors of the investor-owned utilities seem to feel the same way. As long as they do, the industry will continue to raise money at reasonable costs.

NOTES

1. Robert H. Lessin, *The Middle Years: Musings of an Investment Banker* (No place of publication: 1997), p. 24.

2. The Averch-Johnson effect was first hypothesized in a 1962 article: Harvey Averch and Leland L. Johnson, "Behavior of the Firm Under Regulatory Constraint," *American Economic Review* (December 1962).

3. "From the financial point of view . . . earnings are limited but . . . more stable than most industrial companies, bonds . . . are widely used in capital structures, and the risk is usually less than for industrial companies because of the essential nature of the service . . . and protection against competition." Ralph E. Badger, Harold W. Torgerson, and Harry G. Guthmann, *Investment Principles and Practices* (Englewood Cliffs, N.J.: Prentice Hall, 1961) p. 296.

4. David W. Wirick, with John D. Borrows and Steven Goldberg, *Evaluating Water Utility Financial Capacity with Ratio Analysis and Discounted Cash Flows* (Columbus, Ohio: The National Regulatory Research Institute, July 1997), pp. iv–v.

5. Ibid., p. 32.

6. Stephen P. Morgan and Jeffrey I. Chapman, "Issues Surrounding the Privatization of Public Water Service: A Report Prepared for the Association of California Water Agencies," September 17, 1996, p. 39.

7. Ibid.

8. Prospectus for City of Houston Texas Water and Sewer System Junior Lien Revenue Refunding Bonds, Series 1996 A, February 1, 1996, front page.

9. Wirick, Borrows, and Goldberg, *Evaluating Water Utility Financial Capacity*, p. 18.

10. Ibid.

11. Ibid., p. 38.

12. "The Philosophy of American Water Works Company," in 1996 American Water Works *Annual Report*, p. 23.

13. Ambrose Bierce, *The Devil's Dictionary* (New York: Dover, 1958), p. 26.

14. Peter F. Drucker, *Managing for Results* (New York: Harper & Row, 1964), p. 215.

15. Benjamin Graham, David L. Dodd, and Sidney Cottle, *Security Analysis* (New York: McGraw-Hill, 1962), p. 1.

16. Ibid., p. 386.

17. John Burr Williams, *The Theory of Investment Value* (Cambridge, Mass.: Harvard University Press, 1938), p. 397.

18. Eugene Brigham described Modigliani and Miller's work as "the single most important financial research . . . ever published." For a brief explanation and full references, see Eugene F. Brigham, *Financial Management: Theory and Practice* (Chicago: The Dryden Press, 1982), pp. 643–656, or any good finance text. The original articles are: F. Modigliani and M. H. Miller, "The Cost of Capital, Corporation Finance and the Theory of Investment," *American Economic Review* 48 (June 1958), pp. 261–297; "The Cost of Capital, Corporation Finance and the Theory of Investment: Reply," *American Economic Review* 49 (September 1958), pp. 655–669; "Taxes and Cost of Capital: A Correction," *American Economic Review* 55 (June 1965), pp. 524–527.

19. Alfred Rappaport, *Creating Shareholder Value* (New York: The Free Press, 1996) p. 181.

20. Sylvan G. Feldstein and Frank J. Fabozzi, "Municipal Bonds," in Frank J. Fabozzi, T. Dessa Fabozzi, and Irving M. Pollack, eds., *The Handbook of Fixed Income Securities* (Homewood, Ill.: Business One Irwin, 1991), p. 422.

21. Feldstein and Fabozzi, "Municipal Bonds," pp. 465–466.

22. *Re Application of Public Service Company of Oklahoma*, Cause No. 27068, Order No. 206560, Jan. 15, 1982 (Okla. C.C.), p. 63.

23. George Orwell, *Nineteen Eighty-Four* (New York: Harcourt, Brace and Co., 1949), p. 3.

Part VI

International Issues

CHAPTER 34

Introduction

. . . a lot of people say the next war will be fought over water. . .[1]

— Franklin Fisher

The statistics are stark. "Every day, 25,000 people die as a result of poor water quality. . . . Some 1.7 billion people, more than one-third of the world's population, are without safe water supply,"[2] and two billion people "lacked provision for sanitation."[3] Those, of course, are not the issues that cause nations to fight wars. Most water usage goes for agricultural and industrial uses, and disputes arise when one country diverts the flow of water on a huge scale, thereby affecting the agriculture and industry of another country.

From the viewpoint of the commercial water supplier, the fact that people in less developed countries need water does not necessarily translate into opportunity either. The major water supply businesses, using western techniques developed in the industrial world, would have to invest $1,000 to $2,000 per connection. They would require annual revenues of $300 to $500 to support their operations. In those countries with the greatest need for safe water and sanitation, family incomes often are less than $1,000 per year. Those people will have to solve their problems on a communal basis, with financial aid, using appropriate technologies. Do not expect commercial water companies to rush to serve the rural poor.

At the same time, urbanization, economic development, and a trend toward finding market-oriented means of developing infrastructure point to opportunities for private sector water suppliers, for manufacturers of equipment, and for producers of water and sewage treatment supplies.

WHERE IS THE PROBLEM?

On the whole, as indicated in Tables 34-1 and 34-2, the higher the level of income, the greater the percentage of the population that has access to safe drinking water (the definition of which is questionable in some places) and to sanitary facilities. In most developing countries, furthermore, the percentage of the rural population that has access to safe drinking water and sanitation may be half the percentage of city dwellers.

Despite the enormous improvements of the past two decades, a large and growing number of people lack adequate sanitation. While the bulk of those people live in rural areas, the unserved population seems to be increasing faster in urban

Table 34-1

Human Development Index Indicators

	High Human Development Index Nations	Medium Human Development Index Nations	Low Human Development Index Nations
% of population with safe water		69%	
% of population with sanitation		36%	
Life expectancy (years)	85%	67	71%
Gross Domestic Product/capita	83%	$3,288	35%
(1994 $)*	72	993	56
Gross National Product/capita	$8,525		$1,306
(1994 $)	4,963		306

Note:
*Purchasing power parity.

Source:
United Nations, *Human Development Report*, 1997, pp. 164–165.

Table 34-2

Human Development Indicators by Region

Region	1994 GDP per Capita (1987 $)	Life Expectancy (Years)	% of Population with Access to: Safe Water	Sanitation
Sub-Saharan Africa	$507	50	51	45
Arab States	1,595	63	76	52
South Asia	514	61	82	35
East Asia	659	69	68	27
South-East Asia & Pacific	935	64	66	56
Latin America and the Caribbean	1,931	69	75	61
Least-developed countries	254	50	57	36
All developing countries	823	62	71	39
Eastern Europe and CIS	1,370	68	98E	91E
Industrial countries	14,473	74	99E	96E
World	3,402	63	68E	62E

Note:
E = Authors' estimates

Source:
United Nations, *Global Environment Outlook* (1997), *An Urbanizing World* (1996), *Human Development Report* (1997).

areas (Table 34-3). If United Nations projections are correct, the population subject to water quantity problems will increase, as well (Table 34-4).

These calculations for the sufficiency of water quantity in Table 34-4 examine the flows of water in all major river basins, and estimates of rainfall, recharge into aquifers, and usage within each basin. Overall, by sector, the study projects:[4]

	Water Withdrawal Index for 2050 (1990 = 100)
Worldwide water withdrawals for:	
Domestic use	212
Industry	237
Agriculture	106

The doubling of domestic usage is in line with projected population expansion, but the more than doubling of industrial consumption would come in the face of a projected quadrupling of world gross domestic product. And the projected static water demand for agriculture takes place in a period during which caloric intake by the population doubles.[5] To return to the discussion of Table 34-4, then, the absolute population that suffers from water quality problems increases over time. The percentage of world population in that situation remains about the same. But consumers of water in the industrial and agricultural sector must dramatically reduce water consumption per unit of output in order for the relationship between supply and demand to remain at the semi-satisfactory current levels. Given the unrealistic pricing structures, absence of metering, the subsidization schemes that exist in the water sector, and the lack of profit incentives in the provision of water supply, enormous scope does exist to curb wasteful usage. That analysis suggests, however, that the best opportunities, internationally, may lie in conservation measures, water trading that encourages rational use, metering, and sale and installation of low-waste equipment, rather than in investment in expansion of the water supply infrastructure.

Table 34-3

Sanitation and Population in the Developing World
1990–2000

	1990	1994	2000
Population (millions)			
Lacking in adequate sanitation			
in urban areas	452	588	846
in rural areas	2,150	2,280	2,500

Source:
United Nations, *An Urbanizing World* (1996), p. 268.

Table 34-4

Water Quantity and Population
1990–2050

	1990	2015	2050
Population (billions) with:			
Severe water quantity problems	1.5	2.1	2.8
Moderate to no water quantity problems	2.4	3.4	4.7
No water quantity problems	<u>1.3</u>	<u>1.7</u>	<u>2.2</u>
Total	5.2	7.2	9.7

Note:
Calculations for major river basins encompassing about 95% of world population.

Source:
United Nations, *Global Environment Report* (1997), p. 246.

Based on projections for water withdrawals overall (see Tables 34-5 and 34-6), the United Nations must believe that people in all parts of the world except Europe and North America will become far more economic in their usage of water, even though their economies will grow faster and their current usage levels are less than half of those of Europe and North America. Achieving those projections might require a combination of sophisticated water pricing policies that induce conservation in usage, capital expenditures to improve deliverability at the water system, and better management techniques at water suppliers and users. The United States, with one of the most water-intensive economies in the world, has religiously avoided such policies. Perhaps countries with less abundant financial and water resources will ignore the American model. If they do not, the U.N. projection will prove excessively optimistic.

SOCIAL NEEDS VERSUS BUSINESS OPPORTUNITIES

In 1995, roughly 63% of the population of the urban world, but only 18% of the rural population, had access to basic sanitation services. "Projections show," according to the United Nations, "that access to safe water for all can be achieved in urban areas with only a modest increase in coverage. In rural areas a major acceleration in the provision of water supplies is needed."[6] That sums up the issues for policymakers and business people. Conventional private capital will flow to the cities, where water suppliers can run the businesses as they are accustomed to doing. Government agencies can pull capital out of urban systems, or deflect planned capital investments to rural areas.

Having said that, though, large percentages of the population of huge cities such as Calcutta and Jakarta go unserved by public water and wastewater utilities. In many cities, vendors sell water from carts at prices many times that charged by

Table 34-5

Population, Economy, and Water Withdrawals by Region
1990–2050

	1990	2015	2050	% Annual Rate of Growth 1990–2015	2015–2050
Population (billions)					
Africa	0.6	1.3	2.2	2.7	1.6
Asia and Pacific	2.9	4.1	5.2	1.3	0.7
Europe	0.8	0.9	0.9	0.4	0.1
Latin America	0.4	0.6	0.8	1.5	0.7
North America	0.3	0.3	0.3	0.6	0.1
West Asia	0.2	0.4	0.7	2.9	1.6
World	5.3	7.6	10.1	1.4	0.8
Gross Domestic Product (trillions of 1990 US $)					
Africa					
Asia and Pacific	0.4	1.0	4.3	3.6	4.2
Europe	4.7	12.0	30.8	3.9	2.7
Latin America	8.1	15.1	27.3	2.5	1.7
North America	1.1	2.4	6.9	3.1	3.0
West Asia	6.0	13.1	21.6	3.1	1.4
	0.6	1.6	6.9	4.1	4.3
World	21.0	45.1	96.0	3.1	2.2
Water Withdrawals (Thousand Km³/year)					
Africa	0.1	0.2	0.3	1.3	1.0
Asia and Pacific	1.3	1.7	2.0	1.0	0.6
Europe	0.7	0.9	0.9	0.8	0.1
Latin America	0.2	0.2	0.3	1.2	0.7
North America	0.5	0.6	0.6	0.5	0.0
West Asia	0.1	0.2	0.2	1.1	0.7
World	3.0	3.7	4.3	0.9	0.4

Note:
World figures may not add up due to rounding of some figures.

Source:
United Nations, *Global Environment Outlook* (1997), pp. 216, 217.

the local utility. Does this indicate that the local utility could serve those potential consumers if it could raise politically set prices to levels that would finance expansion? (In Brazil, for decades, the government refused to allow the telephone companies to charge enough for service to enable them to install new lines. People could afford to pay higher prices for the lines, but the government would not let the company raise prices. As a result, a black market developed for existing telephone lines. Those who desired a telephone probably paid more on the black

Table 34-6

Gross Domestic Product per Capita and Water Withdrawals by Region
1990–2050

	1990	2015	2050	% Annual Rate of Growth	
				1990–2015	2015–2050
Gross Domestic Product (1990 US$)					
Africa					
Asia and Pacific	$646	$803	$1,956	0.9	2.6
Europe	1,593	2,946	5,958	2.5	2.0
Latin America	10,309	17,465	30,518	2.1	1.6
North America	2,569	3,804	8,425	1.6	2.3
West Asia	21,809	40,830	65,530	2.5	1.4
	2,823	3,821	9,508	1.2	2.6
World	3,971	5,971	9,473	1.6	1.3
Water Withdrawal (m³/year)					
Africa	227	159	129	− 1.4	− 0.6
Asia and Pacific	444	406	397	− 0.4	− 0.1
Europe	905	1,010	1,020	0.4	0.0
Latin America	401	376	369	− 0.3	− 0.1
North America	1,847	1,817	1,740	− 0.1	− 0.1
West Asia	641	409	291	− 1.8	− 1.0
World	564	491	427	− 0.5	− 0.4

Source:
United Nations, *Global Development Report* (1997), pp. 218, 219.

---

market for a line than they would have if the telephone company charged a compensatory price. But the government could say that it kept down the price of phone services.) Or are housing and economic conditions such that the non-connected simply would consume too little to make a utility infrastructure economical? Perhaps, in some situations, the economic solution is the water vendor.

Water and sewage, however, are not the same as electricity or telecommunications. Not only does a large part of the population already have water and sewage service, but the existing customers are not likely to increase their usage over time, either. The water and sewer utilities might have to invest large sums of money to maintain or improve existing services without producing a proportionate increase in consumption on the part of customers.

The players in the international water and sewage management business may find their opportunities in better managing the operations and expansion of existing systems, rather than in the traditional expansion of utility service, which is expansion of plant to serve new customers, and earning a return on that investment. Obviously, in order to earn a return above cost of capital that makes the effort worthwhile, they will have to bid carefully for the properties or for the management contracts. This is not a business in which rapid growth in demand or dramatic technological improvements will bail out high bidders.

CONCLUSION

An unacceptably high percentage of the world's population does not have access to clean water in adequate amounts, or to modern sanitary conditions. That situation leads to disease and death, and it certainly slows economic development as well. It is by no means clear, however, that private entrepreneurs with standard solutions will bring an end to those conditions. Probably the best one should expect is that the application of modern management to both operations and capital investment will bring dramatic improvement to water supply and wastewater utilities in urban areas.

CHAPTER 35

The Need for Clean Water and Sanitation: Regional Patterns

Lo malo era que, la lluvia lo trastornaba todo. . . . La atmósfera era tan húmeda que los peces hubieran podido entrar por las puertas y salir por las ventanas. . . .[7]

— Gabriel García Márquez

For most of the world, clean water and sanitation services are not anywhere near as available as in the United States. However, the particular problems faced by different nations vary from region to region, revolving around issues such as local climate, population density, and level of industrialization.[8]

In general, the extent of a nation's water system can be linked to its per capita gross national product (GNP). But there are many situations in which this is not so. For instance, Jordan has a per capita GNP about 25% smaller than that of the Ukraine, yet Jordan's citizens have significantly better access to water, as shown in Table 35-1. Differences such as this can be caused by both the ways different nations tackle the problems and the causes of the problems themselves. A scarcity of water, for instance, can occur in both a desert country with a low population and a tropical country with a large population and hence large water needs. The U.N., in fact, simply defines water scarcity as having renewable per capita water resources of less than 1,000 cubic meters (m^3) per year. (See Table 35-2.) Another cause of such a difference could be rate of population growth: a nation with a relatively stable population will have more time to put the necessary infrastructure in place than a nation with a rapidly expanding or urbanizing population.

AFRICA

Africa has the unfortunate distinction of having the highest proportion of people without access to adequate water supplies. With the exception of West and Central Africa, most of the continent suffers from an excess of demand over supply due to rapid population growth and to economic development. In addition, many of the freshwater sources are polluted by untreated sewage, industrial effluents, and agricultural pollution. As a result, diarrheal deaths from consumption of contaminated water are the highest in the world. The contaminated water transmits other diseases too, such as schistosomiasis, malaria, onchocerciasis, and filariasis.

Table 35-1

Access to Water and Sanitation for Selected Countries

	1994 GNP per capita ($US)	Housing Units with Piped Water (%)			Housing Units with Flush Toilet (%)		
		Urban	Rural	Total	Urban	Rural	Total
Malawi	170	75	17	22	17	1	2
Haiti	230	22	1	6	5	0	2
India	320	63	10	23	N/A	N/A	N/A
Gambia	330	59	6	22	N/A	N/A	N/A
Pakistan	430	58	5	20	25	N/A	N/A
Bolivia	770	89	31	60	42	3	23
Jordan	1,440	91	55	77	98	89	94
Ukraine	1,910	68	4	45	N/A	N/A	N/A
Poland	2,410	97	67	86	85	46	72
Thailand	2,410	85	17	30	15	4	6
Canada	19,510	100	99	100	100	99	100
Austria	24,630	95	95	95	N/A	N/A	N/A

Source:
United Nations, *Human Development Report*, pp. 164–165, and *An Urbanizing World*, pp. 501–506.

Currently, only 35% of the population lives in urban areas. However, spurred by ethnic conflicts, armed conflicts, natural disasters, population growth, and the search for jobs, the continent is urbanizing rapidly. Urban areas in the least developed nations are growing at nearly 5% per year, putting them among the fastest growing urban areas in the world. Most cities have not kept pace in terms of constructing needed water and sewerage systems.

Africa suffers from many other economic and social problems that make it likely the situation will not improve in the near future. Twenty-one of the 30 poorest nations in the world are in Africa. Many nations have economic growth rates lower than their population growth rates. At the current rate of population growth, the number of people in Africa is expected to double in 20 to 30 years. There is a general lack of funding for the water system infrastructure needed to support that kind of growth. Many countries already have large debt burdens: the continent as a whole had a debt of $313 billion in 1994, equivalent to 83% of its gross domestic product, or GDP. In addition, the conflict and political instability that plague the continent make it even harder to get infrastructure in place. Water issues themselves can create international conflicts, since many river basins cross national boundaries. To date there has been almost no attempt to manage them jointly.

ASIA AND PACIFIC

Until recently, many Asian nations had fast-growing economies. However, the region also contains two-thirds of the people in the world who are residing in absolute poverty (less than $1 per capita income per day). Although the region as a whole has substantial water resources, many areas suffer from a scarcity of water, for a variety of reasons. Certain areas (such as Iran and Afghanistan) have a scarcity of water resources due to their arid locations. Other countries, with high precipitation, are unable to tap into much of their resources because of the highly seasonal nature of the rainfall and a lack of means to collect and store water in many watersheds. Nations with highly seasonal rainfall patterns also tend to be very sensitive to climatic perturbations such as El Niño which cause a failure of the monsoon rains in India and drought in Indonesia and Australia. Coastal areas that rely on groundwater (such as Bangkok, Thailand) are finding their aquifers contaminated by saltwater intrusions because of overexploitation of the aquifer. Finally, parts of China and India have chronic water shortages simply due to high population density.

Using the U.N.'s definition of water scarcity as having fresh water availability of less than 1,000m^3 per year per capita, Singapore is already in a state of water scarcity, Iran and India are projected to be in that condition by 2025, and in that year China will be close to the threshold. Because the 1,000 cubic meters is assumed to be used for domestic, industrial, and agricultural usage, the significance of meeting this definition for scarcity varies from country to country. For instance, because Singapore has very little agriculture, it is able to withdraw significantly less per capita than India or China, as can be seen in Table 35-2.

Water pollution is a major problem throughout the region. Water drawn from rivers is generally heavily contaminated with pollution from domestic sewage, industrial effluents, and runoff from agricultural and mining areas. Pathogenic pollution from untreated sewage is severe in all but the developed nations. For instance, only 18.5% of municipal wastewater in China was treated in 1992.

The main factors driving the problems of scarcity and pollution are the region's high rate of population growth, urbanization, and industrialization. Population growth is putting heavy pressure on the existing water sources, leading to scarcity even in areas that have high rainfall. Rapid urbanization, caused by both population growth and migration from rural areas, is putting increasing pressure on urban water systems. Much of the urban growth is taking place haphazardly in the form of slums and squatter settlements without access to water and sewage systems. These conditions, besides allowing disease to spread easily, result in even greater pollution to waterways and thus increase the problem of contaminated drinking water. Finally, industrialization, an important component of the region's impressive economic growth, also has resulted in increasing heavy metal contamination of water sources. Some nations, such as Singapore, have begun to act to

Table 35-2
Annual Internal Renewable Water Resources and Withdrawals for Selected Countries

	1994 GNP/ capita ($US)	Annual Conventional Renewable Water Resources		Annual Withdrawals (post-1985 unless otherwise noted)		Sectoral Withdrawals (%)		
		Total (km³)	Per Capita (m³)	Percentage of Total Resources	Per Capita (m³)	Domestic	Industry	Agriculture
Africa								
Congo	620	832.0	321,236	0	20	62	27	1
Egypt	720	58.1	923	97	956	6	9	85
Kenya	250	30.2	1,069	7	87	20	4	76
Libya	5,410*	0.6	111	767	880	11	2	87
Zaire	170*	1,019.0	23,211	0	10	61	16	23
Asia-Pacific								
Afghanistan	220	50.0	2,482	52	1,830	1	0	99
China[1]	530	2,000.0	2,292	16	461	6	7	87
India[2]	320	2,085.0	2,228	18	612	3	4	93
Japan	34,630	547.0	4,373	17	735	17	33	50
S. Korea	8,260	66.1	1,469	42	632	19	35	46
Singapore[2]	9,100*	0.6	211	32	84	45	51	4
Europe								
Austria	24,630	90.3	11,333	3	304	33	58	9
Belgium[1]	22,870	12.5	1,236	72	917	11	85	4
Italy	19,300	167.0	2,920	34	986	14	27	59
Romania	1,270	208.0	9,109	13	1,134	8	33	59
Russian Fed.	2,650	4,498.0	30,599	3	790	17	60	23
UK	18,340	71.0	1,219	17	205	20	77	3

Table 35-2 *continued*

Latin America/ Caribbean								
Argentina	8,110	994.0	28,739	4	1,043	9	18	73
Brazil	2,970	6,950.0	42,957	1	246	22	19	59
Colombia	1,670	1,070.0	30,483	0	174	41	16	43
Cuba	2,000*	34.5	3,125	23	870	9	2	89
Mexico	4,180	357.4	3,815	22	899	6	8	86
N. America								
Canada	19,510	2,901.0	98,462	2	1,602	18	70	12
USA	25,880	2,478.0	9,413	19	1,870	13	45	42
West Asia								
Iraq	2,170*	78.4	4,106	63	2,588	8	11	81
Israel	14,530	2.2	467	96	447	16	5	79
Jordan	1,440	0.9	230	98	217	21	5	74
Kuwait[3]	19,420	0.2	112	192	236	77	2	21
Saudi Arabia	7,050	86.2	4,743	19	897	9	1	90
Yemen	280	15.5	1,151	19	215	6	1	93

Notes:
*1992 data
[1]Annual Withdrawals data from 1980.
[2]Annual Withdrawals data from 1975.
[3]Kuwait draws more than half of its water from nonconventional sources such as desalinization and wastewater reuse.

Source:
United Nations, *Human Development Report*, pp. 164–5 and *Global Environmental Outlook*, pp. 32, 46, 65, 84, 99, 109.

control these problems, generally taking a command-and-control approach, rather than making use of more innovative techniques such as economic incentives.

EUROPE AND THE FORMER SOVIET UNION

Unlike the two regions examined so far, Europe does not have rapidly shifting demographics. It is well-urbanized already (except for Turkey), and population growth ranges from negative to 1%. There is great variation in the welfare of its various states, however. Western European per capita GNPs are a minimum of four times as large as those of their Eastern European and former Soviet Union counterparts. Not surprisingly, the water situation varies greatly across Europe and the former Soviet Union as well. Eastern Europe and the states of the former Soviet Union in particular have significant problems with basic water quality issues that the wealthier Western European countries have solved. Even these Western European nations have some basic infrastructure problems, however, with some water systems losing up to 80% of their supply through leaks. For the region as a whole, water use is increasing. As the countries of Eastern Europe increasingly adopt Western-style patterns of consumption in all aspects of their societies, it is likely that this trend will continue. Ironically, however, through the use of conservation programs and increasing efficiency, countries such as Austria, Bulgaria, the Netherlands, Spain, and Switzerland are going against that trend and actually decreasing total withdrawals.

The two major drinking water concerns in Europe are overexploitation (in some localized areas) and water pollution. Overexploitation occurs both in the western countries, due to high population densities, and in the southern countries, due to the drier nature of their climates. Sixty-five percent of the public water supplies are drawn from aquifers. But 60% of the industrial and urban centers of Europe are in regions where the rate of groundwater withdrawal exceeds the rate of recharge. The aquifers of coastal nations are threatened by saltwater intrusions as a result.

Water pollution is both more complex and potentially more solvable in the long run. The Western countries have taken more steps to deal with the problem than their Eastern neighbors. Heavy metal concentrations in lakes and rivers, alarmingly high in the 1970s, have been reduced to levels in compliance with drinking water standards in most bodies of water. Agricultural runoff and munici-pal sewage badly loaded the surface waters with phosphorus and nitrogen in the 1960s and 1970s, creating eutrophication and toxicity problems. In the west and south, reduction of these discharges (particularly sewage discharges) has improved the health of rivers such as the Rhine. However, many problems remain. Two-thirds of European rivers still show increasing levels of phosphorus and nitrogen. Nitrate levels in groundwater often are above healthy levels. Moreover, Belgium, Denmark, Italy, and the Netherlands still suffer from high loadings of organic matter in their waterways due to inadequate sewage treatment. Beach closings from sewage-contaminated water are declining, but there are still an estimated two million cases of gastrointestinal disease annually from bathing-water contamination.

The water pollution problems, and the corresponding drinking water quality problems, are at their worst in Eastern Europe and the former Soviet Union. Much sewage is untreated, and there is a large amount of industrial discharge, including radioactive contamination. Water pollution is so widespread in Eastern Europe that some waterways are not even fit for industrial use. So much inadequately treated sewage is discharged in the Russian Federation that only 21% of its rivers are considered to be at acceptable bacteriological levels. Water pollution extends to the groundwater resources of the area as well, from sources such as sewage and pesticides percolating into the aquifers. Groundwater pollution is expected to get worse in the coming years due to leaks from uncontrolled landfills and petrochemical tanks.

Water treatment facilities in Eastern Europe and the former Soviet Union are simply inadequate to deal with these levels of pollution. In the economic malaise that has stricken the former Soviet Union since the fall of communism, the situation has actually gotten worse. Thirty-one percent of drinking water samples failed chemical standards and 28% failed bacteriological standards in 1993, versus 15% and 23% respectively in 1980. Not surprisingly, the region has many cases of disease resulting from improperly treated water.

LATIN AMERICA AND THE CARIBBEAN

Despite huge river systems such as the Amazon, two-thirds of this region is arid or semi-arid. Many areas have seasonal dry spells, or fluctuate between periods of long droughts and punishing rains. The main problems facing this region are water pollution and urban water shortages.

Although population growth in Latin America, at less than 3% per year in most of the large nations, is at a reasonable level, many cities have grown explosively in the last few decades due to rural abandonment and poverty. Seventy percent of the residents of the entire region, and 78% for South America, live in urban areas today. By 2020 the figure for the whole region is expected to be 80%. Latin America is already home to two of the world's largest megacities, Mexico City and São Paulo.

The rapid and unplanned growth of urban areas has left a ring of shantytowns around most major cities. As a result, many residents do not have piped water available. For instance, 10% of urban residents in Bolivia and 30% in Guatemala do not have access to piped water. Eighty percent of city dwellers in Latin America have access to sewage collection services, but the number varies greatly from country to country, from a low of 40% in Bolivia to a high of 100% in Chile. This is only sewage collection, however. Few cities have adequate sewage treatment facilities in place. In most cities the sewage is piped into the nearest body of water completely untreated. In the Caribbean, the percentage of people served is even lower. In the 11 Caribbean Common Market countries, the population served by sewage systems ranges from 2% to 16%. However, the lack of very large cities in these nations reduces the severity of damage caused by the sewage. On the other hand, many of these nations depend heavily on tourism and cannot afford to have their beaches contaminated at all.

Acute water shortages in many urban areas have been another result of the rapid growth of Latin America's megacities. Mexico City, which gets two-thirds of its water from underground aquifers, is currently drawing water from the ground more than twice as fast as it is recharged. Buenos Aires gets 55% of its supplies from groundwater, much of which is severely polluted. Coastal Caribbean nations such as Venezuela are overexploiting their aquifers and suffering from saltwater intrusions as a result. These aquifers, too, often are contaminated by pollutants.

Rivers, however, are the freshwater sources that are the worst polluted. Megacities are a large factor in this, because of the concentration of raw sewage and industrial discharge they dump into rivers. The high bacterial and organic loads from the sewage cause a number of problems, such as poor-quality drinking water, food contamination, and the spread of waterborne disease. Outside the cities, mining operations and agriculture (especially the use of pesticides) are a major source of toxic contaminants. On some rivers in Bolivia, Colombia, and Peru, cocaine processing is the major polluter! Most cities do not have adequate water treatment facilities in place to clean up the water to drink.

Nations in Latin America and the Caribbean have begun to show interest in the region's environmental problems. Recent years have seen environmentally active nongovernmental organizations (NGOs) proliferate; there were 26 in Colombia in 1990, and 400 four years later. Bolivia, Costa Rica, Mexico, and Peru have founded national councils for sustainable development, composed of representatives from the private sector, NGOs, and the government. Whether or not they will accomplish anything is another matter entirely. The tendencies of the region towards more market-oriented economies has tended to lessen the effectiveness of governmental controls. This may inspire more innovative approaches toward solving these problems, or it may result in no solutions being attempted at all. At least one nation, Chile, has begun experimenting with tradable water rights.

WEST ASIA

All of the nations of West Asia have arid or semi-arid climates. It is one of the few regions of the world where the major water problem is quite simply an overall lack of freshwater. Yet water usage is surprisingly high here, exceeding the per capita usages in Africa, Asia and the Pacific, and the Latin America and Caribbean region.

Five nations in the region (Jordan, Iraq, Syria, Lebanon, and Israel) have access to reliable surface water supplies from lakes such as the Sea of Galilee and rivers such as the Tigris, Euphrates, and Jordan. Many of the other nations are completely dependent on sources such as groundwater, flash floods, desalinization of sea water, and wastewater reuse. Kuwait, for instance, gets almost half of its water from desalinization and another 16% from wastewater reuse. Some of the ground-water sources in the region are deep aquifers in which the water was deposited thousands of years ago and will never be replaced. In effect, these sources are being mined rather than tapped.

There are few formal agreements among nations in the region on sharing trans-boundary water sources. Virtually all the major surface water sources cross national boundaries. Given the lack of alternative sources in these nations, this creates enormous potential for conflict. In the 1960s, in fact, Israel and Syria skirmished for several years over a disputed boundary that lay directly upon a freshwater source.

Agriculture is the largest consumer of water, accounting for more than 80% of the region's total demand. Needless to say, agriculture in such an arid region is a water-intensive proposition, explaining in part the region's high consumption.

Domestic use only accounts for about 9% of total water usage. However, this demand is expected to rise as incomes rise in many countries. Rural dwellers in general have poor access to water and sanitation. City-dwellers, on the other hand, generally have good access to drinking water and sewage collection. However, only about one-fifth of the wastewater is treated. In some areas shallow aquifers are being polluted by the untreated discharge. The relatively high rate of urbanization is worsening this situation. Already, 70% of the population resides in cities, and this number is increasing due to rural populations fleeing rural poverty and land degradation from overcultivation and overgrazing.

Some pollution also results from industrial sources such as the oil and phosphate industries, which have contaminated surface and groundwater sources. Bahrain, Oman, and the United Arab Emirates also have severe problems with seawater intrusions into freshwater aquifers, because they are overdrawing their resources. In Bahrain it is estimated that the interface between salt water and fresh water in the aquifer is advancing at the rate of 75 meters to 130 meters each year. These problems are similar to those faced by many regions of the world. The difference is that West Asia cannot afford to waste any of its already scarce water resources.

NORTH AMERICA

How do North Americans compare to this? Of all the people of the world, North Americans are probably the most fortunate when it comes to water. The region as a whole has an abundant supply of water. The region is affluent enough to build expensive water transport systems needed to supply water to areas with shortages, such as the American Southwest. North Americans are among the world's largest consumers of water. It is part of the pattern of consumption tied into the North American standard of living. Water is priced cheaply; there is no reason not to use it. Undoubtedly much of this use is wasteful and could be done without: one study in Canada found that Canadians who paid volume-based rates used 40% less than those who paid flat rates.

Yet, as we have seen already, there are still some problems. Twenty percent of U.S. citizens are served by a facility that violates national standards, even though the water that comes out of the tap is probably of excellent quality compared to the drinking water available in most regions of the world. In Canada, municipal systems generally meet provincial guidelines. However, 20% of the water systems in Canadian Native American communities pose potential health risks, as do 9% of their sewage systems.

Both countries still have delivery problems in some rural areas. According to the U. S. Department of Agriculture, 2.4 million rural Americans still have a "critical need" for safe, dependable drinking water. Meeting their needs would cost $3.5 billion. Rural areas often suffer from microbial contamination problems, due in part to contamination from agricultural practices. In Canada as a whole, 20% of the municipalities reported problems with water availability, despite the overall abundance of water in the nation.

CONCLUSION

Demand for water seems likely to rise throughout the world. And in most regions, the supply of clean water per capita will decline, in some cases dramatically. (See Table 35-3, which reformats information shown previously.) Such a change in

Table 35-3

Water Withdrawal

	Total (km^3/yr)			Per Capita (m^3/yr)		
	1990	2015	2050	1990	2015	2050
Africa	145	199	280	227	159	127
Asia and Pacific	1298	1654	2048	444	406	397
Europe	715	871	912	905	1010	1020
Latin America and Caribbean	179	241	302	401	376	369
North America	511	582	574	1847	1817	1740
West Asia	130	168	211	641	409	291
World	2978	3715	4327	564	491	427

Source:
United Nations, *Global Environmental Outlook*, pp. 217–219.

availability of water per inhabitant could have a dramatic impact on the lives of those not fortunate enough to live in regions with abundant water resources. Many countries will have to expend a greater effort to keep clean the water that they have and to utilize water with the utmost economy.

As with so many other development issues, providing clean water globally is not an expensive proposition compared to the size of the global economy, but many nations individually cannot afford to provide clean water within their borders. Therefore, it is not surprising that the wealthy industrial nations also are the ones with the best access to clean water. Although industrialization can threaten clean water sources with pollution, the wealthier industrial nations are quite capable of tackling that problem with pollution control measures. It also can be argued that they can deal with the issue by exporting "dirty" industries to other countries. In still-developing industrial areas such as Southeast Asia or Eastern Europe, however, water pollution is a serious threat to clean water. In even-less-developed nations, the problems revolve around issues of providing a basic water supply infrastructure to the population and preventing pollution of water sources by sewage.

CHAPTER 36

Ownership

Now, what is Costaguana? It is the bottomless pit of 10 per cent loans and other fool investments.[9]

— Joseph Conrad

First came General Pinochet and Margaret Thatcher and then the entry of McDonalds into Moscow and the collapse of communism, stock exchanges on the Chinese mainland, and finally a private-sector-is-better ideological movement that has swept the world. Some of the most statist economies on earth now try to harness capitalist greed as a force of social betterment.

Competition does force enterprises to run efficiently, but water companies are monopolies. They do not have competitors. Selling government-owned utilities to private firms simply transfers the monopoly power from the government to the new owner, who may run the company more efficiently, but may not share any of the benefits of the added efficiency with consumers. Therefore, the government must maintain a role as regulator of the private monopoly after the sale. Any plan of privatization must include a regulatory scheme that encourages the private owner to run the water or wastewater company more efficiently, to make necessary investments that improve and expand the system, and to share the benefits with consumers, as well.

OWNERSHIP PATTERNS

In the United States, Canada, and in many parts of the world, public sector institutions dominate the water and sewage industries. The French, in the 19th century, developed a different model that prevails to this day, as well as in other countries. The municipalities in charge of water and sewage may contract out to private operators. The British, on the other hand, sold their state-owned utilities outright to private investors during the Thatcher government. Other countries have sold off water companies, allowed private operators to sell services to government-owned utilities, or, as in the case of Mexico City, contracted the rights to operate parts of the city water system to four operators, with the thought of eventually stimulating competition between them. This movement to privatize offers investment and expansion opportunities for slow-growing water utilities in industrialized countries, could free up capital for social spending in the less developed countries, and might lead to better service for consumers.

Privatization takes many forms. The government utility might do no more than outsource certain services or work that it now performs. As an example, it might contract for a private firm to do its billing, payroll accounting, or meter reading. Or it might hire an outside engineering firm to operate a treatment plant. Outsourcing has become a popular means of reducing costs in the public and private sector. If the outside firm can handle a function more efficiently than the water supplier's internal department, then the supplier should hire the outsider to do the job.

The government-owned supplier might require the addition of a new facility to the system, but might not have the capital or the expertise to make the addition. It decides to contract to buy the output of the needed facility for a given period of time. Private firms offer to build and operate the facility, on the strength of the contract to sell the output to the government-owned utility. Competing private firms offer their terms to the utility, which picks the best offer. The terms include a decision about the disposition of the facility at the end of the contract. For instance, B-O-O-T (build, own, operate, transfer) contracts are popular. The private company builds the facility, which assures that it exercises care in watching construction costs. It owns the facility, which means that it has to raise the money needed to construct the plant. It operates the plant, so it is responsible for efficiency and reliability. Finally, at the end of the contract, it transfers the ownership of the facility to the government utility. Outsourcing requires no changes in regulation. The contract sets the terms. The government water supplier takes the best price, and sets the operating requirements. The operator has an incentive to run the plant as efficiently as possible, because the more efficient the facility, the more profit that it earns.

The French government, as noted, has developed another method of privatization. In France, the municipalities have responsibility for water and sewage services. They run their own operations, or they contract out the operation by means of a public service concession that might have a 25-year to 30-year term. Concessions arrangements can vary, as noted by Générale des Eaux:

> In France, the partnership is based on the concept of incentive management, which requires a long-term commitment on the part of the operator to achieve well-defined quality and price goals. The contract may take various forms. The concession arrangement is a contract that sets a flat rate fee to be paid to the operator for all operations and maintenance work, as well as the construction and financing of infrastructural work for which the operator is responsible.

> Build, operate and transfer (BOT) contracts may be entered into for specific plants. Another type of contract offers a fixed management fee, guaranteed separately from any initial capital expenditure. This is the predominant model in France, and it is spreading rapidly in the United States. There are also intermediate solutions, where the local authority is directly involved in the daily operations and performance of the service . . . .

> Local authorities may decide to delegate the management of public water services for three main reasons. Firstly, they need professional people to imple-

ment . . . modern water treatment techniques . . . . Secondly, they seek greater management efficiency, with substantially higher productivity than the public sector can offer. Lastly, they want to improve the quality of service through better compliance with health standards and more efficient, planned mainte-nance of the infrastructure.[10]

Many French-style concession agreements have characteristics that blur the differ-ence between the contract scheme and ordinary regulation of privately owned utilities. The contracts, for instance, may call for the contractor to invest in new plant, on which it is entitled to earn a profit as well as a return of its investment. (At the end of the contract period, the contractor may have to turn the assets over to the municipality, but it has depreciated the assets in the same way that a utility depreciates its rate base.) The concession agreements also allow periodic adjustment of prices charged, to cover changes in costs, including the costs of new investment, if approved by governmental authorities. As the concession agreement strays farther from a simple outsourcing of management, it resembles an ordinary utility franchise more and more.

Less-developed countries can utilize contractual agreements if they want to raise cash or bring in expertise or capital. They can auction off the concessions, with safeguards to assure an acceptable level of service at set prices. The winner, then, has the responsibility to run and improve the system, but also has the opportunity to collect all revenues and earn profits determined by its ability to run the sys-tem efficiently.

The British government reconstituted the water industry in England and Wales, transforming all the state-owned entities into private corporations, and then selling 100% of the shares of those entities to the public in 1988. The water privatization, in many ways, caused headaches for the government. As a starter, the government was wedded to a regulatory formula for utilities originally devised to control the price of condoms. The regulator, for a five-year period, allowed the utilities to raise prices at the rate of inflation (retail price index or RPI) less a factor to reflect productivity improvements (x). If the utility could increase productivity more than x, it kept the difference as an additional profit. Obviously, when the regulator set prices for the five years, he took into account calculations of expected profit-ability and rate of return, but he did not explicitly set prices based on rate of return. The formula worked for telecommunications, where firms could introduce technological improvements that lowered costs. It worked for electric utility distri-bution companies, which had modest needs to add to plant. It could not work for the water companies, which could produce fewer savings by applying technol-ogy, and which faced enormous capital expenditures to improve water quality. The water regulator had to replace x with a price factor to pay for capital improve-ments (k), and prices ended up rising more (rather than less) than the rate of inflation, and people began to complain about deterioration of service. When the time came to investigate pricing and profitability issues, the reports read like an American treatise on rate of return. The moral of that story is: as long as the water business remains capital intensive, and technology provides the means to make only moderate cost reductions, then return on capital is the key to any regulatory scheme, no matter how that fact is disguised.

In the United States and Canada, so far, most privatization has taken the form of operating contracts, in which a private firm agrees to operate and, possibly, physically improve a facility whose operations are integrated into a government-owned utility. At some time in the future, municipalities might sell entire water or sewage operations, if a combination of the right sales price and the right water bill for consumers produced a benefit for local voters. So far, though, the low financial costs inherent in municipal bonds plus the savings derived from not paying income taxes have created hurdles for potential private operators seeking to take over municipal facilities.

As an example of an American contract privatization, in January 1998, United Water Resources announced that it had signed onto the largest public-private partnership of wastewater operations to date, a 10-year agreement with the Milwaukee Metropolitan Sewerage District (MMSD). That agency, which provides wastewater services to 1.2 million residents, will pay United an annual operations and maintenance fee of $30 million in exchange for the management and operation of the system. (United, incidentally, agree to hire all MMSD employees, at current wages and benefits.)

In the less-developed world, which is short of capital, and sometimes faces serious deficiencies in the management of government agencies, the need to bring in private enterprise may be more pressing.

PRIVATIZATION: A View from the Field

The following discussion on privativation efforts is excerpted from *The Privatization of Public Utilities*.[11] The author, Jose V. Kochen, was chief operating officer of Brazil's largest water and sewer utility before his retirement, and as such has seen first-hand the challenges facing a government-owned industry's transition into a competitive one.

The predominance of government ownership may be due to water's scarcity as well as distance from place of consumption. In the past, building the necessary facilities may have been beyond the capabilities of local private investors, but the community still needed the facilities. Local interests petitioned the government to make the investment in water supply, which was recovered from subscribers in the form of a tariff for services rendered. This was a common model for development. It led many to the comfortable but false belief that water, as an essential for life, was the exclusive obligation of the government to furnish. That induced many people to not bother to pay for the service, especially when the water entities were poorly organized or administered.

This misunderstanding about the obligations of government has led to the deterioration of many governmentally owned water suppliers. In a vicious cycle, a tariff set for political reasons at an unrealistically low level plus inability to collect the bills creates an operating deficit for the water supplier. That, in turn, leads to a scarcity of funds for investment and a deterioration of maintenance, which produces, as a consequence, a drop in the quality and continuity of service, and finally, a water shortage, which, in turn, makes it impossible to charge a realistic tariff because the service is so bad. At this point, the cycle repeats, each time producing worse results.

The government is not the best organizer, operator, or administrator, and the burden of these bureaucratic deficiencies and overheads ends up on the customers, in the form of higher taxes required to cover the operating deficit, or in the form of an unnecessarily high tariff for water services.

In developed nations and in those in which free markets thrive, privatization of public services increasingly is seen as a means of eliminating deficiencies in operations and improving the quality of service. This trend has been most evident in Europe, especially in the United Kingdom. As the experiences of privatization become better understood, more governments may adopt it as a solution.

The Structure of Government Water Suppliers

Normally, the governmental utility has four distinct divisions of management:

1) **The presidency or chief executive**—representing the top management by means of the president or general manager, and the executive directors.

2) **Operations**—responsible for the end product of the entity, which is to produce and distribute water.

3) **Finance**—charged with financial and economic matters and with the collection of revenues.

4) **Administrative**—in charge of support and personnel.

Yet, thanks to the almost constant necessity of modernization and expansion, principally in developing countries, two additional divisions almost always are present, one for planning and design, the other for construction. These two activities, as a result of the resources applied to them, end up assuming an importance even greater than the activity that produces the end product of the business: operations. The bulk of the resources of the corporation, including the best personnel, end up directed to these two areas, to the extent that they almost deform the service provider into a construction firm. The political dividends derived from public works projects end up making construction more important than providing an essential public service.

The planning and design, and construction activities, which are outside the main purpose of the water entities, can be contracted out and executed by private firms that specialize in those fields, probably at lower costs, especially when one considers the factors that influence costs, including the likelihood that these divisions end up as permanent parts of the government entity, even after the construction becomes less important or ends.

For this reason, many private water companies do not ordinarily have planning and design, and construction divisions, other than to supervise those activities, and therefore, they are proportionally smaller and less costly. When those activities are required, they are contracted out to private firms. This difference is one of the factors that weighs in favor of the privatization of water supply.

The supply of water is basically an industrial activity, and private enterprise has the means to run it. The supply operations involve equipment commonly used in industrial activities, and the labor needed is available in the marketplace. Private initiative has demonstrated better managerial performance than the government (in many forms), which leads one to conclude that those activities in which the government plays a role as business manager should be privatized, and water supply is one such industry. The benefits of privatization, derived from greater productivity, should accrue to the community in the form of better service and lower prices.

Difficulties that Public Water Suppliers Face

Governmental water agencies often face a lack of resources for investment due to:

1) Competition from other government sectors for the limited budget resources of the government.

2) Inability to convince society of the importance of investment in the sector in order to improve public health or develop the community as a whole.

3) The water sector's unconvincing lobby in the political arena, unable to raise the sector's visibility or get it the needed recognition.

4) Government interest, to the detriment of the water sector, in putting money into more obvious projects, such as roads, port facilities, and subway systems, that produce more electoral dividends.

The shortage of investment funds, over time, reduces levels of service, leaving part of the population without water and at the mercy of the consequent public health problems. Lack of resources, too, leads to deterioration of equipment, of work habits, of controls, with repercussions on cost and quality of service. If the need to invest in water facilities is great, though, the needs are even greater for sewage. The necessary investments are large, involve expensive construction and equipment, and the industry is far behind the demand for its service.

The extended organization structure, with an excessive number of managers and advisors who work largely to accommodate each other and who resist change, is another issue. These structural deformities often originate with an inadequate salary policy, which has to be circumvented. The majority of employees, who are not favored by the policy, have no incentive to work productively and show a general lack of interest in the employer, which reflects badly on the water agency's image. What makes matters worse is the susceptibility of government agencies to external factors that encourage nepotism, which results in crews not only far greater in size than needed, but often without the necessary qualifications.

The difficulties facing government sewage industries are basically the same as those facing the water industry. Reasons to privatize sewage services are the same as those for water supply, but the most important reason to do so is to raise the capital for new treatment stations and the network.

These disequilibrating factors are difficult to correct in a government agency. Not only do private firms have fewer of these problems to deal with, but when they do occur, they can be corrected more promptly. The private firms can line up resources more quickly, are less sensitive to political pressures, are free to determine the size of crews and salary policy, and can guide themselves by the real needs of the enterprise and by the situation of the labor market.

Principal Failings of Government Water Agencies
Government water suppliers often exhibit deficiencies in the operating sector that are most easily corrected through privatization. These are the most common failings among the government water suppliers:

1) **Loss of water in the system.** It is common to come across water supply systems that lose over 25% of the water produced. This loss is the difference between the volume impounded at the source and that billed. The losses take place at all stages of production through to billing, and are of a size that is unacceptable in any industrial process, especially in an era in which industrialists seek total quality control and reduction of waste to as close to zero as possible. Those high losses require the utility to spend more money for electricity, chemicals, personnel, and capital. The reduction of losses, though, is important not only to eliminate those excess costs, but also to free up productive capacity that can be placed at the disposal of unserved areas and new customers, which also implies the postponement of new (and unneeded) investment.

2) **Automation and remote control.** Entirely automatic equipment for such purposes as pumping, measurement, pressure control, and treatment is available on the market. When installed, it provides the system with greater security,

allows a reduction of personnel, and lowers costs.

Equipment may be operated by remote control, using radio or telephone links, with the same assurances of security and efficiencies. Yet many systems still lack these improvements.

3) **Operational control.** Whoever controls the operations of the supply system— increasing or decreasing volume, directing the water to where it is required, handling emergencies—needs an information system that provides real-time data on rate of flow, volume, elevation, pressure, state of repair, and standards of quality. Such a system permits the operator to rapidly identify alternative actions, make improvements, produce greater efficiency, and allows more rapid and surer decisionmaking in the operation of the water supply system. The use of such information systems is not that common.

4) **Elimination of areas and points of critical problems within the system.** At times, intermittent service or water shortages become chronic problems in certain areas. The solutions for these deficiencies are often postponed either for lack of resources needed to invest in the solution, or because even worse problems take precedence. Chronically poor operations in a particular area is one of the failings that most often depresses the quality of service. Many times, the utility will adopt palliatives such as shifting the supply from one area to another, with the intention of minimizing, rather than resolving, the problem.

5) **Constant modernization of work procedures and materials.** What ought to be routine may not be done at all by government water suppliers. The application of new work procedures and the utilization of modern machinery, equipment, and materials is often slowed down almost always because of shortages of money or unwillingness of the staff to make changes.

6) **Billing and collection.** No economic activity can survive if it cannot identify and know in detail its clientele and costs, and cannot collect enough to cover the costs of the service that it sells. Unfortunately, these pitfalls of the billing and collection process are common. Nonpayment for service is a serious problem unless the water company systematically applies coercive collection techniques, such as shutting off service. Activities so basic to an agency's survival, billing and collection, can be greatly improved by setting standards for them similar to those of private enterprises.

7) **Work rules.** The enterprise must control the productivity of the service crews, by setting the number of members of the crew, time standards for each type of service, and by rationalization of these activities. Doing so not only reduces costs but also improves the public image of the firm.

8) **Information management.** The company should pursue the extensive application of information management to all areas, with the objective of simplifying and speeding procedures, furnishing necessary information rapidly and correctly, and accelerating the decision-making process.

9) **Training.** Constant training and updating of skills should be a part of personnel policy. Workers need to be stimulated by their jobs, have pride in the services they provide, and be certain that their careers will advance based on their own merits.

The deficiencies discussed may seem surprising in that they should not exist in a well-organized firm, but they are commonplace in government water service entities.

Privatization of Water Supply and Reflections on Service

We have described the deficiencies of and the difficulties confronting government water suppliers, many of which could be reduced or eliminated through privatization. The natural struggle to produce a return on investment stimulates the search for efficiencies, and the reduction of losses and wastes. These two objectives, return on investment and reduction of costs, ought to stimulate the utilization of modern work procedures, rationalization of activities, and reduction of crew sizes, but not at the expense of security and quality of service. Reaching these objectives rapidly will not be possible, but long-term actions should be successful.

Private enterprise may be able to move resources into capital investments more rapidly, raising the percentage of the population that is served, modernizing plant and equipment and control systems, all of which should improve quality and security of service. As a private enterprise, the water service company should be less vulnerable to the influence of politicians, who at times could be seen interfering with the organization and its decisionmaking, interference not always coincident with the interests of the community. The personnel situation also should improve from diminished political influence, because with privatization, the internal groups that represent one or another politician should disappear.

Overall, management of the private enterprise will be more transparent to the community, as a result of the audits and controls that will be legally required, and the rules of conduct established by the concession.

Guarantees to the Community

The decision to privatize a government-owned water service agency should be taken only after the new concessionary organization agrees to adhere to conditions involving:

1) **Water quality.** The company must agree to standards set by the law.

2) **Continuity of service.** Service must be furnished in a manner that assures uninterrupted service and adequate pressure.

3) **Prices.** The tariff structure ought to be set up in advance, be appropriate to the needs of the community, with specific rules for residential, industrial, commercial, and other groups. Furthermore, the tariff may have to take into account the social needs of the community, including access to service for those with low incomes.

4) **Investment capacity.** Finances are needed that allow the firm to invest quickly when required to expand service within the community.

5) **Quality of materials and services.** The company must utilize materials and follow work procedures in a manner that adheres to manufacturers technical recommendations.

6) **Emergencies.** To guarantee the continuity of service, the company needs an organization that deals with emergencies, something indispensable for all good service.

7) **Customer relations**. The water company must respect time limitations for the provision of services, and provide quality services to the consumer.

If the water supplier is unwilling or unable to comply with the regulations, the community should have the power to seek immediate correction, to levy penalties and, if necessary, to cancel the concession.

Deciding to Privatize
The decision to privatize a governmental water service agency, in order to reap the benefits of market mechanisms acting on an activity directly linked to collective well-being and public health, should have been discussed vigorously by representatives of the community, so that the decision reflects the views of the majority.

The debate over the advantages and disadvantages of privatization ought to include alternative methods of making the change. A resolution must also be reached before the final decision as to whether the government should privatize the entire activity or part of it, and whether the government should continue to participate in the ownership of the corporation.

The privatization model should be tailored to the peculiar circumstances of each service and to the concerns of the respective communities. The entire process of privatization, from the decision to make a change, to the rules on how to set up the new system, to the choice of the enterprise to do the job, must result from a transparent and open process.

The rules of choice must clearly define the goals to be reached, the parameters of performance, the responsibilities, the penalties, the channels of communication with the community, the previous experience of the competitor for the concession, and in fact, almost every aspect that will regulate the relationship between the enterprise and the community. Privatization will succeed only if the parties develop a climate of familiarity and mutual respect.

Benefits of Privatization to the Community

We can enumerate the results that we would expect from privatization of water supply specifically, although they should be expected in any type of privatization. First, though, note that water supply is a permanent need for society, and it cannot be interrupted or stopped if the private enterprise fails, as would be the case with an industrial activity. The privatization must be accomplished in a way that gives the government sufficient powers and flexibility to act in case the public interest is endangered.

These are the benefits that we expect:

1) Privatization should stem the hemorrhaging of public funds that result from the need to cover the operating losses of water suppliers. That should free up funds for social purposes and other community needs.

2) Privatization will liberate government funds for capital investment in other sectors.

3) Privatization will reduce the role of the government in the economy, on the road to eliminating the state corporation. The state, in turn, We can enumerate the results that we would expect from privatization

4) Privatization should stimulate the growth of new enterprises that will provide services to the concessionaire.

5) Finally, privatization should provide the motive to produce lower costs.

Economic policy in the majority of countries encourages the formation of a market economy, in order to stimulate entrepreneurial creativity, and by doing so, raises the standard of living.

One of the ways to attain this goal is to reduce the role of the state as an owner of businesses, diminishing its interference in private business, and reserving for the state its proper role in education, welfare, preservation of the environment and social services.

The water and sewage industries, without doubt, are enterprises that are privatizable. The benefits of privatization are derived from the rationalization of services, improved water quality, greater efficiency, and reduction of costs. As long as the privatization respects the needs of the community, privatization will be a good solution for the users of the service as well as for the water companies themselves.

CONCLUSION

Privatization is not a magic formula. The government owner could take the same steps as the private owner: bring in capable management, price the product so that consumers use the product wisely, collect the water bills, bring revenues to levels that allow the utility to raise capital for expansion, and run the firm efficiently. In fact, many government-owned utilities do all of the above.

Selling the utility to outsiders brings cash to the government and fresh management to the utility, and hands the unpopular decisions to the new owners. That might speed the process of change. But, in the end, the only way to pay for the new capital is through the revenue stream. Customers pay. If they could not pay for the services before, they still cannot pay for the services no matter who owns the utility, unless, of course, the new owners can provide the same service at a lower cost.

Because the private operator remains a monopolist, consumers must depend on regulators to bring them some of the benefits of the new ownership. The right regulatory framework does that. The wrong framework either stifles the initiatives of the new owners or lets them reap monopolistic profits from public service enterprises.

Perhaps, in reality, a change in ownership, or utilization of outsiders in parts of the supply process, brings to bear expertise and capital-raising ability in an efficient, prompt manner, and provides a means to more easily circumvent institutional and political difficulties.

Demand for clean water and wastewater treatment is strong in the developing nations. In the industrialized countries, the big water supply firms operate in slow-growing markets. Those firms are seeking out opportunities in faster-growing regions. In that sense, privatization serves the purposes of buyers and sellers, and privatization does matter.

CHAPTER 37

Summary

The leader of Albania, Enver Hoxha, warned before his death in 1985 that departures from the true path of Stalinism would end up as a 'bucket of crabs.'[12]

— John Rentoul

Citizens of the United States do face problems of water supply caused by failing infrastructure, uneconomic pricing, more stringent environmental rules and diseconomies of a fragmented industry, but most, at least, begin from a base of adequate and clean water supplies and widespread treatment of wastewater. The industrialized nations of the world are in the same boat, so to speak. For that matter, even if they have to fix what they have, they have the resources to do so.

The situation is not the same elsewhere. Around the world, suppliers not only have to repair and improve the operations of existing facilities, but also make massive additions to plant in order to meet the needs of the growing urban population. They have to levy charges on a population that in many instances cannot afford to pay more, and in some cases may not be paying anything now. Some regions could face critical water shortages within decades, but they may not have the money to clear up current problems, much less plan and invest for the future.

Governments that do not have the funds to rehabilitate or expand water and wastewater infrastructure, or that want greater efficiency from in-place suppliers, have turned to the private sector. They have sold systems, outright, to investor-owned firms, or have entrusted system management to outsiders, usually with a contractual arrangement that provides greater rewards for more efficient operations. To date, the large French and British water suppliers have dominated the international privatization/contracting marketplace. American water suppliers can join as partners with the foreign giants of course, but most American investor-owned companies do not have the requisite size to pursue the biggest opportunities. The government-owned utilities have the size, but they were set up to solve local problems, not to engage in international investment.

The population of a large part of the world, however, may not benefit from the internationalization of the marketplace, because they live in rural areas or do not have the money to pay for better sanitary services. They need small-scale solutions and technology that will make possible access to affordable clean water and sanitary disposal of waste.

Although the global water prognosis has grim elements, finding the solutions represents an enormous business opportunity, not only for the utilities, but also for suppliers of equipment and of technological solutions, and for those who understand how to utilize market mechanisms to achieve goals efficiently.

NOTES

1. Quoted in G. Pascal Zachary, "Water Pressure: Nations Scramble to Defuse Fights Over Supplies," *Wall Street Journal*, 4 December 1997, p. A7.

2. United Nations Environmental Program, *Global Environmental Outlook* (New York: Oxford University Press, 1997), p. 4.

3. United Nations Centre for Human Settlements, *An Urbanizing World* (New York: Oxford University Press, 1996), p. 268.

4. United Nations Environmental Program, *Global Environmental Outlook*, p. 246.

5. Ibid., p. 217.

6. U.N. Centre for Human Settlements, *An Urbanizing World*, p. 109.

7. Gabriel García Márquez, *Cien Años de Soledad* (Buenos Aires: Editorial Sudamericana, 1969), p. 268.

8. All data and information for this chapter has been derived from: United Nations Environmental Program, *Global Environmental Outlook* (New York: Oxford University Press, 1997); United Nations Centre for Human Settlements, *An Urbanizing World*; and United Nations Development Programme, *Human Development Report* (New York: Oxford University Press, 1997).

9. Joseph Conrad, *Nostromo: A Tale of the Seaboard* (London: Harper & Brothers, 1904), pp. 63–64.

10. *1996 Annual Report*, Cie. Générale des Eaux, p. 25.

11. The text that follows is derived from "The Privatization of Water Supply and Sewage," in Leonard S. Hyman, *The Privatization of Public Utilities* (Vienna, Virginia: Public Utilities Reports, 1995), pp. 87–97.

12. John Rentoul, "Privatisation: The Case Against," in Julia Neuberger, ed., *Privatisation. . . Fair Shares for All or Selling the Family Silver?* (London: PAPERMAC, 1987), p. 1.

PART VII

Conclusion

CHAPTER 38

The Future of the Water Business

. . . the . . . children did not beg for coins. With empty tins in their hands they begged for water.[1]

— Antoine de Saint Exupéry

Here is the problem. Between now and 2025, the world's population could increase by one-third. Water supply remains the same. Population could increase by two-thirds by 2050. Water supply remains the same.

That problem of course, creates a business opportunity for those who can efficiently supply the clean water, and safely dispose of the wastewater created by the growing population. What is more, both developed and developing nations will have to expend enormous sums to improve their water systems. In the developed world, where people tend to view water as an almost free natural resource, the distribution, treatment, and waste disposal systems require major repairs and upgrades. Those systems, in many cases, now have to handle volumes in excess of original design. Their owners have not maintained them, due to budget constraints. For some suppliers and their customers, the cost of improving the quality of the water supply could prove prohibitive. In a number of countries, local governments, which still own the majority of the water systems, will have to decide whether to invest in water system improvements or in other social needs less likely to attract private capital.

In less developed nations, where clean water is often a scarce commodity, lack of adequate water and sewage treatment, collection, and distribution infrastructure affects the health of the local population and inhibits industrial development. Installation of modern systems where none now exist, plus meeting the requirements brought on by rapid economic and urban population growth, will require suppliers to raise sums of capital possibly beyond the capability of the local economy.

Meeting the demands of consumers, as efficiently and safely as possible, and providing a compensatory return for those investors who will have to put up the hundreds of billions of dollars required, will require new managerial and regulatory skills, with special emphasis on squeezing the maximum usage out of those fixed assets. How will these demands affect the structure of the industry? How do industry players see the opportunities? What role will local governments and investor-owned water companies play? How will they react to the forces of change?

THE POTENTIAL OF THE INTERNATIONAL WATER MARKET

Water plays a vital role in industrial processes, a fact that gets little attention in all the debates about drinking water. Obviously, soft drink manufacturers use lots of water, but consider these requirements:

- 0.4 gallons to 0.8 gallons of water to produce one kilowatt-hour of electricity;

- 7 gallons of water to process one bushel of corn;

- 150 gallons of purified water to rinse one microchip;

- 100,000 gallons to manufacture one automobile.

The American public spends over $50 billion per year for the services of public water and wastewater systems. Add capital spending and nonpublic services and the market probably exceeds $75 billion per year. On a worldwide basis, the annual market for water and wastewater services could be in the $300 billion range. (See Figure 38-1.) In comparison, the telecommunications market in the United States is estimated to be $150 billion; the electric and gas sector is in the $300 billion range. The size and capital needs of the worldwide water market make it an obvious target for current industry participants, others involved in the infrastructure, construction, and utility sectors, as well as a cross-section of potential suppliers of goods and services.

First, though, the water utility industry worldwide must define its role for the future. What services should it provide, what businesses should it be in, what core competencies will it require in order to compete? In the U.S., the water utility appears to be the last true regulated monopoly, one that is still dependent on traditional rate base regulation. Is it safe for water companies to follow the formula that worked in the past, or must they look beyond their traditional business in order to enhance shareholder value?

The participants in the market each look at it from a different perspective. The two major French water companies have gone the farthest in attempting to form true infrastructure and utility service companies. The French market is dominated by Générale des Eaux (whose name was changed to Vivendi in May 1998) and Suez-Lyonnaise des Eaux, which together control 68% of the water distribution and 36% of the wastewater sector, and account for 90% and 88%, respectively, of the private distribution and wastewater systems in the country. Both companies are conglomerates involved in electric generation, water distribution, wastewater, solid waste disposal, construction, and telecommunications. Interestingly, control is through contracts rather than direct ownership, which could be a future model for municipalities in the U.S. Suez-Lyonnaise des Eaux also is active in the United Kingdom, as the owner—since 1996—of Northumbrian Water.

414

Figure 38-1

World Water Market
Approx. $300 Billion in 1995

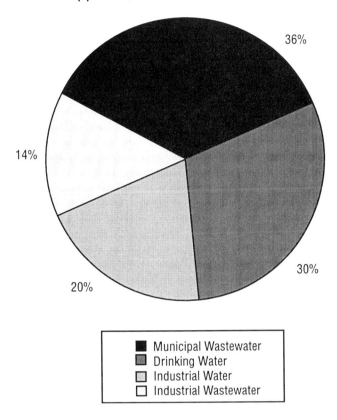

■	Municipal Wastewater
▨	Drinking Water
▦	Industrial Water
□	Industrial Wastewater

Source:
McIlvaine Research, *Smith Barney Pollution Control Monthly*, January 1997, p. 8.

As a result of the privatization of the U.K. water industry in 1989, Severn Trent, which describes itself as "a substantial British-based water, waste and utility services group" that serves "more than 20 million people" worldwide,[2] has chosen to expand aggressively overseas, since in-country opportunities are limited. The company has expanded into areas such as waste management, international operations, and systems and technology. Today these nonregulated businesses account for approximately 30% of sales and 8% of operating profits and are a major component of the company's growth. "These companies operate in the UK and USA—major bases of the operations—but the group is increasingly a global organization with joint projects in countries which include Russia, Israel, China, Peru, Romania, Mauritius, Turkey, Guyana, Swaziland, and the West Indies, and Belgium."[3]

The privatization of both the water and electric systems in Britain has resulted in substantial share price appreciation, leading many to question the government's valuation methodology. In the electric sector, the bulk of the initially privatized utilities have been acquired by American utilities attempting to diversify their industry exposure as deregulation threatens their U.S. business. In the water sector, many of the companies privatized still remain independent, and two actually took over electric utilities serving the same regions, to create what the British call multiutilities. One, United Utilities, was formed when North West Water acquired Norweb plc, an electric distribution company, in 1995. Subsequently, Welsh Water took over South Wales Electricity, to form Hyder. Shortly thereafter, ScottishPower purchased Southern Water, whose customer base is at the other end of Great Britain from the Glasgow-based power company.

United Utilities, like Severn Trent, seems to be following a similar international path, but one with greater integration of services offered to the customers. As United Utilities explains:

> The Regulated Utility Division brings together the regulated water and wastewater and electric distribution businesses in the North West of England. It has the potential to achieve significant synergistic benefits and the ability to exploit its skills, through competition, in non-regulated utility activities elsewhere in the UK. . . . The International Division has continued the successful development of our international water and wastewater activities, whilst adding Norweb's skills of electricity distribution and supply to the portfolio of services it can offer. The cost of entry into the international electricity markets is, therefore, very greatly reduced.[4]

One would expect that many of the new owners of the electric distribution companies in the U.K. would look for business opportunities to leverage the value of their customer bases, which may lead to additional electric/water mergers.

On the other hand, while the largest investor-owned water utility in the U.S., American Water Works, has established a joint venture with Anglian Water, to date this has not been a major initiative. Instead, American Water Works has focused its efforts on consolidating systems in this country, where the majority are still government-run.

> Ninety percent of the country's estimated 60,000 separate water systems serve fewer than 3,000 people each and are finding it increasingly difficult to provide the capital required to remain viable and to provides adequate service. Thus, regional approaches are emerging as the preferred solution to the nation's water service.[5]

Two nonregulated companies, U.S. Filter Corporation and Waterlink, Inc., have become aggressive consolidators of industrial water businesses. In February 1998, U.S. Filter announced its acquisition of Culligan Water Technologies, Inc., broadening its global strategy to include retail sales. Waterlink, a U.S.-based company with a variety of international subsidiaries,

. . . participates in the very large and highly fragmented water and wastewater treatment market. The *Environmental Business Journal* estimates the U.S. market at $75 billion, while McIlvaine Research has projected the worldwide market at $300 billion, growing to $500 billion by the year 2000. The global market growth rate is pegged at 10%. We believe this strong secular growth will be driven by four primary trends:

1) Municipal privatization of water and wastewater treatment plants, eventually forced by crumbling infrastructure.

2) Increasing industrial outsourcing of non-core functions such as water and wastewater treatment needs

3) Industry's need for increasingly purer water in their production process, coupled with the growing scarcity of usable water resources. This is particularly true in developing nations as they seek to industrialize.

4) Rising consumer concerns about the safety of their drinking water.

The market remains ripe for consolidation, with as many as 50,000 companies participating. Even the dominant player, U.S. Filter, controls less than 1% of the global market.[6]

Water suppliers could move into numerous businesses only peripherally connected to their core competency. If they do, they are likely to suffer the same fate as other utilities that have diversified to their regret. (In fact, a number of water utilities already have diversified and pulled back after writing off their losses.) Simply doing what they always did, however, may not serve them well, either. The water business is changing. Or to put it more accurately, some players intend to change it whether the traditional water companies like the idea or not.

THE U.S. WATER INDUSTRY TODAY AND TOMORROW

Let's look at the water industry in the United States and highlight the issues addressed by typical industry participants. The regulated, municipal, and nonregulated water companies all face issues and opportunities that are representative of ones being addressed around the globe. The U.S. market is ripe for a major restructuring.

The U.S. water market is in a state of flux. Many of the water systems are antiquated and need repair. Furthermore, 85% of the distribution systems and more than 90% of the wastewater systems are in the hands of local municipalities, which are coming under increasing budgetary pressure. Publicly traded water companies have seen their share prices rocket because they represent the last remaining regulated utility investment opportunity for dividend-driven retail investors, and because electric utilities have shown growing interest in the water sector, making the water companies acquisition targets.

There is no doubt that the water utility sector will continue to grow and generate regulated rates of return that will appeal to investors who want the continued payment of stable or increasing dividends. Capital requirements will remain heavy, due to the need to build new systems, rehabilitate old ones, and put in place new environmental controls. Regulated water utilities should be well positioned to purchase or manage existing municipal systems. It's likely that water treatment and wastewater services will become a growing area of need based upon water quality and cost issues. Water utilities could find that these markets will account for a large part of their future growth, if the utilities choose to pursue such businesses and are able to do so on a cost-effective basis.

Considering that the price of water has increased 778% since 1960 and is still rising (see Figure 38-2), both industrial and retail customers eventually will come to realize the true value of water and the systems required to insure its quality. In fact, new attention is being paid to water quality in the U.S. One needs only to pick up the local newspapers to see discussions on the risk of chlorination. In the national best-selling book, *Natural Health, Natural Medicine,*[7] a full chapter is devoted to water, the increasing chemical content of our supply, and the risks of treatment methods such as chlorination. The Environmental Protection Agency's Office of Ground Water and Drinking Water Web site covers many of the concerns

Figure 38-2

Water Costs in the U.S.A.

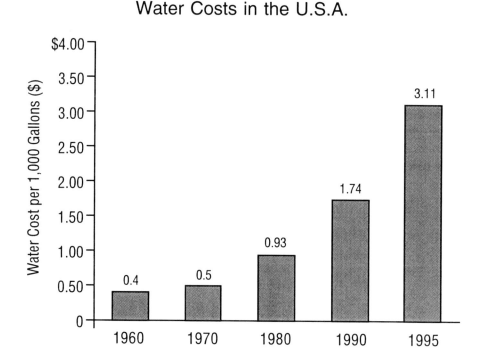

Source:
Smith Barney Research, "Waterlink," July 23, 1997, p. 9.

being raised by the general public. The American public is becoming increasingly aware of water—not only what is in it, but how to use it more efficiently.

How can water utilities ensure that they will be in a position to supply services demanded on a cost-competitive basis? Historically, there has not been competition; utilities' biggest challenges have been in the regulatory approval process. As municipal privatization moves forward, contract management has become a popular method to attract private industry expertise. Unfortunately, to date it has produced thin profit margins, due to cutthroat competition to win contracts. In many cases water utilities are forced to lower substantially their rate-of-return hurdles for these nonregulated transactions in order to win the business. That being said, major industry participants such as United Utilities in the U.K. and United Water Resources in the U.S. see this business as key to their future growth. On the regulated side of the business, acquisition of new systems into regulated rate base is a much safer investment. The issue is that most public systems have 3,000 customers or less. How do you build critical mass with such small transactions? Very slowly! Following the old business models may not generate rapid growth.

All major market participants view the U.S. market as too important to overlook, which should create dramatic competition in pursuit of market share. This competition has been reflected, until now, in the thin margins being realized in the contract water business, the price being paid to acquire residential distribution systems, and the price for nonregulated water assets. U.S. Filter's offer for Culligan, in 1998, was at an implied value of $60 per share, 54% above its prior-day close of $38.875. Municipalities should be able to capitalize on these competitive forces when they sell off utility properties or seek contractors to operate their utilities. Publicly traded, regulated, and nonregulated water companies must be careful of the prices they pay to gain market share, or they will do so at the expense of their shareholders.

As the complexities of water quality and delivery systems increase, many more customers, both industrial and retail, may choose to turn over responsibility for a growing portion of their water needs to qualified suppliers. As consumers face more and more choices for telecommunication, natural gas, electric, home security, and cable television services, and as they are the recipients of increased marketing efforts by numerous providers, many may question the value of customer choice. In the water sector, however, the situation is different. There is only one provider (for good or for bad) in an area. The opportunity to allow other suppliers to provide water through the distribution system of the local water company (referred to as *wheeling* in the electricity industry) seems highly unlikely, due to water quality issues. So the incumbent water supplier will continue to meet water supply, and, in some cases sewerage, needs for the foreseeable future, without the threat of competition.

Based upon this outlook, water utilities probably should have little concern about loss of current customers or the related revenue base. But could another local service company, or utility, offer to provide meter devices to help better monitor water supply and detect leaks? Could a company like Culligan or Waterlink offer in-home filtration or water quality monitoring services? Major retailers, such as Sears, have devoted substantial shelf space to water treatment systems and supplies. Perhaps local plumbers in the future will form a service organization to supply similar services and reduce the role of the water utility to a purely distribution function.

SERVICES BUNDLING

Edward Tirello, of BT Alex Brown, a strong proponent of the need for mergers in the electric utility sector for a decade, has also made his pitch for changes in the water utility sector. Tirello believes that control of the customer bill will be critical to firms that hope to offer more than one utility service to consumers. He predicts that electricity, natural gas, and water; home mortgage payments and taxes; insurance; security systems, cable TV, and telephone service; and appliance repair services could be bundled together in the not-so-distant future as more and more people want to simplify their daily lives.

The bundling of telecom services demonstrates this trend. If AT&T supplies cellular phone service, long-distance and home security systems today, could it not, in the future, also supply electricity, install a metering system, consolidate the billing for all utilities, and offer add-on water services that customers may not now think that they need? Many customers probably will opt for services that save them time and eliminate multiple bills and service options. Some companies are experimenting with Internet-based systems to aggregate customer services, simplifying delivery and payment. It does not take much imagination to envision a migration from the services provided today to a much broader list of future services:

Services Today	Future Services
water supply	point of service filtering and quality monitoring
water treatment	
water distribution	bottled water
contract management for municipalities	plumbing
	well drilling and maintenance
billing and customer service	water marketing and trading
meter reading	managing water rights
monitoring of quality	water conservation
wastewater disposition	resource procurement and management
wastewater treatment	
	shared customer services
	electric aggregation
	aggregation of customer services

It is safe to say that we will see much experimentation in the customer service side of the business. We only need to look at the activities of today's pioneers to realize the range of potential strategies.

As deregulation continues in the telecommunication sector and commences in the electric sector, much experimentation is taking place. It includes the development of new business opportunities, attempts to wrest business from competitors, and the rethinking of goods and services to be provided. There are two main reasons why so many people are attempting to enter these deregulating markets. The first is that, with the elimination of regulation, new market entrants, as well as existing providers, can find ways to deliver products and services at reduced costs, which may drive others out of business. The second, and probably more easily understood driver, is the sheer size of the market.

We have seen electric utilities take an active interest in the water sector as well as water companies look at business opportunities in the electric sector. The reasons given include the ability to manage a regulated business; customer aggregation; more efficient use of customer systems and service systems; the dual needs in developing nations for water and power; and the large privatization opportunity in the United States. Parallels can be drawn from the acquisition of local gas distribution companies by electric utilities, including the possibility that prices paid will be excess of traditional takeover values because of the premium value perceived in buying customer lists and gaining the ability to make new product offerings. Examples of convergence of the industries include:

- NIPSCO Industries purchased IWC Resources, a nearby water utility, in 1996.

- North West Water Group plc, a United Kingdom water distribution company, purchased Norweb plc, an electric distribution company, in 1995. In 1996 the new firm changed its name to United Utilities plc, creating what it calls "The UK's first multi-utility company."

- France's Suez-Lyonnaise des Eaux acquired the U.K.'s Northumbrian Water in 1996.

- In 1997, the Association of California Water Agencies adopted new aggregation rules that allow its 440 member agencies to offer electricity to their members.

- A December 1997 report by HSBC Washington Analysis discussed the 1997 stock price run up of American Water Works and pointed out what a good fit its 850,000 customers in New Jersey and Pennsylvania would be for electric utilities such as GPU and PECO Energy.[8]

Deregulation of the electric and telecom sectors has led to the formation of companies that package utility services. It seems logical to add water to the package. One company, American Residential Services, is consolidating maintenance, repair, replacement, and new equipment installations for heating, air conditioning, plumbing, electric, and air quality systems and home appliances. Service Centers USA, a subsidiary of Northwestern Public Service, has built a similar business unit, and by the end of 1997 it had acquired 14 companies with aggregate sales of $90 million.

It is also becoming obvious that wireless meter reading will affect all customers. Once systems are in place for metering electricity, meter reading apparatus for water, propane, and oil tanks are low-cost additions. Whether regulated water companies believe in a convergence theory or not, they will be at a serious disadvantage if they ignore the possibilities.

WHO THE PLAYERS ARE TODAY

In the United States, government-owned water utilities hog the spotlight. Of the investor-owned utilities, the 15 water utilities publicly traded on an active basis had equity market value of only $4.9 billion at the end of 1997. On the nonregulated side of the business, there are over 50 publicly traded companies pursuing different market segments. Two non-regulated companies worth mentioning are U.S. Filter (equity value $3.1 billion) and Waterlink, Inc. (equity value $190 million), both of which are following consolidation strategies. U.S. Filter revenues grew from $101 million in 1993 to $1.4 billion in 1997. With the pending acquisition of Culligan, consolidated sales are projected to rise to $4.5 billion. Waterlink, which went public in 1997, has seen its revenues grow from $3 million in 1995 to $65 million in 1997. It is estimated that 1998 revenues will exceed $148 million. The American companies, however, are dwarfed by the foreign components of the water industry.

In France, two giants, Suez-Lyonnaise des Eaux (equity value $14 billion) and Générale des Eaux (equity value $18.8 billion), control approximately 90% of the private water sector. (See Figure 38-3.) Both companies also are actively involved in areas such as infrastructure development, electricity, and telecommunications, but these offerings have not yet been integrated into a real package for consumers.

In the U.K., where the water industry has been privatized since 1989, we see the major water companies seeking out expansion and nonregulated business opportunities. The 15 large publicly traded water companies (total equity value $33 billion), are pursuing both regulated and nonregulated initiatives. The two large multisector utilities (with a market value of $5.7 billion) have attempted to provide multiple services to consumers. As the electric sector continues to be restructured, it seems natural that water and electric companies with common customer bases will investigate alliances and ventures to cut costs through shared services and find new revenue sources from their captive customer base. On the regulated side, upcoming price reviews will continue to limit the growth potential

Figure 38-3

French Market Share
1995

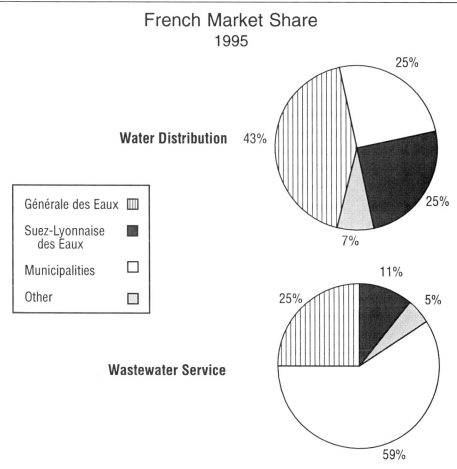

Source:
HSBC Washington Analysis, "Water Utilities," November 26, 1996, p. 21.

of these companies. United Utilities, created by a water company acquiring an electric distribution company, believes that in the future there is a strong likelihood that regulated earnings will decline, due to competitive pressures and the regulatory environment. It is likely that the regional electric distribution companies, many of which are owned by U.S. utilities, will come to a similar conclusion and begin to seek out new avenues to maintain and grow earnings.

CHAPTER 39

Conclusion

The idea of conducting the entire economy on the basis of private greed, as Marx well recognized, has shown an extraordinary power to transform the world.[9]

— E. F. Schumacher

In some ways, the American water and wastewater industry seems to exist in a time warp. One almost expects to see the industry depicted in black and white rather than in color. Government agencies originally set up to provide fire protection, to combat cholera, or to construct vast public works that transported water 30 to 40 miles, still dominate the industry here. They use an operational matrix almost unchanged from Roman days and they purify water with century-old techniques.

In Europe, Latin America, Australia, and in parts of Asia and Africa, governments either have put or are in the process of putting the water and wastewater sector into private ownership or management. That process has begun, slowly, in the United States, but it has not affected most of the huge municipal utilities, or the state or federal water projects. Are America's government-owned utilities more efficient than their international counterparts, or are American governments so flush with funds that they can afford to maintain the necessary capital expenditure programs? The dilapidated nature of some big-city infrastructure, the reliance on tax subsidy, the resistance to making new environmental expenditures, and the creation of elaborate money-funneling operations and use of bond insurance indicates that at least some of these huge systems are not in good shape.

But, to be realistic, the investor-owned water suppliers in the United States have not targeted the major municipal, state, or federal water systems for takeover or operating contracts. U.S. water companies do not have the financial capability, size, or even the operating experience necessary to qualify as rescuers of the large systems, assuming such systems need rescue. That role, probably, would fall to the huge French or British utilities, or to contracting firms outside the utility sector that could create water utility entities that far exceed the size of existing investor-owned water utilities.

Two alternatives do exist, though. One would be to create private companies out of existing water departments, and sell those new companies to the public in securities offerings. The other is to consolidate government utilities into larger, regional entities that could offer lower-cost service and take advantage of marketing opportunities that come with size. The existing investor-owned utilities, possibly as a result of small size, parochialism, or conservatism may find themselves playing a marginalized role in the future, as associates of foreign utilities, as units of newcomers to the industry, or as firms limited to the small markets—unless they transform themselves dramatically and quickly.

Consolidation will play a role in the future of the industry, because the current 60,000 suppliers cannot provide services or raise money as efficiently as a smaller number of larger entities. Consolidation will occur through purchase of smaller by larger entities, merger of government agencies, joint operating arrangements that bring the benefits of scale to smaller entities, or through operating contracts that put effective control of a number of entities into the hands of a nonowner. Consolidation, or better yet, the formation of alliances, could occur for another reason. Utilities seem to be heading in the direction of offering a number of services to customers. Several electric companies have begun to put together packages that include electricity, gas, telecommunications, cable TV, and home security services. They will put in place multiple-product metering and communications links. Adding water as one more product would not be difficult to do with the cooperation of the water company. For that matter, the water company might want to play the dominant role, and offer its customers the other services. Or, the principal packager might decide to buy the water company (or make a deal with a local municipal water supplier) in order to enter a new market. The point is that marketers need large customer bases in order to reach economies of scale in advertising, new product development, billing, and in purchasing their inputs at the lowest possible cost. Most water companies that choose to play in this game as principals will need more customers. Those who choose not to act could end up losing out on the value that their markets offer, and acting out roles as disadvantaged bit players.

Operationally and technologically, the water and wastewater industry is in an odd position. It cleans and delivers the product in roughly the same way that it did a century ago. The industry has not supported advanced research and high technology work of the sort typified by the old Bell Laboratories or the Electric Power Research Institute. The industry tolerates a 20% to 30% wastage rate of the product that it delivers, possibly because the cost of correcting the problem exceeds the value of the lost product, but in some places a shortage of the product could develop, and cost of incremental facilities might soar over the cost of internal water supplier conservation measures. From a structural standpoint, though, the fact that a technological revolution seems not in the offing may give comfort to the existing utilities. After all, one could argue that technological change undermined the monopolistic positions of both the telephone and electric utility industries, thereby loosing on them the forces of competition.[10] Something else could happen in the water business. The rising cost of providing the quality of water demanded by environmental and health regulators and that demanded by consumers (which may or may not coincide), through the public water supply system, may encourage consumers to do the job, instead, in their homes or places of business, with equipment provided by others—not by the public utility. That distributed answer may be the economically correct one, but it could relegate the public water supplier to the role of provider of a regulated-price commodity while others take the high-margin business, acting as the water quality improvement suppliers. Would those new suppliers—if they appear on the scene—work with the other suppliers of utility services, and would they try to cut the water utility out of that picture? If this sounds farfetched, how many people believed a few years ago that any firm other than the local utility would provide retail electricity?

Rate-of-return regulation has the virtue—in theory—of rewarding the utility for making the needed capital improvements. But the delays in the process may prevent the utility from actually earning the allowed return for prolonged periods. What is worse, though, is that the regulatory system provides few explicit incentives for innovation or more-efficient operation. Alternative regulatory schemes have the virtue of using incentives to encourage efficiency, but they also can encourage the utility to cut corners and discourage needed capital expenditures.

The real problem with the current regulatory system, though, is that it sends all the wrong signals to consumers. Because it is anchored in the past (original cost rate base and historic cost depreciation), it does not tell consumers what that last drop of water really costs society. It encourages wasteful use of a precious resource. Admittedly, most water and wastewater consumers do not take their services from regulated monopolies, but rather from government agencies. Those bodies could, in theory, price their services in a way that reflects cost to society, assuming that doing so does not get them in trouble with the Internal Revenue Service for running a highly profitable, nontax-paying business in the guise of a city department. But most government agencies do not look upon economic pricing as part of their charge, and local politicians may worry when the water and sewer bill becomes obvious to the consumer. In other words, both the regulatory system and the nonregulated pricing process seem to make the construction of an economically rational water pricing scheme almost hopeless. The states, if they had the legal right to do so, could impose on water users a fee for the water itself, which would discourage waste, but think of all the opposition from those who now have a free resource.

Barring a rational pricing system, society may benefit from a semi-rational system, based on trading of water rights. In those areas of water shortage, the owners of the rights will sell their water use rights to those who place the highest value on the water. That pricing process will cause users who pay high prices to consume as little as possible, and to demand that the water transporters lose as little water as possible during the transportation. It will cause sellers of rights to cease wasting water because every drop wasted would represent lost profits. It also would encourage the development of alternative water sources and technologies, which would not have been worth developing if the price of water were lower. Conceivably, water trading could even encourage the development of water sources that render certain pipeline or other resources less valuable: the specter of stranded costs in the water business. Admittedly, somebody gets rich in the process—not the taxpayers who developed the subsidized water resources but rather the owners of the water rights received as a gift from the taxpayers—but that solution may be a better one, from a public policy standpoint, than one in which farmers waste water growing subsidized crops and urban dwellers cannot get the water supply for which they are willing to pay. Market-based mechanisms may provide the only way to deal with the dearth of water in the western United States. They should provide major business opportunities for those who can wait out the initial period of opposition and uncertainty.

Financially, most water and wastewater suppliers seem likely to continue to do what they have been doing. That is, they will raise large amounts of external capital to finance expansion, rehabilitation, and environmental improvements until technology produces less capital intensive solutions, or depreciation rises to a higher level, or the utilities get beyond their big spending programs. Credit ratings permit such financing.

All industry participants—whether a public or private water utility or a private water services company here or abroad—have to learn to move with the times, rather than at their accustomed pace. This is imperative for two reasons. First, the company may find ways to cut costs, through new technologies or joint ventures, or increase revenues through new products and business opportunities. Second, whether managements like it or not, they may be faced with an offer from an outsider to buy out the company, manage it, or just work together with the company to enhance competitive position. To just put one's head in the sand and ignore external market forces is to do a disservice to customers, shareholders, and employees.

As different players map out their strategies, it is probable that divergent views will develop as to valuation and future opportunities. As in any market, there may be times when excess valuation levels present an opportunity to sell a business, and conversely when buying opportunities present themselves and the firm needs to be prepared to quickly evaluate such options. Many people agree that for most utilities:

- Competition will increase.

- Technology will play a major role in industry evolution.

- Customers will continue to gain more options.

- Convergence of industry sectors and utility services will continue.

- Market-based solutions will prevail over imposed solutions.

428

They may not agree that those conclusions apply to the water and wastewater sector. But, even if the core utility remains regulated, the regulatory framework can change, and unregulated firms will act to take advantage of all the business opportunities peripheral to that core. (Unregulated firms might even provide the same service as the water utility. The British, for instance, have begun to allow the establishment of "inset" suppliers that sell water to certain customers within the territory of another utility.)

One thing is certain: the size and opportunities in this market sector will drive much activity, and the future will probably bring many changes. As a Severn Trent publication notes:

> And so the era of the multi-utility is born, not so much with a bang or a whimper, more a struggle for survival! ... But just because water is different, [Severn Trent CEO] Vic Cocker insists this is no time for complacency. 'The so-called 'multi-utility revolution' will affect customers' perception of service and will no doubt lead to greater pressure for competition and greater efficiencies in the water business.'[11]

Water companies in the future will have to stay abreast of industry developments, listen to their customers, field a knowledgeable management team, and be prepared! Someone recently said of electric deregulation, "This is not your grandmother's old utility system." The same may be very true for the global water sector, as market forces and entrepreneurialism invade that last, conservative bastion of the old utility system. While there are no clear winners or losers today, breadth of experience, geographic reach and expertise, and financial resources all will be important to grow and succeed in this changing business environment.

NOTES

1. Antoine de Saint Exupéry, *Wind, Sand and Stars* (New York: Reynal & Hitchcock, 1939), pp. 142–143.

2. Severn Trent plc, *1997 Report*, p. 5.

3. Ibid.

4. United Utilities plc, *1996 Annual Report*, p. 10.

5. American Water Works, *1996 Annual Report*, p. 8.

6. Smith Barney Research, "Waterlink," July 23, 1997, p. 3.

7. Andrew Weil, M.D., *Natural Health, Natural Medicine* (New York: Houghton Mifflin Company, 1995), pp. 75–83.

8. Debra G. Coy, "Water Utilities: Electric Utility Takeover Targets," *Environment This Month*, December 3, 1997.

9. E. F. Schumacher, *Small is Beautiful* (New York: Harper & Row Perennial Library, 1975), p. 254.

10. See, Leonard S. Hyman, *America's Electric Utilities: Past, Present and Future* (Vienna, Va.: Public Utilities Reports, 1997) and Leonard S. Hyman, Edward DiNapoli and Richard C. Toole, *The New Telecommunications Industry: Meeting the Competition* (Vienna, Va.: Public Utilities Reports, 1997).

11. *Severn Trent Insights,* Issue 2, 1997.

SELECTED BIBLIOGRAPHY

Selected Bibliography

Readings and source material on the water and wastewater industries vary from technical to tendentious. The industry does not collect, analyze, or distribute statistics as meaningfully or expeditiously as do the telecommunications, natural gas, or electric utility industries. Government-collected information is often stale, as well. The National Association of Water Companies publishes a magazine, *Water*, industry statistics, and other helpful documents that center on the investor-owned industry. The American Water Works Association also collects and publishes information. Many of the best sources of information are now on the Internet. And, that old standby, the *Encyclopaedia Brittanica*, covers the topics well.

Moody's and Standard & Poor's publish the most authoritative industry and utility-specific financial and operating information, and provide thorough analyses, especially from a credit standpoint. Several brokerage houses publish up-to-date industry and utility-specific analyses on a regular basis.

The Statistical Abstract of the United States, and its various offshoot publications, produces a plethora of information. The material is stale, but it is collected in one place, and every library worthy of the name carries copies of it. The suggestions that follow are either classic texts, readable explanations, up-to-date treatments, or one of the few published sources available on this topic.

Operations and Environment

Cessna, Cornelia B., Nancy R. Jacobs, and Carol D. Foster, eds. *Water: No Longer Taken for Granted*. Wylie, Tex.: Information Plus, 1993.
General exposition of water issues.

Kochen, Jose V. "Privatization of Water Supply and Sewage." In *The Privatization of Public Utilities*, edited by Leonard S. Hyman. Vienna, Va.: Public Utilities Reports, 1995.
Succint discussion of operational and organizational issues for both water and wastewater.

Lean, Geoffrey, and Don Hinrichsen. *WWF Atlas of the Environment*. Santa Barbara, Calif.: ABC-CLIO, 1994.
Water and sanitation are discussed from an environmental view. Excellent maps, tables, and graphs buttress the analysis.

Linsley, Ray K., and Joseph B. Franzini. *Water Resources Engineering.* 2nd ed. New York: McGraw-Hill Book Company, 1972.
One of the best overviews of the technology and science of water supply, covering hydrology, design of water systems, and engineering factors that shape water systems. Clearly written.

Miller, E. William, and Ruby M. Miller. *Water Quality and Availability: A Reference Handbook.* Santa Barbara, Calif.: ABC-CLIO, 1992.

Montgomery, Carla W. *Environmental Geology.* Dubuque, Iowa: Wm. C. Brown Publishers, 1992.
Thorough textbook, well-illustrated, which covers hydrology as well as treatment of water and waste.

U.S. Department of Agriculture. *Climate and Man: Yearbook of Agriculture 1941.* Washington, D.C.: United States Department of Agriculture, 1941.
Although some of the science of meteorology has advanced, this volume contains a wealth of climatic data, and excellent descriptions of the climate factors that influence water development in the United States.

U.S. Department of Agriculture. *Water: The Yearbook of Agriculture 1955.* Washington, D.C.: U.S. Government Printing Office, 1955.
Out-of-date, quaint in its outlook, overly focused on agriculture, but an excellent reference filled with good explanations and illustrations.

Wekesser, Carol, ed. *Water: Opposing Viewpoints.* San Diego: Greenhaven Press, 1994.
General information, conservation, and laws are covered.

History and Organization

Blake, Nelson Manfred. *Water for the Cities: A History of The Urban Water Supply Problem in the United States.* Syracuse, N.Y.: Syracuse University Press, 1956.
An indispensable source on the development of the urban water system.

Cross, Gilbert. *A Dynasty of Water: The Story of American Water Works Company.* Voorhees, N.J.: American Water Works, 1991.
A chatty corporate history that emphasizes the human side of the story.

Kirby, Richard Shelton, Sidney Withington, Arthur Burr Darling, and Frederick Gridley Kilgour. *Engineering in History.* New York: Dover Publications, 1990.

Leavitt, Judith Walzer, and Ronald L. Numbers, eds. *Sickness and Health in America: Readings in the History of Medicine and Public Health*. Madison: University of Wisconsin Press, 1985.
This contains several chapters relative to water and wastewater issues.

Reisner, Marc. *Cadillac Desert: The American West and Its Disappearing Water*. New York: Viking, 1986.
The book to read to get an overview of Western water policy. The chronicles of Western water development are far more compelling than much contemporary fiction.

Rosenberg, Charles E. *The Cholera Years*. Chicago: University of Chicago Press, 1987.
A major analysis of the spread and containment of a disease intimately associated with water supply.

Usher, Abbott Payson. *A History of Mechanical Invention*. Rev. ed. Reprint. New York: Dover, 1988.

Regulation and Economics

Bain, Joe S. *Industrial Organization*. New York: John Wiley & Sons, Inc. 1968.
A thorough, practical discussion of the principles of industrial organization, unadorned by formulas of any kind.

Beecher, Janice A. *Sourcebook of Regulatory Techniques for Water Utilities*. Washington, D.C.: National Association of Water Companies, June 1997.
An extraordinarily thorough publication that examines 10 general ratemaking issues and then divides them into 48 subdivisions, all replete with examples, current practices, sources of information, helpful appendices, and even telephone numbers.

Beecher, Janice A., and Patrick C. Mann. "Real Water Rates on the Rise." *Public Utilities Fortnightly*, July 15, 1997, 42.
A succint outline of the conflict between rising costs and regulation.

Bonbright, James C. *Principles of Public Utility Rates*. New York: Columbia University Press, 1961.
The classic text on regulation of public utilities.

Bonbright, James C., Albert Danielsen, and David R. Kamerschen. *Principles of Public Utility Rates*. Arlington, Va.: Public Utilities Reports, 1988.
An update of the 1961 text, with more details on recent events.

Clark, J. Maurice. *Studies in the Economics of Overhead Costs.* Chicago: University of Chicago Press, 1962.
A classic study of the economic issues involved when fixed costs predominate, written in clear English.

Hirshleifer, Jack, James C. DeHaven, and Jerome W. Milliman. *Water Supply: Economics, Technology, and Policy.* Chicago: University of Chicago Press, 1960.
Rigorous analysis of water economics that shows the economic flaws of much water policy. Emphasizes the point that water use is sensitive to price.

Kahn, Alfred E. *The Economics of Regulation: Principles and Institutions.* 2 vols. Cambridge, Mass.: MIT Press, 1988.
The two volumes, "Economic Issues," and "Institutional Issues," examine economic principles and actual situations in clear prose. Looks at all regulated business, not just utilities.

Morin, Roger A., in collaboration with Lisa Todd Hillman. *Regulatory Finance: Utilities' Cost of Capital.* Arlington, Va.: Public Utilities Reports, 1994.
A practical book full of examples; spreadsheet is optional.

Phillips, Charles F. Jr. *The Regulation of Public Utilities: Theory and Practice.* Arlington, Va.: Public Utilities Reports, 1993.
Thorough analysis of regulation and regulated utilities, with much discussion of actual situations.

Welch, Francis X. *Cases and Text on Public Utilities Regulation.* Washington, D.C.: Public Utilities Reports, 1968.
A splendid classic, unfortunately long out of print.

Financial

Brigham, Eugene F., and Louis C. Gapenski. *Financial Management: Theory and Practice.* Chicago: The Dryden Press, 1991.
Thorough text that moves from the simplest to the most complex concepts, with many examples.

Copeland, Tom, Tim Koller, and Jack Murrin. *Valuation: Measuring and Managing the Value of Companies.* New York: John Wiley & Sons, 1996.
The McKinsey method of helping firms make capital budget decisions, determine cost of capital, and measure the value of the enterprise. A cookbook, of sorts, for financial valuation.

Dewing, Arthur Stone. *The Financial Policy of Corporations*. New York: The Ronald Press, 1953.
A massive treasure trove of information on how corporations evolved.

Feldstein, Sylvan G. "Guidelines in the Credit Analysis of General Obligation and Revenue Bonds." In *The Handbook of Fixed Income Securities*, edited by Frank J. Fabozzi, T. Dessa Fabozzi, and Irving M. Pollack. Homewood, Ill.: Business One Irwin, 1991.

Feldstein, Sylvan G., and Frank J. Fabozzi. "Municipal Bonds," and "Analyzing the Creditworthiness of Short-Term Municipal Obligations." In *The Handbook of Fixed Income Securities*, edited by Frank J. Fabozzi, T. Dessa Fabozzi, and Irving M. Pollack. Homewood, Ill.: Business One Irwin, 1991.
A thorough, and readable, analysis of municipal finance.

Graham, Benjamin, David L. Dodd, and Sidney Cottle. *Security Analysis: Principles.* New York: McGraw-Hill Book Company, Inc., 1962.
The classic text on security analysis, in the last edition by all the original authors. Quaint, but full of investment wisdom.

Logue, Dennis E., ed. *Handbook of Modern Finance*. Boston: Warren, Gorham & Lamont, 1984.
Definitions, examples, caveats, and shrewd observations fill the book.

Rappaport, Alfred. *Creating Shareholder Value: The New Standard for Business Performance.* New York: The Free Press, 1986.
An understandable account of making money for shareholders; long on common sense, short on formulas.

Wirick, David W., with John D. Borrows and Steven Goldberg. *Evaluating Water Utility Financial Capacity with Ratio Analysis and Discounted Cash Flows.* Columbus, Ohio: The National Regulatory Research Institute, July 1997.
A brief, well-reasoned analysis, with many examples, cookbook formulas, and sophisticated concepts reduced to simple English.

Woelfel, Charles J. *Encyclopedia of Banking and Finance*. Chicago: Probus Publishing, 1994.

International

Hyman, Leonard S., ed. *The Privatization of Public Utilities*. Vienna, Va.: Public Utilities Reports, 1995.
Discussions of privatization issues by business executives who participated in the process.

United Nations Centre for Human Settlements. *An Urbanizing World: Global Report on Human Settlements 1996.* Oxford: Oxford University Press, 1996.
Detailed discussions on urbanization issues, with many projections included.

United Nations Development Program. *Human Development Report 1997.* New York: Oxford University Press, 1997.
Development issues discussed; numerous examples and voluminous tables of data.

United Nations Environment Program. *Global Environment Outlook.* New York: Oxford University Press, 1997.
Regional concerns and policy responses, plus numerous projections of trends.

APPENDICES

APPENDIX A

Water Conservation

One of the major challenges facing water suppliers today is to meet the needs of customers with minimum environmental impact and at low cost. In the past, planners assumed that water use would grow, simply because it had grown in the past. Water planners sought to meet increasing demand by building new supplies. Little thought was given to using water more efficiently, or questioning the assumption that demand would grow in areas with stable or declining populations. Controlling demand was an unknown concept aside from asking people to reduce water use during a drought.

However, with the rise of the environmental movement in the 1960s, critics began to question the environmental impact of building large water projects to meet growing water needs. That change in attitude slowed the building of new water supply projects. Inflationary pressure in the 1970s that dramatically raised the cost of construction and tight money policies in the 1980s dampened enthusiasm for spending on water projects. Utilities slowly started to look at ways to stretch their water supplies by using water more efficiently.

Physically, a gallon of water is a gallon of water, whether it comes from a brand new reservoir or from water saved by fixing a leaky faucet, thereby stretching existing supply. The questions to ask in determining whether to build a new supply or save water are: which strategy minimizes environmental impacts, and which is cheaper? Conservation of water, through the more efficient use of current supplies, provides the low-cost answer to both the environmental and economic questions. Most conservation strategies rely on reducing use of water by the customer, but some of the biggest returns can be made by the supplier reducing the water it wastes. These are strategies that should be considered in thinking about ways to increase the efficiency of a water system's operation.

METERING

It is not possible to set up any rational conservation plan without metering. Otherwise, utilities cannot charge customers based on the amount of water they use, and that is a pricing system that would discourage waste. Metering also helps the utility to determine where water is going in the system. If a utility does not meter customers, and cannot tell where its water is going, it will not know if increased usage is due to a broken water main or because a customer just installed a giant swimming pool. After Boston started a comprehensive metering program, the city reduced its unaccounted water from 50% to 36%. (Unaccounted water is water a utility distributes, but which disappears into the system.) Water resource experts recommend metering all customers within a system to assure proper accounting for water, and to make those who use more water pay their fair share of water supply development. (Most utilities, though, do not meter water for fire fighting.) Metering also provides the data that a utility needs to set up a pricing system by showing the relation between price of water and volume consumed.

A water utility needs to choose meters that are appropriate for the type of service offered. A meter designed for large water volumes would not be sensitive enough to measure the demand of an apartment dweller, and might underreport demand. In addition, utilities should regularly check on the meters to assure that they work properly and have not been tampered with. Dishonest customers do tamper with their meters, or bypass them, to reduce their water bills. Regular inspection of meters can discourage this, as will prosecutions of water theft. Meters usually should be replaced after 15 years of use, as their accuracy decreases over time.

In the past, meters were located inside homes; this raised the expenses of the water company, because meter readers were not always able to gain access to homes, necessitating repeat trips to read a meter. Recently, utilities have installed meters outside of homes and businesses, allowing utilities to collect billing information regardless of whether the residents are home. Newer meters emit signals that allow a meter reader to record data while driving through a community, which speeds up meter reading and reduces the number of employees required, all of which justifies the higher initial cost of these meters.

The frequency of billing relates to the frequency of meter reading. In the United States, the frequency of bills varies from once a month to twice a year. More frequent billing gives customers feedback on how much water they are using, and can provide an incentive for them to reduce consumption, because they are quickly notified as to the cost of their water use.

PRICING

Pricing is the key to any conservation plan, for financial incentive spurs users to conserve. One of the biggest disincentives to conservation comes about when customers do not pay the full cost of the water they use, usually when a government body subsidizes the water price. In some municipalities, taxes subsidize water bills, discouraging conservation, because tax charges do not reflect the amount of water as accurately as metered water bills. In Massachusetts, this cross-subsidization of municipal water supplies is prohibited by law.

Water utilities tend to use four systems of charging for water use: fixed fees, uniform block pricing, increasing block pricing, and decreasing block pricing. With fixed fees, a customer pays a fee for water use that does not change, regardless of the amount of water used. Flat fees discourage efficient water use because a customer pays the same fee whether he uses one or 100 gallons a day. The homeowner has little incentive to fix a leaky faucet, because a new washer will cost 25 cents, but the leaking water does not cost him anything extra.

With uniform block pricing, the customer pays a charge based the volume of water he uses, for example $25.00 for each 1,000 gallons he uses. (See Figure A-1.) This rate per unit of water stays the same whether the customer uses 1,000 gallons or 10,000 gallons. This pricing system ensures accountability, because the customer is charged for the water he uses. There are two variants on this system: increasing block pricing and decreasing block pricing. With increasing block pricing (Figure A-2), the price per unit of water sold increases as usage increases, making users pay a higher rate for consuming above certain levels. The opposite

Figure A-1

Uniform Block Pricing

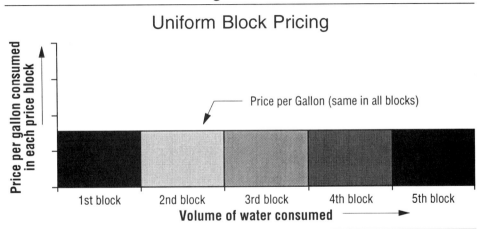

Figure A-2

Increasing Block Pricing

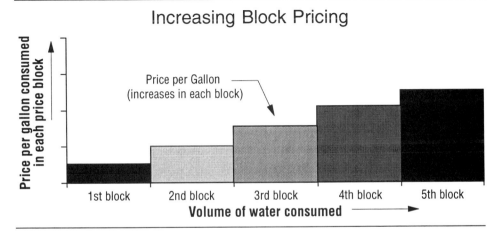

of the increasing block system is the decreasing block system, whereby the price per unit falls as usage increases. (See Figure A-3.) In the past, water systems used decreasing block pricing to reflect the increasing economies of scale from increasing size of water operations.

However, when such increased use requires the water supplier to develop new supplies to meet that increased demand, the average costs of water stop decreasing, and the economies of scale become diseconomies of scale, raising costs to customers. Decreasing block pricing, by encouraging increased use, works against water conservation. Massachusetts has banned decreasing block pricing, in order to encourage efficient water use.

In addition to these basic pricing structures, some water suppliers add other charges to encourage more efficient use of water. Some utilities charge higher prices during the drier summer months to discourage excessive watering of lawns.

There are other ways that pricing can be used to increase water conservation. One is to charge higher rates for water use during the day than at night in the drier seasons. Some utilities encourage homeowners to water their lawns at night by charging lower rates at night, when less water will evaporate due to heat, allowing homeowners to use less water to keep their lawns green. In addition, utilities sometimes place a surcharge on excessive water use that exceeds a norm for that class of customer. Although water for domestic consumption needs to be potable, there is no reason that water for outdoors has to be fit to drink—lawns do not need fluoridated or chlorinated water. Lower-quality water, such as reclaimed sewage, could be used outdoors, and a lower rate could be charged for its use. This would free up scarce, high-quality water for home use. This could be very useful when a treatment plant is nearing capacity, because instead of building

Figure A-3

Decreasing Block Pricing

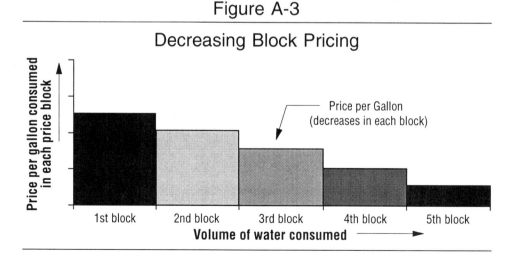

new capacity, water can bypass parts of the treatment process, freeing up capacity to produce potable water. Parts of St. Petersburg, Florida even have a dual system of water distribution for potable and nonpotable water. As another consideration in favor of such a scheme, in the dry season, water for outdoor use can be priced at a higher rate, because of its tendency to evaporate and be lost from the water system, whereas water that is used indoors returns to the water system as sewage, and can be reclaimed for further use.

PUBLIC EDUCATION

Although price spurs customers to conserve, there are often limits to what people know about conserving water. Public education programs by water utilities can show people how to use water more efficiently, whether at home or in industry, and, with a proper pricing system, save money on their water bills. It is essential for a water utility to have a good public education division, because without good communication, it is hard for a utility to implement conservation programs. In addition, in the event of a drought, an unprepared utility will not be able to react quickly to promote emergency conservation programs. Water systems rely on public service announcements, advertising, and bill inserts to communicate with water users. In addition, many utilities have a public service bureau that provides speakers and programs for community groups, including schools. In many areas, water utilities develop curriculum for schools that fits in with studies of the environment in science classes. Those programs help to communicate good water use habits at an early age to students, who, in turn, often police their elders' water use.

DOMESTIC CONSERVATION

Domestic conservation strategies seek to reduce water use of residential customers. Usually, these consist of retrofitting household plumbing systems to make them more efficient. Since faucets, showers, and toilets account for the majority of indoor water use, retrofitting them can reduce the amount of water used, without requiring a change in customers' behavior, or affecting the quality of their water supplies. The amount of water-saving equipment that customers will install depends on the price of water compared to the price of the equipment. If customers see that the savings on their water bills, within a reasonable period of time, will exceed the cost of the retrofit, then they will invest in change.

Domestic conservation is affected by both government rules and the work of the water utility. Building authorities in a state or locality have control over the plumbing code, and can mandate the use of highly efficient water appliances in new construction or renovations. The federal government, through the Energy Policy Act of 1992, even mandated that after January 1, 1997, all toilets sold in the United States had to be low-flow toilets—using no more than 1.6 gallons of water per flush. While this cannot help a utility reduce water use over a short period, such as during a summer drought, over the long run these improvements increase the efficiency of the water supply system, and by reducing water usage, decrease the severity of a water emergency.

Often, when water utilities need a fast way to reduce consumption, they provide and install conservation devices. Many utilities will even provide a no-charge water audit. An expert goes through a customer's house, and shows him how to save water. Often, the utility will retrofit houses at no charge. Studies have shown that to improve the likelihood of having a customer use the devices, it is best to have the water utility install them, rather than just giving the devices to the customers. By controlling installation, the utility can assure that the devices are installed properly. Although some utilities have replaced customers' toilets with low-flow models, usually water companies only provide small-scale devices that reduce flows through faucets, showers, and toilets. In the western United States, in cities such as Tucson, Arizona, utilities help homeowners develop landscaping plans that do not require much water. Some of these utilities help homeowners select native plants that function well in the desert, and require little watering. Although some may question why a water utility is in the landscaping design business, utilities have found that the savings in water use from these programs is cheaper than developing new supply to meet water needs.

NONDOMESTIC CONSERVATION

In addition to aiding residential customers, water utilities work with commercial customers to reduce water usage. Businesses are well attuned to ways they can save money on their utility bills. Although businesses use water in the same ways as homeowners, such as toilets, they also use water in very large quantities for cooling and industrial purposes. The main industrial uses of water are as a solvent and coolant. Since certain industrial uses need highly pure water, many times purer than household water, it is often possible to reuse industrial wastewater for lower quality uses. One of the largest uses of industrial water is for cooling purposes. Water utilities provide industries with the expertise to show how to reduce water usage. They often help businesses find leaks, and help industries develop ways to recycle cooling water. In the American West, electric power plants are starting to recycle the water that runs through their steam turbines, rather than venting it into the atmosphere. In arid areas, industries are encouraged to develop industrial cooling technologies that cool through air processes, rather than water. Given that many industries use large volumes of water, even a little change by a large factory can produce dramatic water savings.

MUNICIPAL CONSERVATION

Given that municipalities are the primary water suppliers in the United States, it behooves them to set a good example in the field of water conservation. Municipalities also can use their facilities as a means to demonstrate the efficacy of water-saving devices, and create informational displays about these appliances. Some towns even have plaques marking low-flow toilets thereby emphasizing the efficacy of this advanced plumbing. During a drought, homeowners are not likely to obey the rules about conserving water when city hall has a bright green lawn, in contrast to the parched yellow plots of homeowners who obey the prohibition against watering. In addition to implementing indoor water-saving devices for home use, municipal governments often have large amounts of park land and golf courses. Efficient application of water outdoors provides one of the most visible means of promoting conservation—especially in arid climates. One factor that can work against conservation by cities is the fact that they own the water system. Municipalities often are not charged the full cost of water they use. Charging a proper price to a city provides one of the simplest ways to encourage conservation by governments.

LEAK DETECTION

Although most conservation strategies focus on the water customer, many utilities are extremely wasteful of water, which can reduce the authority of their pleas to reduce water in a drought. Many utilities lose a significant percentage of their water due to leaks. Water companies should do periodic audits of their own water use and should determine how much they cannot account for. Usually the losses arise from leaking pipes; for every gallon lost another must be pumped and treated, raising treatment and distribution costs. Special audio devices, available at a modest cost, allow crews to locate underground leaks by listening for them. It is recommended that a survey of the water system be completed every two years to check for leaks. One benefit of these regular checks is that if leaks are caught while small, the decaying pipes can be repaired before there are dramatic breaks, which often create bad publicity. Water systems have different criteria for which leaks to fix. The costs of replacing the lost water should be compared with the costs of treating and pumping equivalent amounts. If a system is getting close to the point at which a major plant expansion is required, a concerted leak detection and repair program could bring a water supply system to below the critical point at which a new supply needs to be installed.

BIBLIOGRAPHY

Boston, City of. *Water Conservation Plan.* March 20, 1989.

Easton, Town of. *Water Conservation Plan.* May 11, 1989.

Environmental Protection Agency. "How to Conserve Water and Use it Effectively." Http://www.epa.gov/OWOW/NPS/chap3.html.

Massachusetts Department of Environmental Management, Division of Water Resources. *A Guide to the Application of the Interbasin Transfer Act and Regulations.* December 1985.

Massachusetts Water Resources Authority. *MWRA Long Range Water Supply Program, Program Briefing and Recommendations to the Board of Directors.* January 24, 1990.

Massachusetts Water Resources Authority. Various brochures on conservation.

Massachusetts Water Resources Commission. "WRC Interpretive Guidelines." 1986.

National Regulatory Research Institute. *Compendium on Water Supply, Drought, and Conservation.* Columbus, Ohio: National Regulatory Research Institute, October 1989.

Pioneer Valley Planning Commission in cooperation with the Pioneer Valley Water Supply Task Force. *Pioneer Valley Water Action Plan.* June 1990.

The Central Valley Project: Evaluating Water Pricing Reform[1]

The Central Valley Project (CVP) is a federal water project in California consisting of dams, reservoirs, power plants, pumping facilities, and water conveyances to irrigate agriculture in the Central Valley Basin of California. (See Figure B-1.) The State of California began to build the Central Valley Project at the start of the Great Depression but ran out of money. In 1935, the federal government took over the responsibility for construction and operation of the system of dams, reservoirs, aqueducts, and pipelines. The Central Valley Project supplies approximately one-fifth of California's water, and has helped the Basin become California's leading agricultural region. Despite the agricultural wealth it produces, however, the CVP is not self-sufficient. The federal government, by pricing the water below its true cost, subsidizes CVP water, which ultimately discourages efficient water use.

Underpricing raises the demand for water, leading to intensive building of water projects to meet the higher demand. Water users pay only 5% to 10% of the full cost of supplying the water, so the taxpayer pays most of the cost. Current water allocation rules in the Central Valley reinforce inefficiencies. The regulations favor use of water for agricultural purposes, despite the fact that urban areas need the water, and are willing to pay more for the water than do the farmers. Furthermore, the rules have encouraged wasteful use of water by the farmers, which has brought on environmental problems as well. Congress, in 1992, passed the Omnibus Western Water Law to correct some of the deficiencies of previous legislation. Title XXXIV of that law, entitled The Central Valley Project Improvement Act, seeks to remedy three problems caused by the old legislation:

- Underpricing encouraged wasteful use of water.

- Overwatering (induced in part by underpricing) caused saline pollution.

- Inexpensive irrigation encouraged farmers to produce crop surpluses.

Congress changed the law in order to remedy these problems through the creation of water rights. Farmers growing low value or surplus crops using subsidized water could sell the rights to use that water to cities or to other water consumers who could put the water to better use. In the process, lawmakers reasoned, farmers would use less water, because they could sell excess water to others at a profit. That would reduce overirrigation and the pollution caused by it, the government

Figure B-1

Major Components of the Central Valley Project in California

would not have to buy surplus crops from the farmers or to pay to clean up the pollution caused by overwatering, and urban dwellers could buy water from the farmers at a lower cost than if they had to develop new water projects.

Unfortunately, years after the passage of the law, the envisioned trading market has not yet emerged, in part due to opposition by water districts that purchase CVP water, and because the Department of the Interior repeatedly has failed to meet its deadlines to implement the law. Nonetheless, several major financial organizations and cities have made investments or have begun processes that could lead to water trading.

Chapter 13 of this book discusses Western water issues in detail. This appendix examines the Central Valley Project Improvement Act, and the implementation issues needed to produce concrete results from the legislation.

CHANGING THE LAW

Although relying on government subsidies worked for a while, the 1980s brought trouble to California agriculture. Underpriced water led to inefficient allocation and environmental problems. In the 1980s, fiscal restraint and the opposition of environmentalists halted the building of the large Western water projects popular in the past. Demand for water grew in the 1980s, but supplies dwindled. From the mid-1980s to the early 1990s, a drought gripped California, straining urban water supplies. Urban residents grew tired of paying higher and higher prices for less and less federal water, when farmers paid below-market prices to grow surplus crops. Introducing a free market in water rights appeared to provide an answer to the problem.

The CVP's pricing policies induced both economic inefficiency and environmental damage.[2] Concern over these economic and environmental problems led to the enactment of Title XXXIV of the Omnibus Western Water Law of 1992, which many hoped would provide a remedy.

The goals of Title XXXIV are stated in the law as follows:

    (a) to protect, restore, and enhance fish, wildlife, and associated habitats in the Central Valley and Trinity River basins of California;

    (b) to address impacts of the Central Valley Project on fish, wildlife and associated habitats;

    (c) to improve the operational flexibility of the Central Valley Project;

    (d) to increase water-related benefits provided by the Central Valley Project to the State of California through expanded use of voluntary water transfers and improved water conservation;

    (e) to contribute to the State of California's interim and long-term efforts to protect the San Francisco Bay/Sacramento-San Joaquin Delta Estuary;

    (f) to achieve a reasonable balance among competing demands for use of Central Valley Project water, including the requirements of fish and wildlife, agricultural, municipal and industrial power contractors.[3]

Those goals can be reduced to three specific objectives:

1. To establish an actively functioning market for the trading of water rights. An active market is best defined as the ability of entities in California that are deficient in water, especially municipal and industrial users, to obtain water from those entities that have available water and are willing to sell.

2. To reduce the amount of irrigation water applied per acre of farmland.

3. To reduce salt deposition on the land, salt runoff into rivers, and consequential degrading of wildlife habitats.

The law seeks to increase the efficiency of water distribution and reduce environmental problems by reallocating water through market mechanisms, rather than by building new facilities.

If the 1992 law works as envisioned, farmers, in addition to meeting their individual interests, would contribute to overall economic efficiency and help to protect the environment. This is how it should work:

1. Farmers, because they can market their water, can learn what their water is worth to others and what economic value they lose by applying the water to crops instead of selling the water to those who put a greater value on it.

2. Farmers will be induced (not forced) to change their agricultural practices. It will no longer be desirable to devote water to low-value crops or to wasteful irrigation, for doing so would reduce the farmers' opportunity to make a bigger profit.

3. Farmers, then, will adjust their irrigation practices and introduce technology to reduce water use.

4. Marginal lands will be removed from agricultural use.

5. Removing land from production will decrease runoff from soils, lessening pollution of the aquatic environment, all other things being equal.

6. CVP water used for municipal or industrial (M&I) purposes can be sold at a higher price (known as full cost) than irrigation water. Thus, the federal government stands to earn more from its investment, if those customers take more of the water.

7. Reducing irrigation will reduce salinity problems caused by overwatering. The San Joaquin Valley Drainage Program has determined that increasing the efficiency of water application to the land is the most effective and least costly way to reduce water contamination.

Looking at the willingness of cities to pay for water, and comparing it with the willingness of farmers to sell water, one could predict, conservatively, that farmers might sell about 900,000 acre-feet of water per year to urban users at a price of about $125 per acre-foot. The law has the potential to reduce water use in the CVP, and the shift should reduce salt related drainage problems by at least

10%. All in all, the policy should eventually benefit economic efficiency and the environment.

Formulating policy is not the same as implementing it. The law has only been partially implemented and water transfers to urban areas have not occurred. Proper planning of future implementation will help the law work more effectively. In formulating an implementation plan, remember that bringing about water transfers is the main goal, which requires bringing buyers and sellers together to exchange property. The law stipulates that the purchasers may include:

1. California water users.

2. California water agencies.

3. State and federal agencies.

4. Indian tribes.

5. Private non-profit organizations using water for project purposes.

6. Any user with a purpose recognized as beneficial under California State water law.[4]

Sellers may be individuals or water districts that receive Central Valley Project water. To coordinate those transfers through a bureaucratic mechanism would be a mind-boggling task. The solution is the creation of a market for water transfers. Development of a plan to implement the legislation, though, requires an understanding of the rules governing water transfers contained in Section 3405 of the law. According to the law, all CVP water recipients can transfer water to any of the parties noted above as "purchasers."

All transfers need the U.S. Secretary of the Interior's approval. Additionally, if transfers remove more than 20% of a district's contracted water, the local water district or agency also must approve the transfer. All approvals or denials of transfers must be conditioned on the following criteria:

1. The amount of water transferred cannot exceed the average flow of the last three normal years before the enactment of the law. (The law does not define a normal year.)

2. Water transferred to a non-CVP contractor requires changes in water charges by the CVP:
   a. If the transfers are for irrigation, the CVP contractor must pay the greater of full cost (according to the 1982 Reclamation Reform Act) or cost of service rates (covers operation and maintenance costs).

b. If the transfer is for municipal or industrial use, the payment must be made at the cost of service or at municipal and industrial rates (which include interest on capital costs), whichever is greater.

3. All transfers must be between willing sellers and buyers.

4. All transfers must be consistent with California state law.

5. With water destined for transfer outside the CVP service area, other CVP contractors have first rights to bid for the water before the transfer is made. They must pay the same price that the exporting district would have received if it had exported the water. This provision is scheduled to expire after September 30, 1999.

6. Only a quantity equivalent to water that would have been consumptively used (absorbed by the crops) or irretrievably lost to beneficial use (e.g., evaporated) may be transferred.

7. The transfer should not have an unfavorable impact on the transferrer's water agency or its customers.

Successful transfers require:

1. A mechanism to police buyers and sellers, to assure that they qualify under Title XXXIV criteria.

2. An arena where buyers and sellers can come together and transact water rights at a mutually acceptable price. A central trading arena would reduce information costs associated with transactions. Water rights could be traded on commodity markets, as are air pollution rights. Trading rights on a commodity market provides an easy way for information to flow between buyers and sellers.

3. A clear mechanism for defining and enforcing rights. It will be necessary to quantify water flows precisely and objectively to prevent sales fraud. Also, it will take expertise to quantify consumptive use, which is the basis for all transfers. This will require technical engineering expertise, which the Bureau is highly qualified to provide.

Congress, clearly, did not create an unfettered free market. It imposed numerous conditions on the trading. Making the process work well will require skillful implementation.

IMPLEMENTATION

The law is not likely to achieve its goals unless these questions about implementation are answered:

What cooperation with other government agencies and private groups is likely to be needed for successful implementation? Water districts have to allow their farmers to contract freely for water. The districts must not be allowed to manipulate the rules governing transfers to prevent free-flow of water. Farmers must actively engage in transfers. They are the key to the process, for they hold the water rights.

Are there existing groups whose interests will be affected adversely? Obviously, those who stand to be hurt would oppose implementation of the law. The real question is: can these groups, having failed to prevent enactment of this law, now prevent or stall proper implementation? The de-emphasis on capital-intensive solutions to water and salinity problems will hurt the water project construction industry, although those construction firms could pick up offsetting business from the design, development, and construction of efficient water distribution systems (such as drip irrigation). Ironically, the Bureau of Reclamation could be the most adversely affected by the law. Bureau personnel plan and design new water supply projects. The new emphasis would be on project management and conservation, not on construction of massive projects. But, if the energy formerly devoted to large-scale construction could be channeled into developing more cost-effective and efficient distribution systems, some accommodation might be reached. Farmers often oppose modification of agricultural practices. However, when they realize the potential financial gains to be had from water transfers, they should embrace the new philosophy. As a group, farmers could significantly alter water politics.

Does the law threaten the jobs or status of officials who could block implementation? The law threatens the jobs of those Bureau of Reclamation officials responsible for distributing water through bureaucratic mechanisms. The Bureau might object to losing control over the approval of transfers. The Secretary of the Interior must assure that the Bureau steps back to let the market prevail. By removing elements of bureaucratic control, the law also threatens the power that California water districts have over water allocation.

Do existing staff have the capabilities to perform the work required? The Bureau of Reclamation ranks high when it comes to engineering expertise, but does not have much experience in operating water markets. Under the proposed system of water transfers, the Bureau's role will be minor. Its technical apparatus, therefore, can be put to work designing more efficient irrigation systems to help farmers, and investigating ways to clean up the environmental problems from past practice.

455

Does the law require different behavior on the part of government employees, and how realistic is this? Yes. In recent years, opposition to large public works projects has grown due to the environmental problems they have caused. The Bureau must become an environmental steward, not a construction agency with a penchant for grandiose projects. Budget constraints in the past few years have reduced the Bureau's construction projects, anyway, so the agency should change its behavior, now that Congress has ordained a change in law.

To what extent has public debate already occurred and what effect is that likely to have upon public acceptance of the law? In the congressional debate leading up to the law's passage, there was considerable opposition from certain California water users. Despite this pressure, the law passed by wide margins, indicating overall public acceptance. Growers now can profit from selling water. Pressure for water by urban governments had made maintenance of the status quo politically impossible, anyway. It seems unlikely that those opposed to this law can change it in the near future, given the law's support from cities and environmentalists.

What events have recently taken place that are supportive or harmful to the law? The emphasis on balancing the federal budget supports the law, having curtailed the building of massive new water supply projects. Water users now have to resort to water conservation and trading in order to meet their needs. Furthermore, water transfers should benefit the U.S. Treasury, because water for M&I use can be sold at a higher water rate than irrigation water. In addition, there is increasing concern that excess irrigation contributes to non-point source pollution, so environmentalists support the law. Evolving demographics within California also favor the law. As California urbanizes, agriculture decreases its share of the California economy. Political power is moving from agricultural interests to major population centers. Droughts before passage of the Act raised the spectacle of cities lying parched, while farmers continued to flood the desert with irrigation water. Consequently, in 1991, the state of California moved to cut off much agricultural water and shift it to urban users. Farmers do not wish to repeat these events. Transfers represent a way to avoid these problems in the future. Farmers stand to gain in two ways:

1. Water marketing allows a systematic reduction of water applied to farms. Farmers would have enough time to adjust their practices for less water, rather than being cut off abruptly.

2. The farmers would gain financially from transfers, rather than lose out as they would if the state impounded their water without compensation.

In short, recent trends support the law.

ASSESSING IMPACT

Assessing the impact of the law will take years. Complex trading markets do not emerge quickly, especially markets limited by so many qualifications about buyers, sellers, quantities, and required approvals. The slowness of the Department of the Interior to move, and the fact that different provisions of the law take effect at different times, further complicates the analysis.

Rossi and Freeman recommend that the evaluation should examine outcomes by means of the model shown in Table B-1. The model forces the evaluator to consider whether factors other than the "treatment" (the law) might be responsible for change. Considering these other factors explicitly makes it possible to design an evaluation scheme that lessens the likelihood that they will confound the analysis of the effectiveness of the legislation. In other words, the analysis should measure the effect of the law we are studying, and not the effect of extraneous factors.

What are the possible changes that took place, what are the intended changes, how can they be measured, and what are the possible factors that may confound the analysis?

1. *Efficiency of water use.* How much water does it take to produce each crop? This number would be reduced by introducing more efficient irrigation systems. Changes in rainfall also must be accounted for in determining efficiency. An excessively dry year would lead to a dramatic increase in the amount of water applied through irrigation. Conversely, a very wet year would reduce, temporarily, the need for irrigation water. The best way to equalize these differences is to measure the total volume of water applied on crops per each unit of rainfall:

$$\text{Efficiency of irrigation water use} = \frac{\text{Volume of Rainfall} + \text{Volume of Irrigation}}{\text{Volume of Rainfall}}$$

A long-term decrease in the ratio implies an increase in efficiency of irrigation.

Table B-1

A System for Evaluating Impact

Net Impact	=	Outcomes for participants after treatment	−	Outcomes for participants before treatment	±	Effects of other processes at work during treatment	±	Design effects and stochastic error

Note:
Design effects result from the procedures and measures employed. Stochastic effects are measurement fluctuations due to chance.

Source:
Rossi, Peter H., and Howard E. Freeman, *Evaluation: A Systematic Approach* (Newbury Park, Calif.: Sage, 1989).

2. *Value of water transferred.* An increase in the real price of water, over a long time, demonstrates that a market is developing for water rights. It will be important to assure that this is a long-term change, and not driven by a one-time emergency. Thus, it will be necessary to compare the price of water rights with the hydrologic record, which will allow adjustment for any short-term emergencies. Over the long term, however, the hydrologic record will average out, but the price of water should show an increase, given current urbanization trends. If it does not, there may be bureaucratic or other elements hampering implementation.

3. *Amount of salt present in return flows from irrigation.* 'Return flow' is water that runs off the land and back into the water conduit from whence it came. Decreasing salinity in the return flows (a function of soil salinity) is evidence of a healthier aquatic ecosystem. Applying more water to the soil (through rainfall or irrigation) will increase runoff, so it will be necessary to correct for these differences. Thus, salinity should be considered in units of mass/volume, a common means of measuring concentration of pollutants. Another factor that will affect the amount of salt runoff is a change in land management practices and cropping of land. Varying the crops grown, and the land use, will affect the amount of runoff (volume) coming off the land. This factor must be accounted for in looking at the total mass of salt returning to conduits. Also, the total mass should be reduced when water is moved from irrigation and shipped to M&I uses. The U.S. Department of Agriculture, through its Soil Conservation Service, collects this sort of data regularly, so access to this information should not be a problem. It also will be necessary to monitor the status of the aquatic ecosystems to see if they are becoming healthier. This may be a role for the U.S. Fish and Wildlife Service and California environmental agencies. If the presence of salt and other runoff chemicals is decreasing, and the health of the ecosystem is not improving, then other factors may be affecting its health. Also, other wildlife restoration programs may be responsible for improvements, and not just the reduction of chemicals in runoff. It will be important to analyze more than just salinity changes when evaluating the success of the effort.

4. *Financial health of farmers.* Is the new system helping or hurting farmers? One possible way to measure this is by examining farm failure rates, corrected for other factors such as a general change in the economy. Changes in commodity prices, which may not be affected by the hydrologic situation, also will have a bearing on farmers' economic situation. Finally, some chance event, such as an unchecked insect invasion or rampant plant disease, could ruin crops and financially impact growers. The USDA is a repository for this type of information.

5. *Is the changing price of water affecting crop patterns?* Theoretically, as more water is transferred from agricultural to urban areas, and less is applied to the land,

farmers should shift to less-water-intensive, higher-value crops. However, other factors may influence crop patterns concurrently. A change in demand for a crop could affect the amount of crop planted, masking effects of changing water prices. Changes in federal crop subsidy programs could influence demand for the crops, thus affecting crop patterns. The U.S. Department of the Interior collects data on crop acreage in the Central Valley Project, and the USDA could provide information on demand for crops and subsidy programs.

6. *Land retirement.* Increased water prices should drive marginal land out of production. Significantly increased retirement rates would signal that the policy is working as intended. If many of those retired lands were salt-ridden, this would be an even better sign of success. There are other factors, however, which may influence the retirement decision. First, land may be exhausted or so salt ridden that it is retired simply because it is not suitable for crop production any more, despite water prices. In addition, the Department of Agriculture may create programs that encourage or discourage production of certain crops. This may drive land out of use, notwithstanding water price. It will be necessary to monitor agricultural prices and programs before determining effects. The Department of the Interior collects data on land retirements in the CVP.

CONCLUSION

In spite of the fact that the law authorizing water trades in the Central Valley of California was passed in 1992, trading has not started (as of early 1998), primarily due to the opposition of water districts that buy Central Valley Project water and distribute it to farmers. These districts have delayed implementation by opposing transfers, even when those are permitted by law. The Bureau of Reclamation does not have adequate staffing so it relies heavily on the water district's opinions when deciding to make allow or disallow a transfer. It will be necessary for the Bureau to take an independent role in adjudicating transfers, if the law is to be successfully implemented. Title XXXIV is extremely ambitious and it will take a while before its effects are fully felt, but once existing barriers are removed, transfers should occur on a significant level.

Notes

1. Andrew S. Hyman, *Policy Analysis of Potential Impacts and Other Considerations of the Central Valley Project Improvement Act*, 29 June 1994 (unpublished manuscript).

2. United States General Accounting Office, *Reclamation Law: Changes Needed Before Water Service Contracts are Renewed* (Washington, D.C.: U.S. General Accounting Office, August 1991).

3. Central Valley Project Improvement Act, Section 3402 (106 Stat 4706).

4. 106 Stat 4710.

APPENDIX C

Financial Statement and Market Analysis

This is a simple homework assignment. There are nine questions designed to test understanding of a basic financial statement, followed by an outline of the issues that investors and creditors examine. The answers to the questions are at the end of the section.

I. UNDERSTANDING THE BASICS

Here's the situation. I decide to go into the business of making kachina dolls. I will need $80,000 to buy the needed machinery and another $20,000 to keep in the bank in case of emergencies. I set up a corporation on December 31, 1997, buy the machinery and open up the bank account on the same day. To raise the needed money, the corporation sells $50,000 worth of common stock to me and my father. The corporation borrows another $50,000 from my wicked stepmother, who insists on 10% interest on the loan, which has to be paid off December 31, 2001.

Question #1: What does the balance sheet look like on December 31, 1997?

The machinery will wear out (depreciate) over a four-year period. The firm can produce and sell 1,000 kachinas per year. The doll sells for $100. The labor and materials expense per doll is $40. Salespeople get to collect $5 per doll to sell them. Other office expenses are $5,000 per year. The interest rate on the loan is 10%. The income tax rate is 30%. The business pays out half the net income as dividends, and the rest of the profits go into a noninterest-bearing checking account.

Question #2: Construct a statement of net income and retained earnings for 1998–2001.

There's a saying that cash is king. One Harvard law professor used to say, "There are two kinds of assets: hopes and cash." Some expenses (such as depreciation) do not require an outlay of cash. On the other hand, some outlays of cash (such as purchase of machinery or payments of debts) do not appear on the income statement.

Question #3: Construct a statement of cash flows for 1997–2001. Use parentheses to indicate a reduction of cash.

The balance sheet shows what the company owns (assets) and where the money came from to buy the assets (liabilities). Remember, too, that earnings retained in the business are added to common equity.

Question #4: Construct a balance sheet as of December 31st for each year beginning with 1997 (which you already did in Question #1) through 2001.

II. PER SHARE AND RATIO ANALYSIS

The raw figures only tell so much. They need to be analyzed. Shareowners want information per share. They bought a certain number of shares, not the whole business. The company sold 1,000 shares. A buyer may want to pick up a few shares. What is each share worth? That depends upon the earnings per share (EPS) and dividends per share. What are the assets behind each share? (The total of investment made by shareholders plus earnings retained in the business constitutes stockholders' equity, as shown on the books of the business. Book value per share, then, is the common stockholders' equity dividend by the outstanding number of shares.)

Question #5: Calculate per share figures for earnings and dividends for the years 1997–2001, and the book value per share for the end of each year.

Creditors, on the other hand, want to know whether they are protected by a cushion of stockholders' money (in case something goes wrong, remember that the creditors get what is theirs first and stockholders only collect if something is left), and whether the company earns enough to pay interest charges. Creditors look at two measures. One is the debt ratio: what percentage of the total capitalization (debt plus equity) is accounted for by debt? (The lower the better.) The other measure is the pretax interest coverage ratio: how many times does income before taxes and interest expense cover interest charges?

Question #6: Calculate the debt ratio and pretax interest coverage ratio for 1997–2001.

III. COMMON STOCK RATIOS

Common stockholders do not buy entire corporations. They buy shares in the corporation. The price that they pay depends on overall market conditions as well as their assessment of the safety, profitability, and growth prospects of the corporation. Investors usually judge profitability in terms of return on equity (ROE—the profit earned per dollar of common equity), a figure that also gives them a clue to how fast the company can grow. They watch the dividend payout ratio (what percentage of earnings that are paid out as dividends) to make sure that the company can sustain the dividend. When buying the stock, they judge the stock price in relation to earnings, dividends, and book value per share.

Question #7: Calculate return on equity and dividend payout ratios for 1998–2001.

The stock price at year end was $50 in 1997, $120 in 1998, $100 in 1999, $150 in 2001, and $200 in 2001.

Question #8: Calculate the price/earnings (also called "P/E ratio" and "multiple"), the dividend yield, and the market/book ratio for each year.

IV. UTILITY ACCOUNTING IS DIFFERENT

Right now, utility accounting is different, although it may become less different in the future. It is different because the accounts (especially the income statement) have been rearranged, and because regulation creates a set of assumptions that are unacceptable in an unregulated business.

Start with the rearrangement. Utility regulators want to assure that those who furnish the capital earn a fair return on capital (but no more than that). Capital comes from creditors (who lend money to the utility), from preferred stockholders (who are not creditors, but who collect a fixed dividend that must be paid before common stockholders can collect their dividends), and from common stockholders (who take the greatest risk and expect the greatest profit). We need to know how much income is available to provide a return on capital, after all expenses and taxes have been paid.

Question #9: Calculate the return on year-end capital earned in 1998. First rearrange the income statement into the utility format.

The other aspect of utility accounting is that utilities get to count what others do not. In utility accounting, it is assumed that whatever the regulator says has value, has value. Whatever the regulator says that the utility will collect, it will collect. The utility shows as assets what no other respectable business would show as an asset. The utility also shows fictitious income because the regulator says that it will be able to collect that income for customers in the future. (Nobody asks the customers.) As the utility business becomes more competitive, the likelihood of collecting on those regulatory promises becomes slimmer. As soon as the accounting standards board decides that the promises no longer hold, the utilities will go off regulated industry accounting, which will have a significant impact on their balance sheets and income statements, and, as a result, their ability to pay current levels of dividends, which, in turn will have an impact on stock prices. Until now, the water utilities have avoided the competitive and accounting difficulties of the other utility sectors.

V. ANALYZING THE UTILITY

The equity or credit analyst (whether for municipal or corporate debt) should go through a long checklist of items relevant to the utility's prospects, before deciding to invest.

The seeming lack of competitors singles out water supply and wastewater utilities from other utilities facing deregulation. But water and wastewater utilities still have to think about competitiveness in a number of ways.

- They compete with each other for capital. The utility with the greatest financial strength gets the lowest costs.

- They compete with each other in terms of price and product availability. New industry that requires plentiful, inexpensive water will compare suppliers. City councils judging the efficiency of their municipal water versus that of others will compare the price and reliability of service. Regulators will hesitate to grant price increases to utilities whose prices are out of line with those of others.

- They compete with each other to acquire and develop water resources. The public supplier with the best plan and the wherewithal to execute it captures the opportunity.

- Finally, the investor-owned utility with the strongest financial resources and highest stock price is in the best position to buy out other companies, develop new operations, and take the lead over less-well-off competitors.

But, in spite of the detailed examination of the utility, analysts must remember that outside forces affect results. A change in environmental rules, or in the regulatory framework, or in tax laws, or in interest rates, can have a profound impact on companies so dependent on government actions and ability to borrow money.

The following checklist should help analysts:

A. Income statement
  - Sources of revenues
  - Physical volume growth
  - Unusual items of income or expense
  - Noncash items

B. Capital spending
  - Size of program
  - Purpose of spending
  - Financing of spending

C. Dividend policy
  - Sustainability of past policy
  - Stated policy
  - Impact on stock price of a change in policy

D. Regulation
  - Policy in last case
  - Next case planned
  - Reform proposals
  - Impact of regulatory plans on competitive position
  - Vulnerability to regulation

E. Competitiveness
  - Price of output compared to neighbors
  - Neighbors with surplus supplies

- Cost of production
- Types of customers
- Potential damage to utility from change in competitive position

F. Balance sheet
  - Appropriateness to business risk
  - Assets that may have to be written off
  - Hidden liabilities
  - Hidden assets

G. Diversification
  - Size of program
  - Strategy taken
  - Risks

H. Service area
  - Economy
  - Potential for sales growth
  - Relevance versus other factors of analysis

I. Opportunities Outside Diversification
  - Additional services to existing customers
  - Operating savings through merger or joint ventures
  - Providing services to other utilities

J. Valuation
  - Market context: interest rates
  - Compare to similar companies
    P/E
    Dividend yield
    Market/book
    Potential for growth
  - Risks from contracts or commitments
  - Competitive position
  - Regulatory risks
  - Strength of financial position
  - Uses of cash
  - Truth in accounting
  - Management
  - Diversification for growth
  - Possible change in valuation methods
  - Stock attractive for total return, current income or undervalued assets.

The key to analysis, though, is to understand that all points covered are not equally important, and the same points are not of those same importance for each utility.

ANSWERS

Question #1

Balance Sheet on December 31, 1997

Assets

Cash	$ 20,000
Machinery and equipment (at cost)	80,000
Total assets	$100,000

Liabilities and Capital

Common stockholders' equity	$ 50,000
Debt	50,000
Total Liabilities and capital	$100,000

Question #2

Statement of Income and Retained Earnings
1998–2001

	1998	1999	2000	2001
Sales	$100,000	$100,000	$100,000	$100,000
Cost of producing the product	40,000	40,000	40,000	40,000
Sales expense	5,000	5,000	5,000	5,000
Depreciation	20,000	20,000	20,000	20,000
Office expenses	5,000	5,000	5,000	5,000
Interest expense	5,000	5,000	5,000	5,000
Total expenses	75,000	75,000	75,000	75,000
Pretax net income	25,000	25,000	25,000	25,000
Income taxes	7,500	7,500	7,500	7,500
Net income	17,500	17,500	17,500	17,500
Earnings retained in business at beginning of year	0	8,750	17,500	26,250
Net income for year	17,500	17,500	17,500	17,500
Dividend paid in year*	(8,750)	(8,750)	(8,750)	(8,750)
Earnings retained in business at end of year	$ 8,750	$ 17,500	$ 26,250	$ 35,000

* Note that ( ) indicates a reduction in retained earnings due to payout of dividend.

Question #3

Statement of Cash Flows
1997–2001

	1997	1998	1999	2000	2001
Cash flow from operations:					
Net income	$ 0	$17,500	$17,500	$ 17,500	$ 17,500
Depreciation	0	20,000	20,000	20,000	20,000
Subtotal	0	37,500	37,500	37,500	37,500
Cash flow from investing activities					
Purchase of machinery	(80,000)	0	0	0	0
Cash flow from financing activities					
Dividends	0	(8,750)	(8,750)	(8,750)	(8,750)
Redemption of debt	0	0	0	0	(50,000)
Issuance of debt	50,000	0	0	0	0
Issuance of common stock	50,000	0	0	0	0
Subtotal	100,000	(8,750)	(8,750)	(8,750)	(58,750)
Net change in cash in year	20,000	28,750	28,750	28,750	21,250
Cash balance at beginning of year	0	20,000	48,750	77,500	106,250
Cash balance at end of year	$ 20,000	$48,750	$77,500	$106,250	$ 85,000

Question #4

Balance Sheet
1997–2001

	1997	1998	1999	2000	2001
Cash	$ 20,000	$ 48,750	$ 77,500	$106,250	$ 85,000
Machinery at cost	80,000	80,000	80,000	80,000	80,000
Depreciation reserve	0	(20,000)	(40,000)	(60,000)	(80,000)
Net plant	80,000	60,000	40,000	20,000	0
Total assets	100,000	108,750	117,500	126,250	85,000
Liabilities and capital					
Debt	$ 50,000	$ 50,000	$ 50,000	$ 50,000	$ 0
Common equity	50,000	58,750	67,500	76,250	85,000
Total liabilities and capital	$100,000	$108,750	$117,500	$126,250	$ 85,000

Question #5

Book Value, Earnings per Share, Dividends per Share
1997–2001

	1997	1998	1999	2000	2001
Book value	$50.00	$58.75	$67.50	$76.25	$85.00
Earnings per share	0	17.50	17.50	17.50	17.50
Dividend per share	0	8.75	8.75	8.75	8.75

468

Question #6

Debt Ratio
1997–2001

	1997	1998	1999	2000	2001
Debt	$ 50,000	$ 50,000	$ 50,000	$ 50,000	$ 0
Equity	50,000	58,750	67,500	76,250	85,000
Total capital	$100,000	$108,750	$117,500	$126,250	$ 85,000
Debt ratio (%)	50.0	46.0	42.6	39.6	0.0

Interest Coverage Ratio
1997–2001

	1997	1998	1999	2000	2001
Sales	0	$100,000	$100,000	$100,000	$100,000
− Cost of production	0	40,000	40,000	40,000	40,000
− Sales expense	0	5,000	5,000	5,000	5,000
− Depreciation	0	20,000	20,000	20,000	20,000
− Office expense	0	5,000	5,000	5,000	5,000
= Pretax income before interest expense	0	30,000	30,000	30,000	30,000
÷ Interest expense		5,000	5,000	5,000	5,000
= Pretax interest coverage		6.0x	6.0x	6.0x	6.0x

Question #7

Return on Equity
1998–2001

		1998	1999	2000	2001
	Net income	$17,500	$17,500	$17,500	$17,500
divided by	Common equity	58,850	67,500	76,250	85,000
equals	Return on equity (%)	29.8%	25.9%	23.0%	20.6%

Dividend Payout Ratio
1998–2001

		1998	1999	2000	2001
	Dividend	$ 8,750	$ 8,750	$ 8,750	$ 8,750
divided by	Net income	17,500	17,500	17,500	17,500
equals	Payout ratio	50.0%	50.0%	50.0%	50.0%

Question #8

Price/Earnings Ratio, Dividend Yield, and Market/Book Ratio
1997–2001

	1997	1998	1999	2000	2001
Price per share	$50.00	$120.00	$100.00	$150.00	$200.00
Earnings per share	0	17.50	17.50	17.50	17.50
Dividend per share	0	8.75	8.75	8.75	8.75
Book value per share	50.00	58.75	67.50	76.26	85.00
P/E ratio	—	6.9x	5.7x	8.6x	11.4x
Dividend Yield	—	7.3%	8.8%	5.8%	4.4%
Market/book ratio	100%	240%	148%	197%	235%

Question #9

Return on Capital
1998

	1998
Debt	$ 50,000
Common equity	58,750
Capitalization	$108,750

Normal Income Statement		Utility Income Statement	
Sales	$100,000	Sales	$100,000
Cost of production	40,000	Cost of production	40,000
Sales expense	5,000	Sales expense	5,000
Depreciation	20,000	Depreciation	20,000
Office expense	5,000	Office expense	5,000
Interest	5,000	Income taxes	7,500
Total expense	75,000	Total operating expense	77,500
Pretax net income*	25,000	Operating income**	22,500
Income taxes	7,500	Interest expenses	5,000
Net income	$ 17,500	Net income	$ 17,500

* Income after all expenses except income taxes
** Income available to compensate the people who put up the money to set up the business

$$\frac{\text{Operating income}}{\text{Total capital}} = \frac{\$\ 22,500}{\$108,750} = 20.7\%$$

American Water Works Company: The Largest Regulated Water Business in the U.S.*

American Water Works Company is America's biggest investor-owned water utility, serving a population of over seven million in over 800 communities in 21 states. Assets exceed $4 billion and annual revenue approaches $900 million. The company has 22 operating utilities. Through a subsidiary, it owns a 50% interest (with Anglian Water plc) in AmericanAnglian Environment Technologies, which operates and upgrades community water and sewage systems. The company seems to have no other ambition than to provide "the best possible water service at an affordable cost consistent with adequate compensation for investors and reasonable wages and benefits for its personnel." American has eschewed diversification and international activities. It has grown, however, through the acquisition of other water companies throughout the United States. As investor-owned water companies, all of American's water subsidiaries operate under the jurisdiction of state regulators, most of whom apply the old, rate-of-return formulas. Despite the seemingly unadventurous strategy, the company has produced 9% growth in earnings per share over the past decade, an exceptional record for a utility, and its stock has outperformed those of other water companies, too.

As of the end of 1996, two states, New Jersey and Pennsylvania, accounted for about half of the company's business. About 72% of customers live within 600 miles of the company's headquarters in southern New Jersey.

State	Percent of		
	Customers	Net Plant	Revenues
Pennsylvania	28.1%	31.9%	27.2%
New Jersey	17.1	24.0	22.2
Indiana	8.8	7.1	6.7
West Virginia	7.2	6.7	7.0
Illinois	7.7	5.6	7.2
Kentucky	4.6	4.5	3.6
California	5.4	4.1	7.1
Missouri	4.8	2.9	2.9
Tennessee	3.6	2.5	3.2
Virginia	2.5	2.4	3.1
All other states*	10.2	8.3	9.8
Total	100.0	100.0	100.0

* Connecticut, Massachusetts, Iowa, Ohio, New York, New Mexico, New Hampshire, Arizona, Maryland, and Michigan. In 1997, American announced the purchase of a wastewater property in Hawaii.
Source:
Based on data in the company's 1996 annual report, pp. 18–20.

*Sources: American Water Works Company, *1996 Annual Report,* and public investment sources.

The company's growth has come about largely through major acquisitions. American maintains a leveraged financial structure (over 60% debt) but that leverage has not brought return on equity to high levels. The company has a continuous need to raise capital, which leads to almost always being behind in the regulatory cycle. That is, American invests the money, then has to wait for the completion of a rate case in order to earn a reasonable return on that investment.

Financial Analysis
($ millions)

Income Statement	1994	1995	1996
Revenues	$770.2	$802.8	$894.6
Operating expenses	537.5	558.5	600.6
Pretax operating income	232.7	244.3	294.0
Allowance for funds	10.5	21.3	11.7
Other income	0.5	6.1	1.6
Income before interest and income taxes	243.7	271.7	307.3
Interest expense	111.3	118.3	138.3
Pretax net income	132.4	153.4	169.0
Income taxes	49.9	57.6	63.8
Net income	82.5	95.8	105.2
Preferred dividends	7.8	7.7	7.6
Net income for common stock	$74.7	$88.1	$97.7
Capitalization			
All debt	1,464.4	1,577.6	1,920.9
Preferred stock	101.7	100.3	99.0
Common equity	733.4	818.9	1,057.9
	2,299.5	2,496.8	3,077.8
Ratio Analysis			
Pretax operating income as % of revenue	30.2	30.4	32.9
Pretax operating income as % of capitalization	10.1	9.8	9.6
All debt % of capitalization	63.4	63.2	62.4
Net income for common stock as % of common equity	10.2	10.8	9.2
Pretax operating income/interest changes	2.1x	2.1x	2.1x

Residential customers represent the largest customer class in terms of usage and revenue, and they pay more per gallon consumed, as well. Usage per customer, however, does not grow. Nobody is introducing more water-intensive appliances. If anything, the contrary is the case. At the same time, the water companies must put more investment into plant, in order to upgrade the facilities dedicated to existing customers. In fact, in the five-year period 1991-1996, net plant per customer rose 7% per year but revenue per customer grew only 3% per year and sales per customer actually declined 1% per year. Furthermore, in the same period, net utility plant grew 11% per year but water sales (in gallons) went up only 3% per year. Without additional usage or incremental operating economies to pay for the upgrades, American's subsidiaries have had to raise prices in order to cover costs of operating and paying for new investment.

	Water Revenues and Usage by Customer Class		
	1994	1995	1996
Revenue ($ millions)*			
Residential	$431.2	$451.1	$510.1
Commercial	169.5	175.9	197.3
Industrial	53.0	54.4	62.2
Public and other	90.4	92.6	101.8
Total	$744.1	$774.0	$871.4
Usage (billion gallons)			
Residential	114.0	117.1	119.9
Commercial	60.9	61.7	63.5
Industrial	34.7	34.2	36.1
Public and other	27.0	27.0	27.8
Total	236.6	240.0	247.3
Revenue per gallon (cents)			
Residential	0.38	0.39	0.43
Commercial	0.28	0.29	0.31
Industrial	0.15	0.16	0.17
Public and other	0.33	0.34	0.37
Average	0.31	0.32	0.35

* Excludes other water revenues

	Per Customer Analysis		
	1994	1995	1996
Customers (thousands)	1,706	1,720	1,884
Sales/customer (thousand gallons/year)	138.7	139.5	131.3
Water revenues/customer ($/year)	$440	$453	$467
Gross utility plant/customer ($)	$1,864	$2,021	$2,195
Net utility plant/customer ($)	$1,550	$1,676	$1,833

An analysis of revenues and expenses for American Water Works probably presents a pattern typical of many private water utilities. The actual cash expenses of running the operation make up half of the water bill. Taxes, fixed costs, and profits account for the rest of the bill. The chances are, though, that a large part of the operating expenses themselves are relatively invariable. American has to pay employees whether customers are watering the lawns or sitting inside due to the rain. It has to maintain the pipes and send out bills as well. If the company can add to its sales, with existing assets, it can bring down most of the revenue increment to profits. (Perhaps operating costs rise 20 cents for each $1.00 of added revenue.) Conversely, of course, a drop in sales produces little accompanying fall in expenses and profits suffer accordingly.

Analysis of Revenues and Expenses
Three Year Average 1994–1996

	$ Millions	%
Revenues	$823	100.0
Employee costs	191	23.2
Operating supplies and services	56	6.8
Purchased water	43	5.2
Fuel and power	34	4.1
Maintenance materials and services	23	2.8
Customer billing and accounting	17	2.1
Chemicals	15	1.8
Miscellaneous	27	3.3
Total operating and maintenance	406	49.3
Depreciation and amortization	82	10.0
General taxes	77	9.4
Income taxes	57	6.9
Interest	123	14.9
Profit	$ 78	9.5

The joint venture with Anglian Water had management fee revenue of about $8.0 million in 1995 and 1996. Contracts signed in 1997 could more than double revenue, but the organization may contribute only minimally to American Water Work's income.

American Water Work's capital expenditures averaged close to $300 million per year in 1994-1996. Internal sources of funds (after dividends payment) have run at less than half of expenditures, thereby necessitating outside financing. Almost half of American's plant is in the transmission and distribution category (pipes), but capital expenditures for that category represent a lower percentage of the total, because of the need to add to treatment and pumping facilities.

Plant Account and Capital Expenditure Analysis

	Gross Utility Plant in Service Dec. 31, 1996 ($ Millions)	%	Average Annual Capital Expenditure 1994–1996 ($ Millions)	%
Sources of supply	187	4.6	14	4.8
Treatment and pumping	957	23.7	95	32.6
Transmission and distribution	1,890	46.9	109	37.5
Services, meters, and fire hydrants	703	17.4	45	15.5
General structures	266	6.6	27	9.3
Wastewater	31	0.8 ·	1	0.3
Gross plant in service	$4,034	100.0	$291	100.0

American Water Works, although the largest investor-owned water system in the U.S., accounts for only 4% of the entire water business in the country and 2% of the water and wastewater industry. By overall utility standards, American is a small- to medium-sized firm. The company's rapid growth in earnings per share in the late 1980s has been followed by slow growth in the early 1990s. Do the company's strengths as a straight, plain vanilla water company provide it with the wherewithal to move ahead at a faster pace, or will American suffer the fate of many other utilities of similar size, acquired by a giant that wants access to American's customers?

SABESP: Latin America's Largest Water and Sewer Utility*

Brazil is a country of enormous contrasts. Much of the nation, especially in the rural areas of the north, has characteristics of the developing nations: poverty, lack of services, monoculture, poor schooling. The state of São Paulo, in the south, is another matter—a dynamic industrial, commercial, and agricultural powerhouse that produces over one-third of Brazil's gross domestic product. As has been the case with other Brazilian states, São Paulo's government took an active role in development of infrastructure, owning utilities and even banks. Unlike the United States and Canada, Brazil has a long history of establishing corporate entities, much or all of whose stock is owned by the government, to perform economic functions. For decades, in fact, government-controlled corporations dominated sectors of the economy, and were among the most actively traded shares on the stock exchanges.

Companhia de Saneamento Basico do Estado de São Paulo (SABESP) was established in 1973, as a result of the amalgamation of a number of existing water and sewer organizations. The formation of the company resulted from a political decision: to make viable the operation of the money-losing water and sewer operations of the small- to medium-sized cities of the state by joining them with the megasystem of metropolitan São Paulo and with the systems of the larger cities of the interior, which operated at a profit. The small systems in the interior of the state not only operated at a deficit, but the local governments could not raise the funds needed to expand or modernize their systems. The state and municipalities maintained ownership of 100% of the stock until 1996. Thanks to a small share offering, as of mid-1997, the state owned 91.4%, municipalities 2.0%, and the investing public 6.6%.

The company is an enormous organization, as befits a utility that serves one of the largest cities in the world, with assets of $12 billion and revenues of $2.5 billion. In 1996, it sold 1.7 billion m³ (449 billion gallons) of water and collected 1.0 billion m³ (264 billion gallons) of wastewater. It serves 349 of São Paulo's 645 municipalities. SABESP's service territory has a population of 22 million.

Municipalities in the state grant 30-year concessions (with option to renew) to water and sewer suppliers. If the supplier takes over existing assets from the

*Sources: Thomas de mello e Souza, "Sabesp: Conduit for Growth," Merrill Lynch research report, August 5, 1997, and other documents and correspondence. Note: All monetary amounts are in Brazilian currency, the Real (R$).

municipality, it pays for them in stock. The water supplier then installs and owns all the infrastructure that is put in place. If, at the end of the concession period, the municipality chooses not to renew, it must buy all the former concessionaire's assets or, one imagines, build an entirely new water and sewer system. Peculiarly, while the giant city of São Paulo is the largest municipality served by SABESP, the company does not have a formal concession agreement with the city government. That ambiguous arrangement, presumably, makes the company vulnerable to political maneuvering.

The state and federal governments in Brazil are in the midst of a multiyear privatization effort that has resulted in the sale of numerous government-controlled corporations to the private sector. At present, state law and the corporate charter require the state of São Paulo to maintain control of SABESP. Thus, no privatization is planned, although the state could sell additional shares from its holdings to the public while still maintaining control, or sell shares to a strategic investor.

In some ways the regulatory regime for SABESP is as ambiguous as its relationship with the city of São Paulo. The state sets rates on the basis that they must cover operating expenses, depreciation and amortization, and an ill-defined cost of capital. (In the past, Brazilian governments have adhered to that formula only loosely.) One brokerage house said the return on equity derived from the formula was 10%, a figure the company is far from achieving. The Brazilian government has commissioned a study of water regulation, which will examine whether to levy a tax on water suppliers' intake of water (presently free).

For many years, SABESP struggled to meet the needs of a dynamically expanding economy. Now, it already provides water to 95% of the population and wastewater services to 70% of the population within its franchised territories. Improvement to those coverage levels might cause one to conclude, incorrectly, that SABESP can slow down. That, however, is not the case. SABESP may collect the bulk of the wastewater produced by the population that it serves, but it treats less than one-third, meaning that it dumps most of the waste, as raw sewage, into waterways. The Tiete River, which runs through the center of the city of São Paulo and traverses the length of the state, has a reputation as an open sewer, and stemming the flow of pollution into that river is one of the company's biggest tasks. Thus, in the future, SABESP will have to clean water as well as collect sewage. Furthermore, as a result of inadequate investment in pipes, detection devices, and metering, SABESP loses close to 40% of the water that it transports (roughly 25% from technical failings and 15% from thefts). In the coming years, the company must keep up with growth, clean up pollution, and improve the state of the system. Much of the investment will be required for modernization, automation, maintenance, and operating controls for the small water systems in the interior of the state, and even more will go into sewage and treatment. A substantial portion of the expenditures may be destined for water and sewage systems that produce low or no financial returns on investment. The government, in fact set these goals:

	1994	1996	1998
% population served:			
Water	89%	95%	100%
Wastewater	64	73	83
Wastewater (treated)	25	28	60
% water lost	46	39	24

In 1997, water losses declined to 31%. (Losses, incidentally, were only 24% in 1983.) With those goals, SABESP may have to spend close to $1 billion per year over the five-year period 1996–2000, which would be twice the level of the previous five years. In order to raise the necessary funds, SABESP will have to dramatically improve its level of profitability in order to carry the new debt that it will have to sell. It seems unlikely that the state, itself, could raise the funds required. Thus, SABESP must become self-supporting and reasonably profitable or it must find partners to finance and operate needed facilities on an outsourcing basis.

Financially speaking, SABESP's most recent financial statements, before the flotation of stock, presented a mixed picture. The debt level was a relatively low percentage of capitalization, but profitability was negligible.

	1995	1996
Income Statement (R$ millions)		
Water revenue	$ 1,184	$ 1,495
Wastewater revenue	726	916
Total revenue	1,910	2,411
Operating expenses	1,207	1,565
Operating income	703	846
Net interest expense	1,245	741
Other income (expense)	625	(5)
Pretax income	83	100
Income tax	57	42
Net income	26	58
Capitalization (R$ millions)		
All debt	3,056	3,525
Common equity	8,112	8,166
Total Capitalization	$11,168	$11,691
Ratio Analysis		
Operating income as % of revenue	36.8	35.1
Operating income as % of capitalization	6.3	7.2
Net income as % of common equity	0.3	0.7
Operating income/net interest expense	0.6x	1.1x

Most analysts would argue that SABESP, in order to go forward as a stand-alone entity that could afford to raise the money required to improve and expand service, would need to bring interest coverages up to 3x, and return on common equity up to 10%. Doing so in 1996, exclusive of expense reduction, would have required a price increase of roughly 50%. Price hikes of that sort for a vital public service might not go down well with the public, especially when some of its customers suffer from a water shortage. The company, therefore, has to find ways to improve its operating ratios through better management.

In 1995, a new state government took steps to reinvigorate SABESP, by installing a new management team, which then decentralized the company into 16 business and three service units. The management reduced the work force, renegotiated debt terms, began to coordinate activities better with municipalities, and reduced supply outages.

	1994	1995	1996
Connections (millions)			
Water	4.0	4.1	4.3
Wastewater	2.8	2.9	3.0
Total	6.8	7.0	7.3
Network (1,000 Km)			
Water	41.8	42.3	43.0
Wastewater	26.1	26.9	27.8
Total	67.9	69.2	70.8
Employees (1,000s)	20.5	18.7	18.5
Connections/employee	332	374	395
Water losses (%)	46	44	39

The current ratio of connections to employee might be improved, to reach comparability to other large water systems, but the real savings payoff could come from reducing water losses to more reasonable levels. Just getting paid for an additional 10% of the water, for instance, would have raised 1996 pretax net income 150%.

As is the case with most public service monopolies, SABESP's tariff structure seems to reflect social policies rather than costs. Water and wastewater charges are basically identical, with the exception of lower charges for rural dwellers. Residential consumers pay approximately half the rate per unit of volume as do commercial and industrial customers. Those who live in metropolitan São Paulo (and, presumably have higher incomes) pay more than those who live in other cities or in rural areas. Finally, after the initially high price for a low-usage block (in effect, the access charge), the price of water rises with volume taken. The pricing pattern may produce uneconomical usage patterns, and was under study for revision in 1997.

Water and Sewer
Pricing Indices*
mid-1997

	Initial Usage 0–10 m³/mo	Incremental Usage		
		11–20	21–50	Over 50
Customer Class				
Residential	100	100	100	100
Commercial	215	181	174	172
Industrial	236	196	191	179
Region				
Metropolitan São Paulo	100	100	100	100
Coastal	100	80	80	80
Rural	90	64	63	63
Volume				
Residential	100	20	36	56
Commercial	100	17	29	45
Industrial	100	17	29	42

* Represents simple averages of indices computed for each category.

Moving forward, SABESP is in an odd position. It must spend large sums to improve infrastructure in São Paulo. It could attempt to add on more concessions to its portfolio, including franchises in other states. It might invest or joint venture abroad. Those opportunities will open up once the company can bring its profitability up to reasonable levels. At the same time, the company has little float of shares on the stock market, almost no following among foreign investors, and has all the appearance of a government agency that, incidentally, has some shareholders. The next state government can replace the management and change all the policies. The company is neither fish nor fowl. Moving ahead might require a redefinition of the company.

APPENDIX F

Compagnie Générale des Eaux: The French Giant with an International Scope*

Générale des Eaux is the larger of two giant French utility-based conglomerates, the other being Suez-Lyonnaise des Eaux. Générale was founded in 1853. The company started out by winning water supply concessions in major French cities, beginning with Lyons, then Nantes, adding on other cities, and Paris by 1860. Générale went into the wastewater business in 1884, and entered the construction business in the 1920s. Expansion of water and wastewater ventures continued in France, Monaco, and Spain through the 1970s.

In the 1980s, Generale launched a major and often unfocused diversification effort that included investments in pay-TV, energy, incineration of waste, real estate, more construction, and telecommunications. In 1986, the company established a British water subsidiary, and in 1992 made investments in water utilities in Argentina, Mexico, Venezuela, Australia, and Spain. In 1994, its Sithe Energies subsidiary put into service one of the United States' largest independent power projects, Independence, in upstate New York. In 1996, when management changed and the new chief executive launched an effort to make the organization more cohesive, Générale owned entities in the water, energy, waste management, transportation, construction, media, telecommunications, and real estate fields.

In France, municipalities either provide water services themselves or they contract out the service to a private operator. (Approximately 77% of the water and 60% of the wastewater markets have been contracted out.) Générale controls about 40% of the water and 30% of the wastewater markets. It distributes water to areas with a population of 25 million and collects wastewater from 19 million people, in over 4,000 communities. The company has approximately 6.5 million water customers that take around 1.9 billion m^3 (500 billion gallons) annually, and 3.5 million wastewater customers that discharge less than 0.9 billion m^3 (230 billion gallons) annually. The water operations have around 22,000 employees in France.

Contracts with municipalities come in various forms. Usually, the municipality and the operator sign a 25- or 30-year concession agreement whereby the municipality pays the operator a flat fee. The operator has to provide service, meter, collect bills, and make necessary investments. The private company takes all risks

---

* *Sources*: Générale des Eaux reports. Nicola Mann and Jean-Baptiste Delabare, "Cie. Générale des Eaux," Merrill Lynch reports, July 1997 and January 1998. *Note:* Company shareholders approved a name change to Vivendi in May 1998.

483

of operation. The tariff, which is set annually, covers costs, taxes, recovery of investment, and profits. At the end of the concession period, the operator must convey all assets to the municipality, unless it can renegotiate the concession agreement for another term. In the past, municipalities routinely renegotiated the contract with the incumbent operator. New rules, however, require the municipality to put the concession up for tender. Thus, the French water business could come under competitive pressures. As it is, prices have risen sharply, as operators raised water quality in line with European requirements, although prices rose faster for those water systems still under direct municipal ownership. The government has proposed to limit tariff increases to 5% a year (in real terms) for 1997–2002.

Wastewater treatment could present an opportunity for expansion. In France, the Urban Waste Water Directive requires that all towns with a population of 2,000 must collect and treat domestic wastewater, with the year 2005 as the deadline to meet the requirement. As of now, only half of wastewater is collected and treated.

Internationally, Générale seems not to have moved as aggressively as Suez-Lyonnaise, possibly because of a leveraged balance sheet that discouraged asset acquisitions. In the U.K., General Utilities, an affiliate, owns large shareholdings (19% to 28% of stock) in four small water companies. In the United States, Générale owns over 40% of the stock of Air and Water Technologies, a pollution control and management firm that Générale bills as "the country's leading water and wastewater operator." Générale also owns minority interests in two publicly traded water American companies, Philadelphia Suburban (14.5%) and Consumers Water (20.6%). Générale, to show its worldwide scope, has holdings in water distribution companies in Spain, Portugal, Italy, Mexico, Argentina, Martinique, French Guyana, Germany, Hungary, the Czech Republic, Australia, and Malaysia. Générale emphasizes contract management rather than outright ownership.

Générale has huge investments in nonwater activities. The energy division emphasizes cogeneration, independent power projects and district heating and cooling (of which Générale is the largest operator in Europe). Sithe Energies, 60% owned by Générale, has interests in completed or planned power projects that total 11,000 megawatts, including the recently acquired generation assets of Boston Edison. The waste management enterprise is the biggest in Europe and third largest in the world. The transport business operates bus and rail networks, including two rail franchises in the U.K. The telecommunications investment (44% of ownership and operating control of Cegetel) will furnish long-distance, mobile, and fixed-line telecommunications services in France. Cegetel appears to be one of Générale's principal vehicles for growth in the near future. The media group, which had a bewildering array of holdings, traded most of them for a 30% share of Havas, a French media group. In 1998, Générale announced its intention to raise its holdings in Havas. The huge construction group, a worldwide enterprise, accounts for one-third of revenues but produces a loss. The property division launched a number of spectacular French real estate projects that have produced just as spectacular losses.

The extraordinary diversity of Générale activities becomes apparent from an examination of the source of sales and of earnings before interest, taxes, depreciation, and amortization (EBITDA) in 1995 and 1996.

Revenue and EBITDA
(FRF Billions)

	1995		1996	
	Sales	EBITDA	Sales	EBITDA
Water	38.9	5.0	41.0	5.1
Energy	24.6	3.5	27.9	3.6
Waste management	12.7	1.8	12.7	1.7
Transport	3.6	0.4	6.3	0.4
Communications and media	6.3	− 0.3	7.4	0.7
Construction	57.0	1.9	54.4	1.7
Property	8.7	− 1.6	8.0	− 1.1
Misc.*	11.2	− 0.1	8.2	− 0.3
	163.0	10.6	165.9	11.8

* Includes activities scheduled for sale.

In a sense, the water and other public service divisions are carrying the rest of Générale, although the reported return on capital employed in the water sector in 1996 was less than 10%, and for other public service type operations less than 7%. Those are returns barely acceptable to regulated American utilities. A company that emphasizes contracting as opposed to ownership should do better, and management has targeted returns of over 15% for domestic water and over 8% for other public service sector divisions.

Générale's overall financial picture shows the need to improve profitability and to dispose of assets that do not contribute to profitability or to strategic direction.

	Financial Highlights (FRF Billions and %)	
	1995	1996
Income statement (FRF billions)		
Revenues	167.3	171.2
Operating expenses	165.6	167.4
Operating income	1.7	3.8
Financial charges	3.4	332.2
Pretax ordinary net income	(1.7)	1.6
Non-operating items	(2.4)	0.0
Pretax net income	(4.1)	1.6
Profit sharing and taxes	1.7	1.4
Group earnings	(5.8)	0.2
Equity in affiliates' income	0.9	1.4
Net income	(5.0)	1.6
Minority share of net income	1.3	0.4
Net profit (loss)	(3.7)	2.0
Capitalization (FRF billions)		
Stockholders' equity	30.2	33.7
Minority interests	6.0	5.4
All debt	81.5	79.7
	117.7	118.8
Ratio Analysis		
Operating income as % of revenue	1.0	2.2
Operating income as % of capitalization	1.4	3.2
Net income (loss) as % of common equity	(12.3)	5.9
Operating income/net interest expense	0.5x	1.7x

Almost 17% of the shares of Générale des Eaux are in the hands of four French companies (Saint-Gobain, Axa-UAP, Alcatel Alsthom, and Societe Générale). Générale, in turn, owns large blocks of stock in those four firms. At some point, Générale and its large shareholders may conclude that those cross-holdings have less purpose in the more free-wheeling capitalism that is growing in Europe. For that matter, Générale may need to address its many small and disparate holdings, and whether they add value to the company. To further complicate matters, GBL, a firm that is associated with Générale in the ownership of media properties, is also a major shareholder of Générale's rival, Suez-Lyonnaise.

Générale is one of a handful of huge European, utility-based conglomerates with worldwide ambitions. Management has begun a process of focusing on profitability and rationalizing assets. Much of the ongoing effort is going into the development of a major telecommunications and media presence in France, to which water expansion could temporarily take a back seat, given Générale's financial structure, unless Générale chooses to dispose of some of its disparate holdings. Over time, however, Générale is bound to expand its presence as one of the world's most important water companies.

United Utilities plc: The Convergence Model in the United Kingdom*

In 1995, North West Water Group plc acquired Norweb plc, a neighboring electric distribution utility, creating United Utilities plc, the first multi-industry utility company in the U.K. The combined company would become a multimillion-pound, world-class business involved in providing electricity, gas, telecommunications, water, and wastewater services.

At the end of fiscal 1997, United had gross revenues of £2.4 billion, pretax profits of £444 million, and operating cash flow of £519 million. Based upon customers served, North West Water was the third-largest water utility in the U.K., with 6.8 million water and 6.8 million wastewater customers, and Norweb was the fifth-largest electric distribution company, with 2.2 million customers.

Here's how a regulated water utility transformed itself into a leading worldwide supplier of high-quality utility and business support services.

STRATEGY

As is the case with many utilities, the overlapping service territories and customer bases of North West Water and Norweb had been noted by many and had been the basis of discussions between the two companies in the past. In 1995, these and other factors led to merger discussions, resulting in the consummation of the merger in November of that year. The drivers for the merger, in addition to customer and service territory overlap, included shared services, anticipated cost savings, cash flow and tax synergies, as well as enhanced growth prospects. Norweb was viewed as a strong candidate on a stand-alone basis due to its financial strength, superior market position, being a low-cost supplier, and the potential for incremental efficiencies.

After the consummation of the acquisition, United undertook a comprehensive review of the company's divisions and strategic plan. As the company moved from a single- to multiple-industry utility provider, it realized the need to evaluate each business unit and its role as United mapped out its plan to continue to enhance shareholder value. This review concluded that earnings from the regulated portion of the business would decline over time. Based upon upcoming regulatory price

---

*Sources: Annual reports and accounts for 1996 and 1997; company press releases and company Web site.

reviews in the year 2000, and the fact that cost reduction and efficiency gains could not continue at the rates of the past, the prospects for continued growth were marginal. Realizing the negative impact of such earnings declines on shareholder value, management felt that they had to focus on how to grow shareholder value beyond the year 2000.

Management concluded that it was possible to continue to increase earnings post-2000 by adhering to the following strategy:

● Be fully prepared for the upcoming price review process.

● Continue cost reduction efforts and planning.

● Create three specific vehicles for growth: energy and telecommunications, facilities management, and international.

Table G-1

United Utilities
Main Business Units

Water and wastewater—North West Water serves approximately 2.9 million customers in northwest England. Manages the U.K.'s largest environmental improvement program.

Electric distribution—Norweb delivers electricity locally in the northwest of England.

Electric supply—Provides electricity to two million customers in the Northwest, as well as to others in England.

Contracting—Norweb Contracting does installations.

Gas supply and telecom—Has secured 12% of the Northwest's gas market. Now providing telephone service to business customers in the region as well.

International—North West Water Overseas manages utilities serving 25 million customers outside the U.S. and U.K. Norweb International is seeking electricity and transmission opportunities. U.S. Water, owned with Bechtel and Kiewit, operates 30 municipal system in North America. International Water, a joint venture with Bechtel, seeks opportunities outside the U.S.

Facilities Management—Vertex Data Sciences acts as a services outsourcing firm for United Utilities and to others.

The expectation was that the growth vehicles would help offset earnings pressure in the regulated business, and become an increasing contributor to earnings over time. The plan was for those vehicles to contribute 20% of pretax earnings by 2000/01.

As part of this review process, it was determined that certain business units did not fit in with the core business and should be divested. Businesses to be sold included insurance, electrical contracting, generation assets, retail electricity and process equipment companies. Initial estimates for sale proceeds were £350 million. Actual proceeds will be approximately £460 million, which includes the retention of the insurance and electrical contracting business.

BUSINESS UNITS

The company is organized into four major lines of business: Utilities, Energy and Telecommunications, International, and Facilities Management. The Utilities division forms the bulk of the company's operations based upon earnings and assets, while the three remaining divisions will be the areas to fuel future growth. Summarized below are revenues and operating profit data for fiscal 1996 and 1997:

United Utilities*

	Revenues		Contribution	
	1996	1997	1996	1997
Water and Wastewater	828.2	866.7	49.4%	33.6%
Electric Distribution	154.1	329.0	9.2%	12.8%
Electric Supply	596.9	1,105.3	35.6%	42.8%
Gas Supply and Telecom	11.8	26.2	0.7%	1.0%
International	9.9	6.9	0.6%	0.3%
Facilities Management	0.0	185.2	0.0%	7.2%
Other	74.3	60.9	4.4%	2.4%
Total	1,675.2	2,580.2	100.0%	100.0%

	Operating Profit		Contribution	
	1996	1997	1996	1997
Water and Wastewater	364.2	383.3	80.8%	64.1%
Electric Distribution	70.4	132.1	15.6%	22.1%
Electric Supply	10.8	45.8	2.4%	7.7%
Gas Supply and Telecom	−1.7	−2.7	−0.4%	−0.5%
International	5.9	4.6	1.3%	0.8%
Facilities Management	0.0	27.1	0.0%	4.5%
Other	1.4	7.7	0.3%	1.3%
Total	451.0	597.9	100.0%	100.0%

*Amounts in British pounds, millions, prior to intercompany eliminations and extraordinary items.

UTILITY

This sector consists of the regulated water, wastewater, and electric distribution sectors. Due to the upcoming price review in the year 2000 and the level of cost

489

reductions already attained, prospects for future earnings growth are limited, if not negative. The competitive price pressures and regulatory climate in the U.K. are forcing companies to seek out nonregulated business opportunities to offset the lack of growth in the regulated business. This division accounted for 46.4% of revenues and 86.2% of operating revenues for 1997. In many ways, this situation is not dissimilar to what we see in the U.S. today, with many regulated utilities utilizing their regulated business cash flow to seek new business opportunities.

The acquisition of Norweb and the integration of the two utility units continues, with investments in new advanced customer systems to centralize customer support, and the establishment of a new BusinessCare service to provide dedicated services and support for commercial and business customers.

ENERGY AND TELECOMMUNICATIONS

This division includes electric and gas supply, Norweb Communications, and Norweb Connections.

Electric supply (that is, procuring and selling the actual electricity) in the U.K., as in the U.S., is a very low margin business. The result, for Norweb, is a 4% operating margin as compared to 40% for its electric distribution (the wires infrastructure) division. In the future, electric supply providers will need to try to pass on the commodity/price risk, which has a dramatic impact on margins to customers. The gas market is smaller and generally less appealing than the electric market. That being said, it will be key for suppliers to be able to offer customers both commodities in a deregulated market.

The earning impact from the telecommunications business is seen as one of the more promising opportunities. As the electric and water utility already have access to the customer, it seems logical that adding telecom services to the menu can add profits. To the extent that meter reading technology becomes widespread, there is an even better argument for combining the services. Norweb Communications has established an advanced fiber-optic system in major business centers, becoming the leading alternative supplier of choice to British Telecom. Major customers include Manchester Airport, British Nuclear Fuels, and Fujitsu. Norweb Communications recently announced contracts with Lancashire County Council, a municipality serving 1.4 million people, and Tplc, a major information technology company. This is a sector that is expanding rapidly worldwide as advanced systems and increased bandwidth become a necessity. Norweb Connections will provide connection services to new residential and business sites, further unbundling the services required for customer access.

INTERNATIONAL

This division is pursuing water and electric opportunities outside of the U.K. Today North West Water Overseas Services manages operating contracts serving more than 25 million people. The company has set up two partnerships to pursue international water opportunities. U.S. Water, a joint venture with Bechtel and Peter Kiewit, will focus on opportunities in the U.S. as that market evolves. Currently, it operates 30 municipal and industrial water and wastewater systems in North America. International Water, a joint venture with Bechtel, will pursue international projects outside of the U.S. International Water has been successful in winning contracts in Manila and Australia, and is also pursuing projects in Asia and South America. On the electric side, United Utilities International Energy is pursuing supply, distribution, and transmission opportunities worldwide.

FACILITIES MANAGEMENT

This division was formed by merging the similar activities of North West Water and Norweb into a new company, Vertex Data Science. Vertex today provides a wide range of services to divisions of United to assist in efficiency improvement and cost reduction on an incentive driven basis. Vertex has begun to actively market its outsourcing capabilities to third parties and has entered into contracts with Bromley Health Trust and the Comet retail business, and has announced the formation of a joint venture company with Northern Ireland Electricity to provide services to that as well as other companies in Ireland. The Northern Ireland contract has an initial term of seven years and contract value of over £175 million.

Vertex also has formed units to pursue business opportunities in the training and metering markets. The management training market is a fragmented one. Vertex, due to its large parent company employee base and training requirements, should be well-positioned to be a consolidator in this market. The meter reading segment of the power market is one that is expected to expand as a result of deregulation. In addition, as we see further unbundling of customer services there is a strong likelihood that the meter will be an important communications link to supply customers multiple products and services.

COMPETITIVE POSITION

United Utilities has embarked on a unique strategy, not because the company realized that the customer focus of the electric and water sectors was a logical fit, but because North West Water instituted a long-term strategic plan before it was forced to do so. It is one of the few regulated water utilities to embrace the changes that may occur in its sector. NIPSCO Industries, in the U.S., acquired a neighboring water utility, IWC Resources. Suez-Lyonnaise des Eaux is a majority shareholder in Trigen Energy and Tractebel. Générale des Eaux controls Sithe Energy. But, to date, water utilities, as a group, have not seen the need to take the major strategic steps that United Utilities has taken.

Other utilities in the U.K. such as Severn Trent and Hyder have embraced the multi-utility concept. In the U.S., with deregulation moving forward, many companies are experimenting with such arrangements. In many ways, the industry and its evolution will determine how successful are such strategies. Companies such as United are developing skill sets, management teams, and insights that will be critical in order to evaluate and act on future industry opportunities as they arise.

The New York City Water and Sewer System: Big Apple Byzantine*

New York City has one of the largest water and sewer systems in the nation. It also has devised one of the most convoluted ownership and management structures in the industry. The city owns the properties. The New York City Water Board leases the properties from the city. It hires the city's Department of Environmental Protection (DEP) to operate and maintain the system. The Board sets rates for services, which are not subject to any approvals by other regulators. The New York City Municipal Water Finance Authority issues the bonds needed to raise funds to expand and improve the water and sewer system. The Board agrees to set rates that cover all operating expenses plus 115% of debt service in the years in which the Authority's bonds are outstanding. It deposits all revenues into a Water Fund, and the Authority has a first lien on those revenues to assure that it receives enough money to pay its debt service.

The system serves New York City, which has a population of approximately 7.3 million people. It provides water in upstate countries in which it has water supply facilities. Those counties have a population of about one million. Approximately 5,600 employees service the system's 820,000 accounts. The system is second only in size to the Metropolitan Water District in California.

In 1987–1996, average daily consumption for New York City and upstate service areas ranged from 1.4 billion gallons to 1.6 billion gallons, as opposed to consumption of around 1.5 billion gallons per day in 1970 and 1975. Peak flows have exceeded 2.0 billion gallons per day. Sewage flow in dry weather runs around 1.4 billion gallons per day. (A large proportion of the city system combines storm and sanitary systems, hence the measure of flow on a dry day is a more reliable indicator of volume.) The system calculates dependable yield (the amount "that can be safely drawn from a watershed during the worst period in the drought of record") at about 1.3 billion gallons per day. The two large water tunnels that connect the reservoirs to the distribution system have a total capacity of 2.0 billion gallons per day. A third tunnel is under construction,with completion scheduled for 2004. The collecting and storage reservoirs have capacity of about 580 billion gallons above the amount needed for minimum operating purposes.

The New York City system residential load accounts for roughly 80% of accounts and 65% of billings. The combined water and sewage charges, for a standardized

---

*Sources: New York City Municipal Water Authority prospectus, August 7, 1997, and public documents.

level of consumption, are close to or even below the average rates charged in big cities, an unusual situation for New Yorkers who are accustomed to paying high prices. (The fact that the system loses money may account, to some extent, for the low prices.) The tariff system does not discriminate between classes of users.

Combined Water and Sewer Annual Charges
March 1997

	Single Family Residential	Commercial	Industrial
San Francisco	$761	$9,042	$885,573
Boston	725	7,408	773,151
Jacksonville, FL	631	5,381	486,881
Houston	590	6,279	620,975
Washington, DC	544	5,445	544,465
San Jose	528	4,957	409,886
Los Angeles	403	4,644	453,834
New York	391	3,913	391,270
Indianapolis	376	2,841	195,580
San Antonio	331	2,400	225,024
Baltimore	313	2,716	240,279
Detroit	277	2,263	186,031
Chicago	185	2,630	263,019
Average for 24 large cities	$465	$4,251	$389,535

Approximately 202,000 accounts pay a flat rate for service. The rate is based on frontage of the building, number of stories, number of dwelling units and number of water-using fixtures. Another 618,000 accounts have water meters. The city plans to meter all accounts by the end of 1998. Sewer charges for accounts with full water and sewer service has been set at 159% of the water bill since 1992. As of July 1997, the city charged metered customers $1.20 per hundred cubic feet (ccf), which is the equivalent of 0.16 cents per gallon. (The water suppliers in upstate communities receiving water from the city pay the city about 0.03 cents per gallon. That price, however, is a wholesale rate for water only, and does not include the distribution services for which city dwellers pay.) From July 1, 1986 to July 1, 1997, the metered water rate has increased 65.5% and the metered sewer charge has increased 339.1%.

The revenues and expenses breakdown shown below includes the activities of all three entities on a consolidated basis, but has been rearranged to emphasize operational revenues and expenses. Due to large adjustments to bad debt expense and depreciation, operating income was highly variable as reported in 1995 and 1996. It is probably safe to say, though, that personnel costs are stable, and that a minimum of 70% of expenses are relatively fixed, when one includes the more than $100 million in annual lease payments to the city. The financial ratio analysis shows poor returns and coverages for the entire system, if one uses the method of analysis that would be applied to private corporations. Calculations of coverages for particular series of bonds within the structure, however, are more complicated, and, presumably, the system's income and revenue segregation procedures are such to assure that it meets bond covenant requirements.

Financial Statements and Analysis
Fiscal Year ended June 30

	1995 ($ Millions)	% of Revenue	1996 ($ Millions)	% of Revenues
Revenues				
Water	504.6	39.9	532.2	39.9
Sewer	717.5	56.7	765.8	57.5
Other	43.6	3.4	35.1	2.6
	1,265.7	100.0	1,333.1	100.0
Operating expenses				
Water operations	203.8	16.1	206.8	15.5
Sewer operations	340.0	26.9	323.3	24.3
Bad debts and other	298.2	23.5	523.0	39.2
	842.0	66.5	1,053.1	79.0
Excess of revenues over operating expenses	423.7	33.5	280.0	21.0
Depreciation and amortization	273.1	21.6	223.9	16.8
Operating income	150.6	11.9	56.1	4.2
Other income (expense)				
Interest charges	(338.0)	(26.7)	(368.4)	(27.6)
Other income	74.4	5.9	78.3	5.9
Net income (loss)	(113.0)	(8.9)	(234.0)	(17.6)
Personnel expenses				
Water	89.6	7.1	94.4	7.1
Sewer	156.0	12.3	152.5	11.4
Total	245.6	19.4	246.9	18.5
Plant account				
Gross plant in service	9,962.4	- - -	10,476.6	- - -
Construction work in progress	3,182.6		3,638.3	
Depreciation	(3,084.3)		(3,304.2)	
Net plant	10,060.7		10,810.7	
Capitalization				
All debt	5,665.6	- - -	6,659.3	- - -
Equity	5,448.9	- - -	5,266.9	- - -
Total	11,114.5	- - -	11,926.2	- - -
Interest coverage	0.4x		0.2x	
Operating income as % of capitalization (loss)	1.5%		0.5%	
Net income as % of Equity	(2.1%)		(4.4%)	

The breakdown of gross plant in service as of June 30, 1996 was:

	$ Billions	%
Water supply and waste water treatment systems	$ 6.2	59
Water distribution and sewage collection systems	4.2	40
Miscellaneous	0.1	1
Total	$10.5	100

The 1998–2007 capital improvement program gives a breakdown of future capital allocations:

	$ Millions	%
Water supply and transmission	$ 888	10.3
Water distribution	2,094	24.3
Water pollution control	4,019	46.7
Sewers	1,332	15.5
Equipment	280	3.2
Total	$8,613	100.0

Of the total, $1,828 million of the 1998–2007 program is destined for reconstruction, replacement of old facilities, and for replacement of chronically failing components. Of the system's 6,048 miles of water pipe, and 6,417 miles of sewer pipe, more than one-third of the mileage in each category has been in the ground for 75 years or more. The city actually has pipe in place that was installed before 1870. The major tunnels and aqueducts still in operation date from 1893 to 1970. The four largest, however, have an average age of over 60 years. Broken water mains are a regular feature of morning traffic reports.

The city's greatest challenges, however, could come on the environmental front, especially if the federal government decides to order the installation of filtration for the water supply of the Catskill and Delaware Systems. Until now, the city has avoided doing so by implementing environmental controls in its watersheds, in accord with an agreement with the Environmental Protection Administration. Cost estimates of installing filtration range from $4 billion to $8 billion. The EPA could make a further determination about filtration in 2002. Putting in facilities of that magnitude would be a big project even for the New York City system. The water system in the meantime has to deal with the need to build a filtration facility for the downstate Croton Reservoir system, a plant that could cost $500 million to $900 million, cover 10 acres, and rise nine stories. On the sewage front, the system has planned an upgrade of its largest treatment plant, Newton Creek, scheduled for completion in 2007, at a cost of $1.2 billion. Fortunately for the city, water conservation programs have reduced the flow from several of the offending treatment plants.

The New York City Water System, despite over 25 years of static demand for its services, has had to make substantial expenditures and raise prices at a faster pace than inflation in order to pay for the capital programs. This situation is typical of many mature, urban water systems, and, unfortunately, it looks as if it will continue to remain typical for a number of years to come.

APPENDIX I

Tariffs

Tariffs, or the schedule of charges to consumers, vary from utility to utility, depending on the cost structure of the utility, the demands of the consumers, and the politics of the price-setting process.

Many utilities assess a one-time charge to turn on service, or to install additional equipment to an existing connection. More importantly, suppliers assess one-time service charges when they have to make the expenditures necessary to connect the new customer to the existing system. Those charges—known as reservation, tapping, or demand charges—may vary from several hundred to several thousand dollars, depending on the type of service requested and the cost of the installation.

After paying the front-end charges to get access to the system, the water or sewage customer must pay for ongoing service. The utility might charge a flat rate for service, regardless of usage. The utility, for instance, might charge $10 per month if the customer has a one-inch pipe coming in, and $20 per month if the pipe is two inches in diameter, on the assumption that consumption is in some way proportional to size of the intake. Or the utility might charge a given amount per month, per number of water-using appliances, or connections, or even by size of the building.

Flat-rate prices, however, do not necessarily properly allocate the costs of providing service. People who conserve water, for instance, might pay too much, while those who waste water pay too little. The water and wastewater utilities, therefore, have moved toward tariffs that charge more to those who use more. Usually, the utility starts off with a minimum charge that covers the cost of keeping the customer on the books, even if the customer makes little use of the facilities. The utility might assess this charge in addition to the charges based on volume of usage, or it might charge for a minimum amount of usage, whether the customer takes it or not. For example, the utility might charge $5 per month, plus 1 cent per gallon taken. Or it might require a minimum payment for 500 gallons (at 1 cent per gallon), whether the customer takes that much or not.

The volume usage charges come in three types: price remains the same no matter how much is consumed, price rises as volume taken rises, or price falls as volume taken rises.

Finally, some utilities change the price schedule to reflect seasonal costs. For instance, the water utility in a winter resort might charge more in the winter, when demand is greatest, and a desert community might charge more in the summer, when everyone wants to water the lawn.

Sewer rates often parallel the water tariffs. In fact, unless the utility meters the sewer discharge, it may impose its charges based on the amount of water taken, on the theory that most of the water ends up going down the sewer pipe, anyway.

The sample tariffs that follow provide examples of charges for both water and wastewater. The examples shown may or may not include the complete tariff, but do illustrate the concepts discussed. (All information is taken from bond prospectuses issued by the water utilities.)

BALTIMORE (1996)

Baltimore, Maryland, uses a *declining block tariff*. In other words, the more you use, the less you pay per gallon. Note, too, that the minimum consumption allowed increases in proportion to the area of the pipe (the term "meter size" used in tariffs refers to the diameter of the incoming connection). The area of a circle is:

$$A = \pi r^2$$

and the radius (r) is half of the diameter. In other words:

Meter size (inches in diameter)	Area (square inches)	Minimum Consumption (gallons)
1	0.785	40
2	3.14	160
4	12.56	640

The tariff schedule is:

Minimum Quarterly Charges for Metered Water Service

Meter Size (inches)	Rate	Consumption Allowed (ccf)
⅝	$ 9.50	10
¾	17.10	18
1	38.00	40
1½	59.18	70
2	111.74	160
3	181.82	280
4	366.44	640
6	570.95	1,150
8	831.60	1,800
10	1,132.35	2,550
12	1,934.35	4,500

Consumption Charges

Quarterly Use Block (ccf)	Rate ($ per ccf)
First 50	0.950
Next 450	0.584
Over 500	0.401

The consumer with a two-inch meter who takes only 50 ccf (hundred cubic feet) of water would have to pay the minimum charge of $111.74, despite the fact that 50 ccf at $0.950 per ccf equals only $47.50.

The consumer with the two-inch meter who takes 550 ccf, on the other hand, pays:

$$
\begin{aligned}
50 \text{ ccf @ } \$0.950 &= \$\ 47.50 \\
+\ 450 \text{ ccf @ } 0.584 &= 262.80 \\
+\ \underline{\ 50} \text{ ccf @ } 0.401 &= \underline{\ 20.05} \\
=\ 550 \text{ ccf} &\qquad \$330.35
\end{aligned}
$$

The $330.35 more than exceeds the minimum $111.74. The average cost for 550 ccf is $0.6006 per ccf, incidentally.

BIRMINGHAM (1996)

The Birmingham, Alabama, tariff sends mixed signals. Water rates rise with increased usage for residential and irrigation customers. Other users (presumably large industry) get a break as they take more water:

Monthly Rates for Each 100 cubic feet of Water Delivered

	Rate
Residential and Irrigation Rates	
For the first 1,000 cubic feet	$ .98
For the next 1,200 cubic feet	1.21
All over 2,200 cubic feet	1.45
All Other Water Users Rates	
For the first 2,700 cubic feet	1.16
For the next 97,300 cubic feet	1.14
For the next 3,233,300 cubic feet	1.07
For the next 1,333,300 cubic feet	.97
All over 4,666,600 cubic feet	.98
Minimum charge—per month for 5/8" meter (in addition to the above)	4.71
Varied minimum charges for other meter sizes	
Fire Hydrant Rental Rates (per year)	105.00

The sewer system has two divisions, Riverview and Moody. They have different tariffs:

Rate Schedule for Sewer Service Charges

Riverview System

1. *Reservation Fee.* The reservation fee is $9.90 per gallon of reserved capacity per day. This is a one-time charge to offset capital expenditures associated with additional capacity.

2. *Treatment Charge.* The monthly charge consists of the sum of the Demand Charge and the Use Charge as set forth below:
   A. Demand Charge is $62.64 per month for each 1,000 gallons per day of reserve capacity.
   B. Use Charge is 90 cents per 100 cubic feet discharged.

Moody System

1. *Tap Fee.* The tap fee is $9.90 per gallon of estimated daily use. This is a one-time charge to offset capital expenditures associated with additional capacity.

2. *Treatment Charge.* The monthly charge consists of the sum of the Monthly Minimum Charge and the Use Charge as set forth below:
   A. Monthly Minimum Charge is $5.61 per month.
   B. Use Charge is $2.69 per 100 cubic feet discharged.

BUFFALO (1994)

Buffalo, New York, sits atop Lake Erie, so the city should not lack water. The schedule shown simply charged for usage per billing period:

Volume Charges

First 3,000 cubic feet (cf)	$10.23 per 1,000 cf
Next 9,000 cf	9.25 per 1,000 cf
Over 12,000 cf	7.18 per 1,000 cf

Senior citizens get a 60% discount.

DeKALB COUNTY (1996)

DeKalb County, Georgia, in the Atlanta metropolitan area, combines a fixed monthly charge with a usage charge that does not change with volume. The industrial wastewater tariff includes special surcharges depending on what the user dumps into the system. The tap fees increase with the size of the installation.

Readiness-to-Serve Charge: (A base monthly charge for providing service availability regardless of volume used, based on capacity of meter.)

	¾" (or less)	1"	1½"	2"	3"	4"	6"	8"	12"
Bi-Monthly Billing									
Water	$5.20	$8.80	$17.40	$28.00	$56.00	$88.00	$174.00	$280.00	$436.00
Sewer	$5.20	$8.80	$17.40	$28.00	$56.00	$88.00	$174.00	$280.00	$436.00

Commodity Charges: (Based on volume of water metered.)

Water .... $1.10 per 1,000 gallons
Sewer .... $1.70 per 1,000 gallons

Industrial Waste Surcharge: (Based on routine laboratory tests of commercial and industrial customer discharges to the County Sewer System and on volume of water metered.)

1. BOD (Bio-Chemical Oxygen Demand) level: An additional $.0006 per 1,000 gallons for each milligram per liter (mg/l) of BOD in excess of 250 mg/l.

2. SS (Suspended Solids) level: An additional $.0006 per 1,000 gallons for each mg/l of SS in excess of 250 mg/l.

3. P (Phosphorus) level: An additional $.024 per 1,000 gallons for each mg/l of P in excess of 15 mg/l.

4. NH_3 (Ammonia Nitrogen) level: An additional $.006 per 1,000 gallons for each mg/l of NH_3 in excess of 30.

Water Meter Tap Fees

Meter Size	Fee
¾" or less	$ 750
1"	850
1½"	1,825
2"	3,625
3"	6,550
4"	7,600
6" compound	10,100
6" fire service	12,000
8" compound	13,550
8" fire service	16,500
12"	direct cost plus $230

Sewer Tap Fees
Residential: $600.

MESA (1995)

Mesa, Arizona, makes no bones about the need to promote water conservation, considering its location in the dry Southwest. If you use more, you pay more per gallon.

Schedule of Water System Fees and Charges

Description of Water System Services	Fee/Charge
Monthly Minimum Bill—All Classes, All Zones	$ 7.81
¾ Inch	9.33
1 Inch	14.89
1½ Inch	21.00
2 Inches	46.25
3 Inches	75.99
4 Inches	149.84
6 Inches	224.20
8 Inches	305.40
10 Inches	

	Western Zone $/Mgal	RWCD Zone $/Mgal	Eastern Zone $/Mgal
Monthly Volume Charge (Residential)			
First 12,000 Gallons of Water	1.15	1.22	1.50
Additional Usage	1.71	1.84	2.25

Note:
$/Mgal = $ per 1,000 gallons.
Western Zone = lies west of Eastern Canal
RWCD Zone = lies between Eastern Canal and Roosevelt Water Conservation District Canal
Eastern Zone = lies east of Roosevelt Water Conservation District Canal

Schedule of Wastewater System Fees and Charges

Description of Wastewater System Services	Fee/Charge
Residential Sewer Service—Inside City	
Monthly Bill	
Minimum	
Capital Related Component	$4.77
User Charge Component	$1.49
+ User Charge Component (average winter water consumption)	$0.57/1,000 gallons
+ Capital Related Component (average winter water consumption in excess of 5,000 gallons)	$1.11/1,000 gallons
General Commercial Sewer Service—Inside City	
Monthly Bill	
Minimum	
Capital Related Component	$4.99
User Charge Component	$1.49
+ User Charge Component (all water used)	$0.57/1,000 gallons
+ Capital Related Component (all water used in excess of 5,000 gallons)	$1.11/1,000 gallons
Multi-Unit Dwelling Sewer Service—Inside City	
Monthly Bill	
Minimum	
Capital Related Component	$4.99
User Charge Component	$1.49
+ User Charge Component (all water used)	$0.57/1,000 gallons
+ Capital Related Component (all water used in excess of 5,000 gallons)	$1.11/1,000 gallons
Industrial Sewer Service—Inside City	
Monthly Bill	
Capital Component	
Flow (in excess of 5,000 gallons)	$1.094/1,000 gallons
BOD (in excess of lbs. contributed in first 5,000 gallons)	$0.089/lb.
SS (in excess of lbs. contributed in first 5,000 gallons)	$0.072/lb.
User Charge Component	
Flow	$0.313/1,000 gallons
BOD	$0.159/lb.
SS	$0.094/lb.
Minimum—Capital Component (includes use of 5,000 gallons)	$5.90
User Charge Billing Component	$1.49

MIAMI BEACH (1995)

Miami Beach, Florida, is a city whose water usage varies with the flow of tourists, and the rate schedule shows that seasonality.

Monthly Water Rates:

Service Size (Inches)	Min. Monthly Service Charge		Min. Gallons of Water Per Month
	June 1–Nov. 30	Dec. 1–May 31	
¾	$ 6.55	$ 7.70	5,000
1	9.17	10.78	7,000
1½	14.41	16.94	11,000
2	22.27	26.18	17,000
3	52.40	61.60	40,000
4	104.80	123.20	80,000
6	157.20	184.80	120,000
8	262.00	308.00	200,000
Water Rate Per 1,000 Gal.	$ 1.31	$ 1.54	

Ancillary Charges:

Size of Meter (inches)	Minimum Deposit	New Service Tapping Charges
¾	$ 40.00	$480.00
1	50.00	600.00
1½	60.00	840.00
2	100.00	1,300.00
3	500.00	$ 600.00 + Estimated Cost + 10%
4	600.00	$ 800.00 + Estimated Cost + 10%
6	1,000.00	$1,200.00 + Estimated Cost + 10%
8	1,500.00	$1,600.00 + Estimated Cost + 10%

The city has various additional charges, too:

Table of Additional Water Charges

Type of Charge	Amount of Charge
Returned check	$20.00 or 5% of the check, whichever is greater
Turn on after requested turn off	$ 2.00
Turn off for nonpayment	10.00
Turn on after turn off for nonpayment	10.00
Unauthorized turn on	15.00
Meter tampering	15.00
Insertion of solid washer or removal of meter	25.00
Installation of water meter on existing tap	60.00

The wastewater usage charge is $2.14 per 1,000 gallons of metered water consumption, except for water separately metered for delivery to swimming pools, lawn sprinklers, or other uses that do not require use of sanitary sewers.

SUFFOLK COUNTY (1996)

Suffolk County, New York, sits at the eastern end of Long Island, over an aquifer in need of protection. The rate structure of the county water authority is simple:

General Rates

Service Classification No. 1 Quarterly	Service Classification No. 1A Monthly
Service Charge $11.43	Service Charge $3.81
Commodity Charge $.9375/hundred cubic feet	Commodity Charge $.9375/hundred cubic feet

CONCLUSION

Tariffs encourage, discourage, or ignore usage. They may or may not reflect the costs of serving different types of customers. Social or economic development goals may take precedence over sending the right cost signals to society. The fact that the utilities use so many different measures of volume, with such varied tariff structures, makes price comparisons difficult, as well. Probably, in most instances, as long as the total revenue collected by the utility equals the cost of operating the utility's facilities plus the cost of capital, few people care what else the tariff does. And that attitude is just fine as long as we have water to waste and we do not care what it costs.

Subject Index